ON STAGE 1

Bob Cameron

GLOBE/MODERN CURRICULUM PRESS

Editor: Marion E. Raycheba

Design: Christine Alexiou

Illustration: Harry Black (page 304)
Irma Coucill (pages 14, 56, 120, 194, and 274)

Cover Photograph: Robert C. Ragsdale/Miller Services

Typesetting: Jay Tee Graphics Ltd.

Canadian Cataloguing in Publication Data

Main entry under title:
On stage 1

Includes index.
ISBN 0-88996-094-1

1. Drama — Collections.   I. Cameron, Bob.

PN6112.067 1984   808.82   C84-098902-4

Printed and Bound in Canada
0 9 8

Contents

Foreword

More than any other artist, the playwright depends on other people. The play itself is a blueprint which needs people, such as actors, directors, set designers, and stage hands, to bring it to life. It also needs the fuel of money, provided by people willing to pay to see it performed. No director will stage a play unless he or she has reason to believe that audiences will be interested in paying to see the production, and no playwright is likely to even bother writing a play unless he or she is reasonably sure that there will be public interest in the work.

The audience is, in this sense, the beginning of every dramatic work. For those involved in the theatre, the audience is the most elusive, capricious, unpredictable, feared, and loved gathering of people. Without the audience, nothing in the theatre would make much sense.

Playwrights must have a strong sense of conviction that they have something worthwhile to tell and show about themselves, about the people they know, and about the society of which they are a part. They must have a sense of commitment and excitement which drives them to put their ideas on paper in a way which will attract and excite that elusive audience — people who are willing to give up an afternoon or evening and, moreover, pay for the privilege.

Recently, in Canada, there has been an upsurge of public interest in drama. The *On Stage* series is responding to this interest by providing students with an exciting range and variety of contemporary dramatic works. Each play was selected with the student in mind. Each will appeal to high school students, and each will extend their experience and knowledge.

The *On Stage* series is also responding to an urgent need. The high school students of today are the audiences of today and the writers, directors, actors, and audiences of tomorrow. This series — with plays by some of the world's greatest playwrights — will give students the opportunity to discover the magic, riches, and excitement of the theatre, something which will have value throughout life regardless of the role they may play.

———————— • ————————

What Is a Play?

Drama comes from the Greek word meaning "to do". *Theatre* comes from the Greek meaning "to see". These two ideas — seeing and doing — define drama in the largest sense. They include both the play *and* the performance.

There are many definitions of the play. One of the most useful for its scope and clarity is Clayton Hamilton's. Hamilton, a respected American drama critic, defined the play this way: "A play is a story devised to be presented by actors on a stage before an audience." This definition covers an entire theory of the theatre and gives the basis for dramatic criticism.

When we speak of the story of the play, we usually mean more than the immediate physical action on stage. For example, jugglers and acrobats perform actions on stage. Are they, then, performing drama? Certainly, they are performing actions of an immediate kind, but they are not usually considered as performing drama. Movement on the stage, then, is not *by itself* enough to distinguish drama from other kinds of performances.

When we speak of the action in drama, therefore, we usually mean the whole pattern of events which the performers are enacting. So, the definition of *story* in the context of drama suggests another dimension of human action. We see the pattern of events in the drama as telling some kind of story *and* as reflecting human life or being based on human life. The action on stage is not abstract or decorative movement. It is action which tells a story, using the devices of speech and pauses as well as gestures and movements.

The first concern of the action of drama is conflict. The action imitates the human actions of aroused passions, rises and falls in fortune, the conflict of wills, misadventures and disasters, bold deeds and words, defeats and triumphs — the stuff of human life. No matter how complex the drama, it is possible to detect the threads of such elemental human conflicts and emotions.

Some people question whether it is necessary to study plays. They say that it is enough just to enjoy them. Perhaps they do not understand that knowing the *why* of liking — or not liking — will add to the enjoyment of the experience.

One way to begin that understanding is to look at the four parts of Hamilton's definition. Once you understand the scope of the play, you will have some of the tools you need to understand why a play is a success or a failure.

A Play Is a Story

A play, like any story, is based on plot. What the audience sees is a story about life recreated on stage. Daily life can be boring and repetitive, however, and so the play presents daily life in a livelier way.

The events of the play — the story — will not be "slices of life" taken and shown exactly as they would happen in life. Instead, the play will be arrangements of words (*dialogue*), which make up *episodes* (a new episode begins whenever an important character enters or leaves the stage).

Several episodes make up a *scene*. Scenes are used to indicate that the time or place has changed.

Several scenes make up an *act*. There are usually two or three acts. Each act is a sign that there has been a major change in time or place.

There is a convention (a tradition) in the theatre that the performance of a play should take no more than two or three hours. This means that there is no time to waste. The story must be prevented as quickly and as clearly as possible.

Devised to be Presented by Actors

This part of the definition sets the play apart from all other forms of literature. The dramatist must always be aware of how the play will *sound*, rather than of how it will be read.

The dramatist is called the *playwright*. In English, the suffix "wright" means "maker". So, a playwright is a *playmaker*, not a playwriter. He or she is an artist who designs, shapes, and builds the narrative — the story we call a play. The playwright uses the tools of words — just as the poet and novelist do. But the playwright also uses *human* tools — the actors, their bodies and faces, their voices and movements — and *mechanical* tools — the stage itself, sets, lighting, props.

On a Stage

This part of the definition of a play may say more about written drama than any other part. The way in which the stage itself — the physical area — developed has had an important effect on the ways in which plays have been written.

To judge any play honestly, it is necessary to have a clear mental picture of the limits on the playwright at the time when the play was written. What did the stage look like? Was it in the open air? Was it in a building? What stage equipment was available? Where did the audience sit? How close was the audience to the actors?

Figure 1. The Greek Theatre

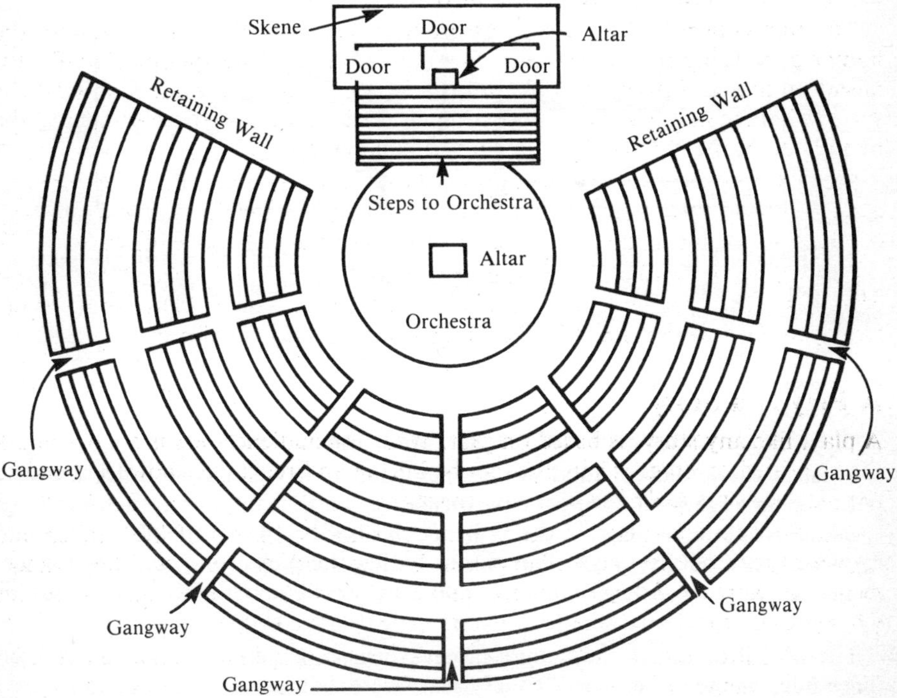

Take a look at the theatre of the ancient Greeks (Figure 1). It was a huge, open air theatre which could seat an audience of from 15 000 to 20 000 in a circle. The main actors were in the centre so that everyone in the audience could see them. There was no curtain, and so the playwright had to deal with the problem of getting the actors on and off the stage without stopping the action. Another problem for the playwright was the tradition of having the chorus and its leader on stage throughout the play. One result was that dramatic scenes tended to be presented as formal debates rather than as informal talks.

Figure 2. The Elizabethan Theatre

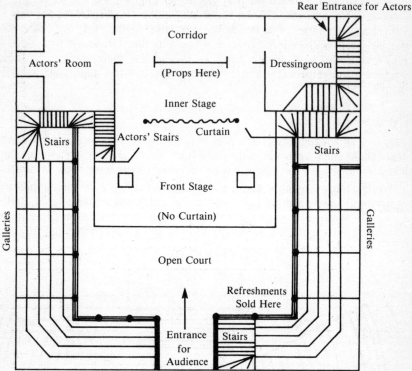

The Elizabethan stage allowed quite a different kind of playwriting (Figure 2). The shape of this stage allowed the playwright much more freedom to create action, mood, setting, and characters.

The front stage jutted out into the audience, and so the play could be seen from three sides. It wasn't curtained. The inner stage, or alcove, was used for scenes that needed setting up ahead of time. The upper stage, which was curtained, was used for seating musicians and for presenting special scenes.

Most of the audience stood in the open court. They could buy refreshments, talk, and move around during the performance. This meant that the actors had to speak above some noise from the audience. It also meant that the playwright had to write very exciting plays. The more exciting the plays were, the less the audience would move around and make noise that could interrupt the play or bother the actors.

The Elizabeth theatre had some more expensive gallery seats on each of the three sides of the stage. These gallery seats were divided into boxes, rooms, and tiers. The gentry sat here.

The Elizabeth playwright did not have scenery on stage, but there were elaborate props and costumes. With the help of these — and a huge, open playhouse — the dramatist could use a great deal of physical movement to help tell the story.

Figure 3. The Modern Stage

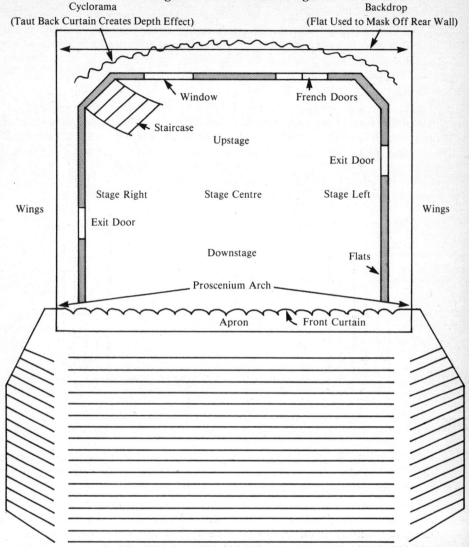

The stage in use today (Figure 3) began to develop during the 1700s and 1800s. The stage apron became smaller, and the performance was pushed back more and more. Scenery came into use. It was painted on wings and backdrops, and much of it looked artificial. But it allowed the playwright to make more of a point about the setting for the play.

The first box set appeared early in the 1800s. This was a three-sided room. The missing fourth side gave it its name, the *peephole* stage. It created a realistic effect — the effect of looking into an actual room. As a result, playwrights began writing what became known as realistic drama.

Electric lighting came into use towards the end of the 1800s. Scene shifting devices, such as the sliding or revolving stage, were invented. Sound recordings and other mechanical devices were added as time went on. All of these played a part in making the theatre stage as we know it today.

Before an Audience

This is the last part of Hamilton's definition of the play, and it is a very important one. Audiences change — from century to century, from country to country. The playwright always has to be aware of the character of the audience. He or she must be aware of what people of the time will enjoy, be interested in, be thinking about. The playwright also has to be aware that many different people will see — and judge — his or her work.

This text presents six plays written at different times for different audiences. It is hoped that by reading and studying these plays, you will develop some sense of drama as a form of art and get some sense of the excitement of the dramatic experience. You will not learn all there is to know about the theatre, but you will gain some understanding of the richness of dramatic literature.

—————————— • ——————————

The Fighting Days

by Wendy Lill

The Playwright

Wendy Lill was born in Vancouver, British Columbia, in 1950. She spent her childhood there and in London, Ontario. After attending the University of Toronto, she began writing poetry, children's stories, radio documentaries, dramas, filmscripts, and plays.

Lill's first play, *On the Line,* was based on the 1980 garment workers' strike in Winnipeg. This play sparked her interest in transferring real events into a dramatic form. She became, as she put it, "hooked on telling stories I see around me". She also became interested in historical drama, which she sees as a way for people to understand the present in the light of their ethnic, religious, and philosophical roots.

Today, Lill, who lives in Nova Scotia, continues freelance writing, mainly for the National Film Board, the CBC, Manitoba School Broadcasts, and various Manitoba theatres. She is also working on a television adaptation of *The Fighting Days*, which is to be filmed in 1985.

The Play

In 1983, Wendy Lill was commissioned by the Actors' Showcase and the Prairie Theatre Exchange to write a play that would address the contributions of women to Manitoba history. *The Fighting Days* grew out of Lill's historical research and the connections she saw between the concerns of women at the turn of the century and the concerns of women today.

Lill chose to tell the story through the experiences of three women, all active participants in the suffrage movement, and within the context of the themes of pacifism, racism, and feminism because, as she put it, "I realized that the story of those early suffragettes was not all rosy. As a feminist myself, I was torn between wanting to glorify the impressive achievements of those early women and telling the real story — whole story — which naturally involves their fears and intolerances and limitations."

According to Lill, the play was written very quickly, then rewritten and workshopped a number of times. This collaborative approach resulted in the first production of the play in March 1984.

The Fighting Days should be considered in the light of the time period in which it is set.

As the 1900s got underway, Canadian women held a position that was inferior to that of Canadian men. It was generally believed that women should not be interested in political or business life. They should, it was thought, stay home, keep house, and raise healthy babies for a rapidly growing Canada.

Women could not vote in elections or hold public office. They were not encouraged to hold jobs outside the home; in fact, many jobs were closed to them. When they were employed outside the home, they were paid less than men who were doing the same work. Men who wanted to farm were given free land on the prairies. Women were not.

Life was hard for everyone in those days, but it was particularly hard for women. They were responsible for cooking, cleaning, making clothing, and, of course, looking after the children (often ten or more as families tended to be large). Farm women were especially hard pressed. They were expected to do out-door chores as well, such as tending the vegetable garden, looking after the livestock, operating farm machinery, and helping with the harvest.

By 1900 one out of every seven women was working outside the home. Most of them were limited to routine jobs in factories, in stores, or as servants in the homes of the wealthy, all of it work entailing long hours for very poor pay. Some women, however, were finding better jobs — as teachers, nurses, and newspaper reporters — and they were also improving themselves by becoming better educated and active in Canada's social, religious, and political life. Women active in such groups as the Young Women's Christian Association (YWCA) and the Women's Christian Temperance Union (WCTU) tackled many of Canada's social problems.

Some of the most active women's groups were formed on the prairies, where women were concerned about such issues as poor working conditions, equal pay for equal work, and the franchise. The fight to get the vote for women was perhaps the most bitter of all, and it began long before the turn of this century. Sir John A. Macdonald introduced bills to give women the right to vote in 1883, 1884, and 1885. All were defeated, but the battle continued with women such as Nellie McClung taking up the banner of leadership.

Nellie Mooney was born on October 20, 1873, to a farming family in Grey County, Ontario. The agricultural depression of that decade made life difficult for Ontario farmers, and so in 1880 the Mooneys made the long trip west by train and Red River cart to start again on a farm near Milford, Manitoba.

In 1889, Nellie spent a year in Winnipeg, training as a teacher, and then took her first teaching post near Manitou. She began writing articles and short stories, and she became an enthusiastic member of the WCTU.

In 1896, Nellie married Wes McClung, a pharmacist. Their first child (of five) was born in 1897, the same year that she made her first public speech at a WCTU provincial convention. Her performance was a great success — witty, eloquent, and stimulating — and she became a sought-after public speaker. By 1900, she was deeply involved in the fight for the franchise, something in which the WCTU had become involved.

In 1911, the McClungs moved to Winnipeg where Nellie found great opportunities for study and service. She decided to concentrate on the suffrage issue, and she joined the movement in Winnipeg, making friends with such activists as Francis Beynon and Lillian Beynon Thomas.

Convinced that a subtle approach would be more effective than violence, Nellie and her friends rehearsed for the famous Mock Parliament, which was held in the Walker Theatre in Winnipeg on January 29, 1914. The Mock Parliament was a clever satire on the views of Sir Rodmond Roblin, Manitoba's premier who was dead set against votes for women on the grounds that they were too emotional to handle the responsibility. Nellie played the role of a woman premier who was dead set against votes for men because "men's place is on the farm". The show was a great success.

On January 27, 1916, Manitoba passed an amendment to its Election Act, becoming the first province in Canada to give women the right to vote (just a few days before Alberta and Saskatchewan passed similar legislation). The next year, nurses serving with Canada's armed forces on the battlefields of World War I were allowed to vote in the federal election. It was not until 1920, however, that Parliament gave all Canadian women the right to vote in federal elections.

In 1921, Nellie was elected to the Alberta Legislative Assembly. (The McClungs had moved to Edmonton.) As an M.L.A. sitting on the opposition bench, she advocated improved social welfare and working conditions, prohibition, a minimum wage law, birth control, and more liberal divorce laws. She had strong views of what was right and wrong, views which often got her into difficulty with her own political party (Liberal). Her opposition to the sale of liquor never changed, but the prohibition movement began to lose its strength as a popular cause. Nellie, who continued to stand for it, lost her seat in the election of 1926.

In 1933, the McClungs moved to British Columbia, where Nellie lived until her death in 1951. Her last few years were not easy, but despite her suffering she never lost her sense of humour. Just before she died, she said to her husband, Wes, "Oh, I'm still here. I'll never believe I'm dead till I see it in the paper." She was buried in Victoria. On her gravestone is the simple epitaph, "Loved and Remembered".

In 1957, the Women's Institute of Grey County, Ontario, honoured her memory by erecting a beautiful cairn on the property on which Nellie was born.

The spirit of Nellie McClung lives on in women like Martha Hynna, who was a member of the Canadian delegation to the United Nations' Commission on the Status of Women for International Women's Year in 1975. In her address to the United Nations, Hynna said, "In the long run, all the hassles of Women's Lib and women's groups will have been well worth the effort if the barriers of human prejudice can be worn away and everyone can share equally in the responsibilities of our society."

Wendy Lill

The Fighting Days by Wendy Lill is reprinted with the permission of the playwright.

The Fighting Days

Wendy Lill

The First Production Was Staged
On March 15, 1983
At the Prairie Theatre Exchange
In Winnipeg, Manitoba

With This Cast

Francis ....Laurel Paetz
Lily ....Terri Cherniack
Nellie ....Linda Huffman
McNair.........................Morison Bock

Act 1: 1910-1914
Act 2: 1916-1917

Directed by Kim McCaw
Set and Costume Design by Kathrine Christensen
Lighting Design by Larry Isacoff
Music by John McCulloch
Stage Manager: Steven Gregg

SCENE 1

Dark Stage. Funeral music fading into sound of a train. Lights up. FRANCIS and her sister LILY are on the train. FRANCIS, 18, LILY, 25. FRANCIS is looking out the window, lost in thought. LILY crocheting.

———————•———————

LILY: Do you think father's up there right now watching us?

FRAN: I never really believed in that part. Did you?

LILY: No, I guess not. Some things just sort of stick with you. I remember you saying that if he was going to heaven, you didn't want to go there. That you'd rather go to hell.

FRAN: But I never really stood up to him. Had I been braver Lily, I would have defied him.

LILY: You were braver than the rest of us. It was you father went after. You seemed to bring out the worst in him.

FRAN: Why do you think that was?

LILY: Mother says it was your questions that made him angry. He thought they sprang from an "undisciplined spirit" . . . whatever that means.

FRAN: You know when he used to ask "are you right with God?" What did you say?

LILY: I said "yes" every time and then he stopped bothering me.

FRAN: But how does one know whether they're RIGHT with God?

LILY: I don't know, Fanny.

FRAN: Do you believe deep in your heart that Methodists are the only ones with immortal souls?

LILY: Not anymore. Not since I moved to the city.

FRAN: What happened then?

LILY: I guess I started to think . . . bigger. I met people who believed in all sorts of things. Some of my friends are Presbyterians. Vernon, the young man I'm seeing at the newspaper, is an agnostic.

FRAN: An agnostic? I've never even heard of that church. What does he believe?

LILY: Well . . . he believes . . . well, he's not sure there really is a God . . . he's just not sure.

FRAN *(concerned):* Oh.

LILY: But he's very nice, Fanny. He went to school in England. He reads a lot . . . just like you.

FRAN: If you like him Lily, I'm sure I will.
  (Silence)
Lily, what about the Catholics?

LILY: What about them?

FRAN: Are they alright too?

LILY: Yes, they're alright too.

FRAN: That's good. I always thought it was sad that Mrs. Sawatsky was going straight to hell after raising all those kids. Lily, what do you remember most about him?

LILY: "Serve the Lord with fear, with trembling kiss his feet, lest he be angry and you perish . . . for his wrath is quickly kindled." There was always so much wrath.

FRAN: I'll always remember looking to see if his workboots were by the kitchen door. That meant he was in the house and I'd get that frightened feeling in my stomach. Lily, did you think he was ever going to die? I didn't. The horse died on its feet on the hottest day of the summer. Gippy and Rex crept off by themselves and died. I was scared that mother would die in the yard with a load of wet laundry in her arms and that look on her face and I'd be left alone with him. I shouldn't have said that.

LILY: You can't help the way you feel. I just wish I could have come for you sooner. Let's not talk about it anymore.
  (Pause)

FRAN: Lily, does this mean I'm free now?

LILY: Free?

FRAN: Free. Free to sing in the house, push peas around on my plate, to screw up my face, play cards, read books . . . .

LILY *(laughs):* All of those things! And mother will be sixty miles away with Uncle and not worrying over your soul any longer.

FRAN: Thank heavens!

LILY: I'm going to take care of you now. We'll get a nice bright room in the West end with elm trees out front. We'll go to picture shows and tea rooms and libraries . . . .

FRAN: Libraries!

LILY: And you can meet my newspaper friends and join my suffrage club.

FRAN: Your what?

LILY: My suffrage club. Oh, you'll learn about that soon enough.

FRAN *(looks doubtful):* Do you think I'll fit in?

LILY: Of course you will. You're going to love the city!

FRAN: Do you think so?

LILY *(hugs her):* I do, and furthermore, the city will love you! Oh Fanny, you're a brick!

SCENE 2

Women's Press Club. Sound of climbing stairs, voices. NELLIE, LILY enter room in mid conversation. FRANCIS following behind.

NELLIE *(reciting):* "I do not want to pull through life like a thread that has no knot. I want to leave something behind when I go. Some small legacy of truth, some *word* that will shine in a dark place. . . ." What word? What word? I want that word to be. . . .
(They become aware there is no heat in the room.)

LILY: Warmth!

NELLIE *(goes to radiator, bangs it):* Didn't Isobel pay our rent this month?

LILY: Maybe they think they can get rid of us by freezing us to death.
(LILY, NELLIE continue working on speech. FRANCIS walking around room, fingering things.)

LILY: I would start the other way, Nellie.

NELLIE: With the alarm clock? You don't think McNair will call me a drippy tap in need of a washer?

LILY: Well it would not be as bad as when he said you rattled along like an old tin can.

NELLIE: Or the time I squeaked along like a set of rusty bagpipes.

LILY *(laughing):* But it will never top the time he called Isobel as useless as a button on a hat.
(They all laugh.)

NELLIE: The perils of public speaking!

LILY: You won't believe this fellow, Fanny.

FRAN: Who is he?

NELLIE: He's a wart on the nose of progress. He's a loose nut in a machine trying to go forward!

LILY: He's the editor of The Rural Review. We won't be much longer, Fanny. Anyway, I'd leave the alarm clock in. It's an idea that strikes people right between the eyes.

NELL: You're right. I'll leave it in. *(To FRANCIS)* Your sister gives me my best ideas, yet never gets any of the credit!

LILY: Nor any of the abuse. Suits me fine.

NELL: Whenever I see you Francis, I seem to be working on some silly speech. There's more to life than that. I haven't even had a chance to get to know you. I want you to sit down here and tell me all about yourself. *(Indicates sofa)*

FRAN: There's nothing to tell.

LILY: Don't be shy Fanny. *(To NELL)* She devours every book she can get her hands on. She knows more about newspapers than I do after four years at The Free Press. *(To FRANCIS)* You've got lots to tell!

FRAN: Well, I grew up on a farm. . .

NELL: So did I! We've already got something in common! When I was a girl, I loved to read books too, but I was always the first one yanked out of school to herd the cows. I would tear around from one field to another, chasing cows and hating every one of them!

FRAN: I felt exactly the same way!

NELL: Did you?

FRAN: But they had to be moved or they'd eat through all the grass.

NELL: Oh I know they had to be moved, but I couldn't understand why I had to chase them all the time. It was always Nellie that had to do it. Never my brothers.

FRAN: But they had to go to school so they could handle the affairs of the farm.

LILY: But she wanted to go to school too! She wanted to learn to read.

NELL: I wanted to learn how to read more than I wanted to sing in heaven!

FRAN: But what was the point if you were just going to get married?

NELL: But if I was going to be a mother and a wife, wasn't I the most important of all? Didn't I have to be a light . . . a beacon?

LILY: With a husband and all those children in her care?

NELL: Just imagine Fanny . . . imagine how wonderful it would have been if your mother had read Tennyson before you fell asleep at night . . .

Willows whiten, aspens quiver,
little breezes, dusk and shiver,
through the wave that runs forever
by the island in the river
flowing down to Camelot.

Four gray walls and four gray towers
overlook a space of flowers
and the silent isle imbowers
the Lady of Shallot.

FRAN *(entranced)*: Oh, how beautiful! I always wanted to write . . . just like you and Lily! I thought if I could write things down, they'd be clear to everyone . . . all the things I felt inside. I would be clear to everyone and I wouldn't feel so alone.

NELL: Did you ever try?

FRAN: Yes, but I didn't really have anything to say.

NELL: Don't ever say that, Francis! Not ever. Any woman with a mind, a pair of eyes and a heart, already has more than it takes to write for any newspaper in this country!

LILY *(laughs):* Oh Nellie!

NELL: That's a good line! I should use it somewhere.

FRAN: You make it sound so easy.

NELL: It's not easy, but it's worth the effort. Isn't it, Lill?

LILY: That depends on whether you ask me before or after my editor has torn apart my story.

NELL: Details. But the point is we women have finally got a chance to write for one another now. Do you agree?

LILY: I agree.

NELL: Good! *(Turns to FRANCIS)* Francis, we're not chasing cows anymore. We've got no one to blame now but ourselves for not doing what we want. Do you understand? *(FRANCIS nods)* Which leads us back to the problem at hand, the speech for tomorrow night. You're coming aren't you?

FRAN: Oh yes, I'll be there!

NELL: Good!

---· ---

SCENE 3

Auditorium. FRANCIS and LILY enter, sit down. A gentleman, late thirties sits down beside them, takes out a notebook. NELLIE takes podium. Applause begins. FRANCIS riveted.

NELL: My name is Nellie McClung and I'm a disturber. Disturbers are never popular. Nobody likes an alarm clock in action, no matter how grateful they are later for its services! But I've decided that I'm going to keep on being a disturber. I'm not going to pull through life like a thread that has no knot. I want to leave something behind when I go; some small legacy of truth, some word that will shine in a dark place. And I want that word to be . . . DEMOCRACY! Democracy for Women. Because I'm a firm believer in Women, in their ability to see things and feel things and improve things. I believe that it is Women who set the standards for the world and it is up to us, the Women of Canada, to set the standards . . . HIGH!
(Applause)
Maybe I'm sort of a dreamer, maybe I'm sort of naive . . . but I look at my little girls and boys and I think I want a different world for them than the one I was born into. I look at them and my heart cries out when I see them slowly turn towards the roles the world has carved for them; my girls, a life of cooking and sewing and servicing the needs of men; and the boys, scrapping and competing in the playground, then right up into the corridors of government, or even worse, the battlefields. I want them to have a choice in about their lives. We mothers are going to fight for the rights of our little girls to think and dream and speak out. We're going to refuse to bear and rear sons to be shot at on far away battlefields. Women need the vote to bring about a better, more equitable peaceful society, and we're going to get it!
(Standing ovation, LILY and FRANCIS. Gentleman looks on without enthusiasm. NELLIE comes over.)

LILY: You were superb!

FRAN: Oh yes!

NELL: Was I loud enough?

MAN (aside): Excruciatingly.
(NELLIE notices him, stiffens.)

NELL: Why Mr. McNair. I thought I saw a bit of tartan in the crowd. I hope you found my talk . . . enlightening.

McNAIR: It's always interesting to hear a woman speak in public. It's sort of like seeing a pony walking on its hind legs. Clever, even if not natural.

NELL: Well, I hope this time you'll have the decency to spell my name right. There are two "c"s. It is McCLUNG not MCLUNG.
(McNAIR gets out notebook, corrects spelling.)

McNAIR: What a pity. It was a rather good play on words.

LILY (steering NELLIE away): I see Isobel over there. Let's go and see what she thought. Fanny, why don't you have some lemonade and I'll be back in a minute. Good day, Mr. McNair.
(FRANCIS goes over to refreshment table, McNAIR follows.)

McNAIR: At least I can be assured of a little refreshment at these events . . . for what it's worth.
(FRANCIS ignoring him, looking off in direction of LILY and NELL. McNAIR studies her.)

McNAIR: So . . . are you their newest recruit?

FRAN: I am Lily's sister.

McNAIR: Oh they have no shame! Dragging out their relatives to fill the seats.

FRAN: No one dragged me out tonight. I came of my own accord.

McNAIR: Well you'll find that once is enough. It gets very repetitious. Nellie said the same thing at the Walker Theatre last week.

FRAN: It sounded spontaneous to me.

McNAIR: That's a knack she's got.

FRAN: Well why did you come a second time if you thought so little of it the first?

McNAIR: I'm a reporter. I never give up hope.

FRAN: I see. I understand that you edit The Rural Review.

McNAIR (flattered): That's correct. Does your husband take The Review?

FRAN: I'm not married. But if I was, I'm sure he would, since it's the best farm paper this side of Kingston.

McNAIR: What's in Kingston?

FRAN: The Advocate, of course.

McNAIR: The Advocate? It's a rag!

FRAN: I disagree.

McNAIR: It's a liberal propaganda sheet . . . and it's weak on markets.

FRAN: You're weak on crop summaries.

McNAIR: You don't say? Well I suppose your sister fills you up with all of her "opinions".

FRAN: Mr. McNair, that is MY opinion. There is no need to blame it on Lily.

McNAIR: Well I didn't mean to offend . . .

FRAN: Oh no! You seem to delight in it.

McNAIR: I happen to think that Lily's not a bad little writer . . . despite all of this. *(Indicates suffrage meeting)*

FRAN: Well, I'll tell her you said that.

McNAIR *(uncomfortable):* Fine.

FRAN: I think Lily's a good writer too . . . .

McNAIR: Good. That's good. *(Attemps an exit)* Well I'd better get back and write this up.

FRAN: But I think her Paper's soft . . . soft on facts, soft on the truth, soft on the banks, soft on the railways . . . but HARD on farmers!

McNAIR: You do have "Opinions"!

FRAN: And even harder on the Woman Question.

McNAIR *(disappointed):* Then you're a suffragette?

FRAN: I believe the word is . . . suffragist.

McNAIR: Gist! Gist!

FRAN: Yes, I guess I am.

McNAIR *(attempts another exit):* Well, time is marching on . . .

FRAN: I'm curious Mr. McNair, why didn't you send your Women's Editor tonight?

McNAIR: Couldn't. She went and . . . passed away.

FRAN: Oh, I'm sorry to hear that.

McNAIR: Well, she was over 70. She wouldn't have taken to this type of event much either. Anyway, she's history and I'm stuck without a living soul to attend these interminable meetings!

FRAN: Perhaps you might think of hiring someone with more modern ideas.

McNAIR: Easier said than done, little Miss.

FRAN: Perhaps you might think of hiring me.

McNAIR: You? Hiring you? I don't even know you.

FRAN: Sir, I come from a farm and I am a woman. I know all about bedbugs and woodticks, runny eyes in chicks, cracked tits on milkers, cakes without eggs . . . and how to avoid the minister's visit.

McNAIR: I'm sure you do.

FRAN: My grammar's good. Lily taught me how to type. And I wouldn't wallow in sentimentality like that last one. No offence meant.

McNAIR: Miss Beynon, you're making a speech. It's unwomanly.

FRAN: It's not unwomanly Mr. McNair. It's 1912. And I'm simply trying to interest you in my qualifications.

McNAIR *(is interested):* Well, perhaps you should try to interest me in the cold light of day. Shall we say nine o'clock tomorrow morning? Mind you're not late!

FRAN: No!
(McNAIR walks towards the door, then turns.)

McNAIR: And don't forget to bring your lunch. *(Exits.)*

FRAN *(to herself):* I think I've got myself a job!

---•---

SCENE 4

FRANCIS approaches desk, sits down, begins to write her first editorial. Tentative.

FRAN: It is my great pleasure to begin my new task as editor of the Homemaker's Page. I have lived on a western farm myself and when I was a girl, rode the calves home from the pasture and chased the wild geese off the wheatfields back of the granary. In my mind's eye, I can still see my mother, standing alone against the far away fields of wheat, sunhat in hand, her skirts blowing away with the wind, looking for a rare visitor to come down the road.

I now know that she was only one of the thousands of lonely women of the prairies . . . far from neighbours, far from towns, far from doctors.

Within this page, I hope you will all be able to get closer to one another. I hope you will begin to see this as YOUR page, where you can write and think and dream and rage . . . and in every way, help one another.

The page is now YOURS.
(Throughout the play, women of the prairies will respond to FRANCIS' editorials through letters.)

DEAR MISS BEYNON
This is my first letter to your Homemaker's Page — though I've had talks galore with you up here . . . *(points to head)*

I live on the prairie with not many neighbours but I'm really not at all lonely. I had a serious operation last May and then a few weeks after, our little house and everything in it, burned down. But in the midst of it all, God has blessed us with another little baby. *(Weak smile)* Our eighth. So life is never dull.

Could you please send me your little booklet HOW TO TELL THE TRUTH TO CHILDREN? It is comforting to know that children can be told . . . . the truth, and still retain the cleanness of thought and purity we wish for them. I've enclosed 5 cents for postage.

My husband says what a rigamarole letter . . . though I can't write in a hurry . . . so please forgive. Your sincerest reader,

SUNBEAM

DEAR MISS BEYNON:
I got something to say to your reader — Titewad's Wife.

I have had three husbands and I think you got to have three husbands before you gets your fair av'rige. My first was terrible thin. My second was terrible fat.

Men run that way. Always one thing or the other. Either terrible drinkers or don't drink at all. Either terrible tempers or no tempers at all. Some as cheap as pig dirt, others with an open hand. Don't see how us women folks stands em.

Mens upsesses and downsesses has wore me out.

My third husband was just plain averige. He just wasn't one thing or another. He was just so ordinary I couldn't stand him any longer and I divorced him.

So to you lady I say, it's only after you have three husbands you know what you really want, and that's no husband at all.

ALWAYS YOURS . . . CHUCKLEHEAD

———————— • ————————

SCENE 5

Women's Press Club. FRANCIS is answering letters from her readers. LILY and NELLIE are helping. NELLIE is pregnant.

FRAN *(holds up letter):*   How do you remove warts from animals and humans?

LILY: Apply the water you pour off beans after they're boiled soft.

FRAN *(reads):*   I am five months pregnant and I have a terrible time lacing my corset good and tight. Any suggestions?

LILY: That's your department, Nell.

NELL: Tell her to throw her corset in the closet. That's what I've done. *(Pats her stomach)* Otherwise, our children will grow up with a terror of small rooms.

FRAN: Is there any way to lengthen the life of my stockings?

LILY: Tell her to rub parafin on their soles.

FRAN: What is the best colour of paint to go with oatmeal wallpaper?

NELL: Either bone or brown.

FRAN: Do I have any advice on how to keep baby chicks in the pink?

NELL: For heaven's sakes Francis, you don't have to answer everything. Give that one to the Hen Department at the paper!

FRAN *(laughs):*   There is no Hen Department.

NELL: Well there should be.

FRAN: I don't know how I'd answer all of these without you.

NELL: Well we wouldn't want you to lose your job.

LILY: Don't worry Fanny, you'll be able to answer this kind of stuff in your sleep in no time.

NELL: I have better things to do. Let's stop now and practice.

FRAN: There's just one more. "Would someone be so kind as to tell me how I can clean feathers. I have an owl and would be very pleased if I could find out how to clean it?"

NELL: An owl? Is it a dead owl?

LILY: What would anyone want with a dead owl?

FRAN: I have an "owl" is all she wrote.

LILY: Maybe she wants to clean it out, then cook it.

NELL: Cook an owl? How disgusting!

LILY: No, I think it must be a stuffed owl if she's interested in its feathers. It's probably been sitting on her mantlepiece for years and the feathers are dirty.

NELL: Cornstarch then. How would you cook an owl anyway?

LILY: Probably just like a duck.

NELL: But there wouldn't be much to it, would there?

FRAN: Maybe she has a pet owl . . . like some people have pet crows.

NELL: I had a pussycat. Animals don't need anyone to clean them. They clean themselves. I wish people would be more concise.

LILY: It must be dead then. Tell her to rub the feathers in cornstarch and, if by chance, she wants to eat it, tell her to clean it out like a duck and cook it with lots of spices.

NELL: Great! Let's get on with the practise.
(NELL cranks up gramophone. FRANCIS puts away papers. NELL hands out scarves, begins to demonstrate dance.)

LILY: Don't strain yourself Nell. You might shake it loose.

NELL: Would that be so terrible?

F & L: Nellie!

NELL: Well I've had four already. How many does a modern woman need. My Jack is already 15. How about you and Vernon?

LILY: I would like three but Vernon thinks it would interrupt his concentration.

NELL: I think Vernon concentrates far too much! *(They laugh)* And you, Francis?

FRAN: No one will even want to marry me.

NELL: Oh, don't be so hard on yourself! Come here now and I'll show you how to do this.
(FRANCIS gets up, moves about awkwardly at NELLIE's tutelage.)
This is an Interpretive Dance. You just let your body move in whatever way you feel. It's very naughty. I saw it at The Palladium last time we were in London. They go mad for dancing over there. If the British Suffragists can do it, so can we. Imagine you're a swan.

FRAN: I feel like a prairie chicken!

NELL: Close your eyes. It helps you forget about yourself. Stick out your hips Fanny. Farther.

FRAN: If McNair could see me now. He thinks its queer for a woman to speak in public!

LILY: What's he going to think when he sees us doing an interpretive dance at the Press Club Christmas party?
  (They laugh.)

NELL: Maybe he'd go back to Glasgow where he belongs, working for some reactionary tabloid. He's like a scotch thistle bristling for a fight. And you know, he drinks.

LILY: Don't be too hard on McNair. Fanny doesn't mind him. She told me that under all that bluster is a good heart.

NELL: Well his mind skids when it comes to suffrage! And he drinks.

LILY *(laughs):* You've already said that! I think your mind skids when it comes to McNair.

FRAN: He's not that bad, Nellie.

NELL: What's good about him?

FRAN: Well . . . he wears plaid ear-muffs to work on cold mornings. And sometimes during the day, I can hear him in his office humming to himself . . . Bonnie Dundee.

NELL: Francis, you've taken a shine to him. He's almost old enough to be your father!

FRAN: No I haven't.

NELL: Then why are you blushing?

FRAN: Because I feel preposterous doing this dance.

LILY *(comes to her rescue):* You're doing fine. Here, let me tie your scarf.

NELL: I think she's going to miss you when you marry Vernon. Who will do up her buttons and make her hair nice?

LILY: She can look after herself.

NELL: Well, now that we've got warts and matching wallpaper out of the way, we'll have to get her working on the larger issues. Tomorrow you can come along to my Women for Peace Committee. We've started a world disarmament campaign, and then, after that, we'll drop in on the Christian Temperance meeting. We can always use new recruits, Francis. It's always the same old girls in everything.

FRAN: I'd love to come.

NELL: Good. Alright now, let's all three try it together . . . from the top.
  (Music crossover into next scene.)

———————————•———————————

SCENE 6

The newspaper office. FRANCIS is practising her dance step, door opens, she hears McNAIR approaching. She slides back behind her desk. McNAIR enters.

McNAIR: Let's see what you've got on your page this week?
   (Pulls page out of typewriter, begins to read aloud.)
"We have too long been contented with the kind of motherhood that can turn its back on mere children toiling incredible hours in factories making bullets and ammunition and uniforms for some far away war and yet calmly say, 'Thank God it's not my children.' What we need now is a new spirit of national motherhood." And someone who can write shorter sentences. National motherhood. National motherhood? You make it sound like the railway, Miss Beynon.

FRAN *(deflated):*   I quite liked that expression.

McNAIR: Is it yours?

FRAN: Well . . .

McNAIR: It sounds like something off of Mrs. McClung's bat. You seem to have an opinion about everything lately. National motherhood, intemperate husbands, the German War Machine, the profession of parenthood, the Boy Scout movement, and suffrage ad nauseum. But I find myself wondering . . . what happened to your columns on mothers and babies, ginger snaps and peonies? What about the little crocheted sweaters for the wee ones. Hmmmm? What about those things? They're important too.

FRAN: Do you think they are more important than freedom from cruel husbands and fathers; from hypocritical ministers, from war mongering politicians?

McNAIR: Oh don't bludgeon me with adjectives. Just say what you mean.

FRAN: I'm sorry.

McNAIR: Unfortunately, the things you mention will always be with us. Scotchbroth and shortbread and a garden full of bluebells make them a bit more tolerable. My mother knew that. She would never have bothered herself with voting and chasing the men out of bars.

FRAN: But was she happy?

McNAIR: Happy? I don't know. She seemed content. She smiled alot.

FRAN: You mean she just put up with it.

McNAIR: Perhaps. But the point is, she had enough to do in the home. You'll be wise to keep that in mind.

FRAN: If you think that women belong in the home, why did you hire me?

McNAIR: I had no choice. What self-respecting man would want to write about "women's things". Unfortunately, you don't seem interested in writing about them either.

FRAN: Mr. McNair, are you not finding my work satisfactory?

McNAIR: Did I say that?

FRAN: You imply that.

McNAIR: I do not. I think that the suffrage question is . . . interesting, but you take it much too far. Mrs. McClung need only pen one of her silly little verses and it somehow finds its way into your editorials.

FRAN: Mrs. McClung is at the forefront of the suffrage cause.

McNAIR: She is a dilettante and a debutante. And a hypocrite. She's an upper class snob who wouldn't have given my poor mother the time of day.

FRAN: That's not true. Nellie McClung is fighting for the vote for women.

McNAIR: For women who don't need the vote. For women who've got something better than the vote! Influence! And furthermore, the proper lineage!

FRAN: No!

McNAIR: No? Then tell me why your suffrage club list is full of names like Steward, Titheradge, Ward, Galbraith, Gordon and not . . . Lewycky, Schapansky and Swartz?

FRAN: Well maybe their husbands won't let them come.

McNAIR: They're not there because your suffrage club doesn't want them there. Neither do they want them living next to them on Chestnut Street nor their children sitting beside theirs at school.

FRAN: Mr. McNair, I believe in democracy for *all* women. I do!

McNAIR: Then you're in the minority. Isobel Graham has gone on record saying she's afraid the entire western hemisphere is sinking under the weight of the immigrants.

FRAN: Isobel has . . . a blind spot.

McNAIR: And Laura McLaughlin, another one of your leading lights, is heading up the fight to eliminate any foreign language in the schoolyard.

FRAN: That's because Laura thinks it's important that newcomers learn English.

McNAIR: That's because she hates the very idea of them. And that includes their women!

FRAN: I admit there are some members who don't feel comfortable with all the strangers in our midst, but that will change. It takes time to alter attitudes. It takes time to remove the walls of class and privilege and ethnic differences that . . .

McNAIR: Oh don't haul out your rhetoric again. It doesn't suit you. The fact is the suffragists are an exclusive club. And you'd do well to stay away from it.

FRAN: I find it curious how you suddenly spring to the defence of foreign women. Because in the year that I've known you, you have never shown interest in ANY women having the vote . . . whether their name was Gordon or Schapansky! I'm beginning to think that you just enjoy muddying the waters!

McNAIR *(winks):* I enjoy arguing with you. You argue like a man!

FRAN: Well I am not.

McNAIR: And I'm glad you're not.

FRAN *(flustered):*   I believe in the vote for women, all women, and I am going to keep fighting for it.

McNAIR: Now don't get so ruffled. It's not that important, is it?

FRAN: Mr. McNair, let me try to explain something to you. When I was a child, on the farm, I was constantly asking questions. Does God ever change his mind? Why was he angry all the time? Why couldn't I talk to the Polish kids on the next farm? Why didn't my father help them out like the other neighbours? But nobody wanted to answer them. My father, and the Methodist minister and later my teachers . . . thrashed and sermonized and ridiculed me until my spirit shrank and I began to doubt my very worth.

McNAIR: It didn't seem to have been a lasting affliction. You seem to have quite an unswerving confidence.

FRAN: Well I don't. I still cower at the voice of authority. Even now, I tense up as you, my editor come into the room. Do you understand what I'm talking about?

McNAIR: Yes, I think so, but I'm not sure what it has to do with suffrage.

FRAN: Oh, but it's all connected! When I came to the city, I met women fighting for the freedom to think and worship and question for themselves. Women who challenge authority . . . who look it right in the eye and say prove you're worthy of respect! I felt like I'd been let out of prison. I felt like a great gleam of sunlight had broken through the fog. And I didn't feel alone anymore!

McNAIR: You're a funny one. You remind me of those little birds. I found trapped in the house when I was a child. My mother would make me catch them and let them go free outside. And whenever I caught them, I could feel their little hearts beating in my hand, and I wanted to tell them not to be afraid, that I wasn't going to hurt them. You're like one of those little birds. Miss Beynon, I understand you live alone since your sister married. Perhaps you might be needing someone to look in on you once in a while.

FRAN: Well I would like that very much.

McNAIR: Good then, I will do that. It's time you associated with someone who still holds womanhood sacred.

FRAN: No! I don't need anyone to hold womanhood sacred. I hold womanhood sacred myself. I do!

McNAIR: Well you hold it at quite a distance. It might help your cause if you applied some rouge to your cheeks occasionally. Goodday, Miss Beynon, I'll let you get back to national motherhood.

(McNAIR exits, FRANCIS sits down at desk, begins typing angrily.)

FRANCIS *(editorial):*   Men say that women have enough to do in their homes without worrying about going to the polling station. I have been doing some thinking about this. Prairie women have been trapped too long inside the home, lonely and dependent from the day they wed til the day they die. And yet, aren't we as necessary to Prairie society as the sun and the rain is to the fields? Don't we deserve to be seen as whole people, with the same rights and responsibilities as the men we work beside? That's why I want the vote, because a vote is like being given a voice when before we were silent. It's like being set free after years of captivity. In the end, isn't what we're really talking about Freedom? I think so. But I've talked long enough. Please write and tell us what Freedom means to you.

F.M.B.

DEAR MISS BEYNON:
Some go to the Bible for proof that woman should not have the freedom to vote. I can see nothing there to convince me that women have no interest outside her house. The very fact that God placed Eve outside in his big garden and not inside the four walls of a kitchen ought to prove she was intended to be a companion to her husband and to see and understand whatever interests him.

I want to thank you and your sister Lily and Nellie McClung for all the wonderful work you're doing in elevating women to their rightful place as queen of the home.

SINCERELY WESTERN SISTER.

P.S. Could any of the readers tell me how to take rust out of a white dress?

DEAR MISS BEYNON
Freedom for me would be a public restroom in town. A place where a woman could go after a long trip in from the country. Please work on that.

SUNFLOWER

DEAR MISS BEYNON:
I agree with you that freedom would come with getting the vote. If women had it sooner, there wouldn't be so many laws on the books which are a disgrace to civilization . . . not to mention Humanity.

DEAR MISS BEYNON
I am 31 years old, the mother of 7 children, the eldest 11 years, the youngest 8 months, I would like to have any information I can get about birth control. That would be freedom for me.

DEAR MISS BEYNON
With all this talk of women's freedom, maybe there's something you're forgetting. And that's the foreigners. Haven't we got enough trouble with them over there, without letting them think they can run our country too? Can we bear dilution by the ignorance, low idealism and religious perversity of the average foreigner? I say no! We must keep them back. Give us good sound British stock women, already civilized, already subject to both earth and heaven for conduct.

WOLFWILLOW

FRAN (editorial):   I have to take exception to a recent view from Wolfwillow about immigrants within our country. It seems tragic to me the number of people, who without being able to give a single reason, instinctively hate or fear or distrust every person who does not belong to the same race or religion as themselves. I think it's because society forces everyone into the same mould, and persecutes those who refuse to be shaped in regulation pattern. But what is the harm of people being different? Is anyone who is original in their thinking really so frightening?

(LILY is reading remainder of editorial at beginning next scene)
If our country of Canada is going to achieve its potential as a great nation, we must begin to recognize and cherish the contributions of people from all lands who decide to make it their HOME.

For my part, I would say, that the real foreigners, are not those who have been raised in different countries, but those whose standards and ideals of life are so immoveable as to not allow for communication with others.

---•---

SCENE 7

Women's Press Club. LILY is reading FRANCIS' editorial in newspaper. NELLIE seated.

LILY: It's beautiful Fanny.

FRAN: You mean that?

LILY: Yes I do! I knew you'd put your heart and mind to work and come out with something that rang absolutely true! *(Hugs her)* She's quite a girl, isn't she Nell?

NELL: At least she doesn't come to us for advice on Hens anymore.

LILY: Is that all you've got to say?

FRAN: Do you like it Nell?

NELL: I'm surprised that McNair let you run such an idealistic little piece.

FRAN: He said he thought it was sort of . . . hopeful.

LILY: Well it is hopeful, and I'm proud of you! Nell, aren't you?

NELL: She's a quick learner.

FRAN: Nellie, do you like it?

NELL: Like it? I think the sentiments are admirable, but I wonder if it takes everything into account.

FRAN: What do you mean?

NELL: Such as what's going on in Europe right now. Some of the countries where these Foreigners hail from are rattling their sabres at Britain even as we speak. People are frightened. God only knows what might happen over there. That's all Fanny.

LILY: Well I think we should go have an icecream to celebrate her efforts.

NELL: You two go along. I've got to finish some work first.
(LILY and FRANCIS leave. FRANCIS crestfallen.)

---•---

SCENE 8

FRANCIS' suite. FRANCIS straightening things, looking in mirror, nervous. Doorbell rings. It's McNAIR.

FRAN: Good afternoon, Mr. McNair.

McNAIR: Good afternoon, Miss Beynon. I hope I'm not disturbing you.

FRAN: No, not at all. Won't you come in.

McNAIR: I guess you're wondering why I dropped a note about visiting today.

FRAN: I thought perhaps you were going to be in the neighbourhood.
  (McNAIR takes a letter out of pocket, hands it to her.)

McNAIR: Not exactly. Here's a letter I received from a group of your readers in the Zid District. It seems they take exception to your column on the Foreign question.
  (FRANCIS reads, looks upset.)

FRAN: I thought it was the most heartfelt thing I'd written.

McNAIR: It was mercifully short of adjectives.

FRAN: It sounds as if they hate me.

McNAIR: Not you, Miss Beynon, just what you're saying.

FRAN: Maybe I was a bit outspoken. Even Nellie seemed cool when she read it.

McNAIR: Did you believe in what you wrote?

FRAN: Yes.

McNAIR: Well then?

FRAN *(FRANCIS reads on):* They're asking for my resignation. That's why you've come, isn't it?

McNAIR: I wouldn't be much of an editor if I could be intimidated by bigots such as these. I follow a hardy little gleam myself called Freedom of the Press. You're doing a good job, Miss Beynon. I've never seen as much mail as you've generated. I'm not saying I agree with everything you write. Believe me, I don't. I'm not a big reformer, as you know. But as long as you write with fairness and reason, and punctuation. . . . I'll back you. I came to tell you that.

FRAN: But what about this? *(The letter)*

McNAIR: Forget about the letter. Your column obviously struck a chord in some of your readers, and they don't like the sound of it. But that's not your problem.

FRAN: Except that I have this tight feeling in my stomach that I haven't felt since I was a child.

McNAIR: If you want to be liked by everyone, you're in the wrong line of work.

FRAN: Perhaps I am.

McNAIR: Don't say that. You'll grow a thicker skin in time. Look at me.

FRAN: Is that what that is?

McNAIR: I think you're a fighter, and when the occasion arises, you'll come out strong.

FRAN: Thank you. I hope you're right. Could you stay for a while and have some tea?

McNAIR: That would be lovely, Miss Beynon.

FRAN: Please call me Francis.

McNAIR: Alright Francis, please call me McNair.
(FRANCIS gets up, goes for tea.)

McNAIR: How does one occupy one's time when not fighting for women's rights?

FRAN: I've been known to go to concerts in the park and even some plays. Lily and I have frequented every tea room in the city. Sometimes her husband Vernon takes us out to the country in his roadster.

McNAIR: Perhaps some afternoon you might enjoy a trip up to Winnipeg Beach. I hear it's a popular spot with the fashionable crowd. Though being seen with me would perhaps not be quite so fashionable.

FRAN: I would be delighted to be seen with you.

McNAIR: Perhaps some time the two of us could go to Church . . . or did the fierce God of the Methodists scare you off altogether.

FRAN: No, I've made my own truce with God. In fact, I met God one afternoon in a corner of the pasture.

McNAIR: Did you?

FRAN: I'd gone out before a thunderstorm to find the cows. I remember looking all around and seeing nothing but a few shacks between me and the far away edges of the world. Then over the east, a snake of fire wiggled down the sky, followed by a crash of thunder. Then a breeze stirred my hair and I felt I was riding on the wings of a bird. I knew God passed by in that breeze because for a moment, I wasn't afraid of anything — not my father, or the minister, or doing compositions, or Lily's warts . . . or anything at all.

McNAIR: I don't know whether you're a heathen or not, but you breathe a clean wholesome look upon life. My mother would have liked you Francis. Perhaps getting that letter wasn't so unpleasant after all. It's given us a chance to . . .
(McNAIR notices an orange sash on a chair, with the words — VOTES FOR WOMEN. He goes over and picks it up.)

McNAIR: What trumpery is this?

FRAN: That's my sash for the suffrage parade.

McNAIR: Your sash?

FRAN: Yes. We're all wearing them . . . for effect.

McNAIR: Surely Francis, you're not going to make a spectacle of yourself like that?

FRAN: Well that all depends on what one calls a spectacle.

McNAIR: I call an army of matrons marching down Main Street in orange sashes a spectacle. My God, you'll have the whole city staring gape-mouthed at you. Laughing and hooting and hollering. It's outrageous.

FRAN: Now wait a minute!

McNAIR: A whole generation of women being turned upside down, turned into shrill opinionated harpies, when they should be at home, having lots of good strong children!

FRAN: Like a bunch of good breeding hogs!

McNAIR: There's nothing wrong with good breeding. And there's not enough of it happening anymore. None of you ladies seem to care that we'll be at war in a month, and there'll be real armies marching down Main Street.

FRAN: Of course we care, but we can't just drop women's suffrage because a bunch of countries can't settle their differences.

McNAIR: You're a babe in the woods.

FRAN: And you're a. . . . You're unspeakable! You're everything that people say about you.

McNAIR: Well if what you mean is that I don't delude myself and that I'm not a dreamer, then it's true.

FRAN: Well I am a dreamer! And I believe there are changes coming. Wonderful changes . . . that will allow everyone to live in freedom. Those days are coming but we have to fight for them.

McNAIR: There is something very wrong with you. I would not permit my wife, if I had one, to carry on the way you do.

FRAN: Well I would certainly not permit my husband, if I had one, to substitute his conscience for mine! Good day McNair!
(Melodramatic sweep of her hand, indicates door. McNAIR leaves. FRANCIS picks up sash, turns it over in her hands, looks miserable.)

———————— • ————————

SCENE 9

At the suffrage parade. FRANCIS is standing in the crowd, listening to NELL McCLUNG speak. Atmosphere jolly, excited.

NELL *(with megaphone):* Alright sisters, you've got your instructions for the parade. Afterwards, we're invited to Government House for tea and sandwiches with the Premier of the Province and the Mayor of Winnipeg. You look beautiful out there. We've come along way sisters. The day has finally arrived when we've beaten back the bigotry which says that Men are better than Women. This day strikes a blow for social equality!
(Suffrage march begins. Victorious moment. FRANCIS in the midst, elated.)

FRAN: Oh I am thankful to be living in these fighting days, when there are so many things waiting to be done, that we have no time to sit and feel sorry for ourselves, when Humanity is seething and boiling and stirring with a thousand conflicting interests, which in the end will work themselves out to the final good of the race. And we women have just begun to dabble with our fingertips in this great eddying stream of life!

(Suddenly suffrage music turns into military music. Parade sounds into sound of heavy boots. The expression on FRANCIS face changes from victory, to confusion and fear.

A drill sergeant calls out:

"Company halt!")

END OF FIRST ACT

ACT: 2

SCENE 1

FRANCIS is in her apartment. It's Christmas time. She is writing her Christmas editorial. 1916.

FRAN *(editorial):*   The Christmas edition of The Review will have to go out this year without a Christmas editorial on the women's page. Vainly I have tried to call up the old jubilant spirit of Christmas . . . without success. To observe this great celebration, while Christian Europe is busy contradicting its teaching "Peace on Earth, Good Will to men", seems almost a sacrilege.

   The pen writes haltingly and unconvincingly upon the subject . . . and finally stumbles and stops altogether.

   (Light up on LILY, seated on sofa, rolling bandages. FRANCIS pacing.)

LILY: We took bones last night. It's astonishing how many ways there are of being injured. We learned that anything ending in "itis" is an inflammation. First Aid is a rude sort of thing. You just grab an old gent's cane or umbrella for splints and a lady's clothing for bandages. Carrie Markham says she just knows she'll be wearing her best and Frenchest lingerie when she'll have to tear it into bandages for some poor private.

   Then we did drowning . . . with a REAL man to demonstrate. In one method, you have to hold the tongue of the drownee out with a handkerchief. The tongue is a rather slippery member. Sometimes one has to put a needle through it to keep it outside the mouth. That's in case there is a lot of blood in the throat . . . .

FRAN: Lily, what are you talking about?

LILY: My first aid class.

FRAN: The war is three thousand miles away. Why are you taking first aid?

LILY: It's good to be prepared.

FRAN: Prepared for what?

LILY: Prepared in case we have to do our bit.

FRAN: Are you off to France to save men . . . drowning on the battlefield.

LILY: Of course not.

FRAN: Is the conflict going to spread to Canada?

LILY: That's not the point.

FRAN: Then what is the point of these endless first aid classes? To me, it all seems . . . daft.

LILY: Everything seems daft to you lately. Even what I'm doing!

FRAN: That's cause you're doing the strangest things.
   (LILY gets up to leave.)

FRAN: Where are you going?

LILY: I shouldn't have come. I hoped maybe we could talk about . . . just talk . . . but you're being . . . oh I don't know how to describe it!

FRAN: I'm sorry Lily. Please don't go. I need to talk too.

LILY: Alright then. You start.

FRAN: Lily, do you remember when Ned Stone's father came back from the Boer War. He said he'd seen British soldiers rounding up women and children and putting them in compounds. He said he saw them dying like flies. I walked home across the field, trying to imagine people dying like flies . . . you and mother and Mrs. Gregory and the Hawkin girls. . . . Lily, that's what's happening over there! Last month, one hundred thousand men died in one day!

LILY: I know. I read the paper.

FRAN: Lily, what do you really think of the war?

LILY: I don't want to think about it.

FRAN: Why not?

LILY: It gives me a headache.

FRAN *(exasperated):* Well that's a small price to pay compared to some!

LILY: There you go again!

FRAN: I'm sorry. It's just that I look at those boys on the parade ground. There almost too young to shave yet, and yet there they're marching around, waving their bayonets, making funny noises, jumping to attention. It all seems so . . . pointless.

LILY: How can you say that? They're fighting for democracy, so that you and I can live in freedom. Isn't that what they're fighting for?

FRAN: So they say. I heard Vernon talk last night at the Labour Temple. I thought you'd be there.

LILY: I couldn't miss my class.

FRAN: Couldn't pass up splints and tourniquets to hear your husband speak out against the war?

LILY: I know what he said. He gave me a private rendition last night when he came home. The British peers own part of the armaments plants in Germany. The first guns captured from the Germans were made in England. The only people who will win the war will be the munitions makers. Conscription is a violent attack on the rights of the individual. . . .

FRAN: Well?

LILY: Well . . . it makes sense . . . and I believe him. But I just don't know how to put it all together . . . what Vernon's saying, what others are saying. I . . . it would be alot easier is if he wasn't giving public lectures.

FRAN: Lily! Vernon has a right to speak in public.

LILY: Except that half the paper won't talk to him now and the copy editor checks my stories twice before they go to press. He assumes I think like Vernon.

FRAN: Well don't you?

LILY: Well yes but . . .

FRAN: Then you've got to stand up for him Lily! You've always fought for people's right to express themselves. The issue here is Freedom!

LILY: But I thought it was freedom that we're fighting for over there? Well whatever it is, there are millions of young men going out and fighting for it. How can they all be wrong?

FRAN: But how can you ever be free by killing people or being afraid that someone's going to kill you?

LILY: I can see why father hated your questions.

FRAN: Now's not the time to be quiet Lily. My God, even McNair's not hoodwinked by all this flagwaving hysteria! He's getting his teeth into war graft and profiteering.

LILY: Well that's fine for him, He's too old to have to worry about it.

FRAN: What do you mean?

LILY: Conscription is coming Fanny.

FRAN: Lily, is that what you're upset about? Vernon wouldn't go, would he?

LILY: No. He's a pacifist.

FRAN: Well that's good, isn't it?

LILY: I suppose.

FRAN: You don't sound happy!

LILY: I am. I am. It's just that if he won't go, does that make him . . . a coward?

FRAN: Do you think he's a coward?

LILY: No. But I think . . . if Vernon won't go, what about Nellie's Jack? He enlisted the day he turned eighteen.

FRAN: Oh I hate this!

LILY: So do I! *(LILY bursts into tears.)*

The Fighting Days

LILY: Isn't it strange, Fanny. One day we're collecting signatures for the vote, and the next, we're signing up people for the patriotic fund. I can't even remember anymore who signed what. Last July at Nellie's cottage, Vernon was playing football with Jack on the beach, and all of us were lolling in the hammocks. . . . I don't know what to think anymore, Fanny. I'm trying not to think. That's why I'm taking these silly classes from women in red white and blue dresses. I have to DO something!

FRAN *(comes over and comforts her):* I know Lily.
(A knock at the door.)

FRAN: That must be McNair. He's early. I'll be right back.
(McNAIR enters, sees LILY.)

McNAIR: Lily! *(Notices she's crying)* I hope I haven't interrupted anything. I could come back later.

LILY: No, please don't leave on my account. I'm alright now.

McNAIR: I just thought I'd peruse the papers in pleasant company before going to the party.
(He sits down on sofa, opens papers)
Just pretend I'm not here. *(Awkward pause)* Here, this will cheer you us! *(Reading)* "The Boer War has brought us the khaki brown and the mopish scout hats, and just as we were feeling at home in these sombre shades, war was declared in the Balkans, and that brought us, blessedly I might add, those pretty peasant waists and rich bright-hued embroideries of the southern climes. Let's hope we never go to war with the Eskimos."
Fantastic mind behind that report.

FRAN: Why would that cheer us up?

McNAIR: Well, at least neither of you is responsible for it.
(FRANCIS laughs.)

McNAIR: Listen to this. *(Reads)* "The patriotism of those war manufacturers who are skinning kin and country with their faulty gear and second-rate "holey" boots is the kind of patriotism that should be recognized by a coat of tar and feathers. But instead, they'll probably get a title!" My God that man can write!

FRAN: Who wrote it?

McNAIR: I did!
(LILY and FRANCIS both laugh. LILY collects up her things.)

LILY: Oh you're a ray of sunshine on a cloudy day, McNair. I'm going home to get ready now.

McNAIR *(stands):* We'll see you later then.
(FRANCIS goes to door with her. They hug.)

FRAN: We'll see you soon.
(FRANCIS comes back into room, starts pacing. McNAIR watches.)

McNAIR: You've got a bee in your bonnet.

FRAN: Would you ever think of fighting in the war?

McNAIR: It's a bit late in the day for me to enlist.

FRAN: But if you weren't too old, would you even consider it?

McNAIR: I suppose I would.

FRAN: Why?

McNAIR: Why? Because it's getting bloody hard to stay out of it! If you're of age and not in uniform, women look at you as if you're not quite complete. And the men simply hate you.

FRAN: But why is that? What business is it of theirs? It's your life!

McNAIR: Am I catching the tail end of an argument?

FRAN: Yes, you are. I'm sorry. *(She sits down beside him)*

McNAIR: If I was younger, I would go to war, Francis. I have a responsibility to fight for the freedom of my country.

FRAN: What does that really mean?

McNAIR: Well, it means to protect our homes, our loved ones . . . our women. Men are supposed to sacrifice their lives for women. Haven't you noticed? Since the war started, I haven't heard a peep from your Women for Peace Committee. Why do you think that is?

FRAN: They're knitting socks and rolling bandages.

McNAIR: But why do you think that is?

FRAN: I don't know. I don't know.

McNAIR: Because when it comes right down to it, women need protection, and they know it. At least most of them know it. And that's why they swoon into the arms of the first waiting soldier.

FRAN: Why do you say things like that to me?

McNAIR: I can't resist. Your cheeks colour up in such a pretty way.

FRAN: Well I'm tired of knitting socks. It's time to DO something!

McNAIR: You could put on your coat and we could go to the party.

FRAN: I'm serious.

McNAIR: You've taken some pot shots at the Patriotic Fund. You're always haranguing us about the treatment of foreigners. *(FRANCIS dismisses this)* My editorials started the ball rolling towards the investigation on rotten boots. I think we're doing our part by keeping the war honest.

FRAN: McNair, I remember my first column about the war. *(Recollecting)* "We women will keep our Purpose clear — true democracy — and with our purpose, transport our men, our country, through the troubled waters of war!" I saw Womanhood as some great unsinkable ship which would buoy up everyone!

McNAIR: That's an admirable image.

FRAN: Except that it was wrong! We thought we were sailing the vessel of freedom, but there seems to be a thousand others out there with the same claim. How can freedom take so many forms? I don't know what to think anymore. Lily's on the verge of tears all the time and Nellie's a flagwaving patriot. We've got the vote now, but we're too anxious or terrified to figure out what to do with it. The letters I get are filled with war and loss and fear. . . .

McNAIR: And while you're at it, you're the worst of all! You're brooding constantly over every war report as if you'll learn something new by counting up the stacks of dead.

FRAN: You're right. I am the worst of all. I feel so utterly useless!
(McNAIR puts his arms around her, leads her to the sofa.)

McNAIR: Come here and sit with me. You can't do anything more than you're already doing. War is always hard on highstrung women.

FRAN: That's a fine remark.

McNAIR: It was meant by way of comfort. I know it's hard on you.

FRAN: And not on you. In your heart, you believe this war is right, don't you?

McNAIR: Of course it's not right. War is never right. But God almighty woman, it's Christmas Eve. Can't you just be content to watch the candles flicker and the snowflakes fall? Do you have to notice every tragic face, every heinous act? Why can't you just notice . . . . Me!

FRAN: I'm sorry McNair. I do notice you. All the time. I do!

McNAIR: Well then why don't you try to imagine a little house with a garden full of bluebells, and a trellis and a little baby in your arms . . . a little pal. That's what I do. Makes me feel better.

FRAN: You're such a romantic.

McNAIR: And what's wrong with that?

FRAN: Nothing, except why do you always picture me in a garden with a baby? Do you think I'd be happy just doing that? If I stopped thinking altogether?

McNAIR: Well give it a try. Just put your wee mind to it . . . little pink and white gurgling bundles . . . tiny fingers . . .

FRAN *(laughs):* Oh how unfair that men can't give birth. You'd be such a perfect mother.

McNAIR: Oh the world is too unfair.
(They kiss.)

———————————•———————————

SCENE 2

The Press Club Christmas Party.

LILY: And now for a bit of light entertainment from the carefree sisters of the interrogation mark and the typewriter. Nellie McClung with our assistance, will give her musical rendition of her much loved poem . . . LETS PRETEND.

NELL *(accompanied by LILY and FRAN)*
Let's pretend the skies are blue,
Let's pretend the world is new, and the birds of hope are singing all the day.
(chorus) All the day!

Short of gladness, learn to fake it,
long on sadness, go and shake it!
Life is what you make it, anyway.
Let's pretend the skies are blue, let's pretend the world is new,
There is wisdom without end . . . in the game of Let's Pretend!
(McNAIR applauds. The three women join him.)

LILY: That was splendid Nellie!

FRAN: Oh yes! Wasn't it? *(To McNAIR)*
McNAIR: A frothy little delight, I must say.

NELL: A rare compliment!

McNAIR: As rare as your rhymes!

FRAN: Shall I pour the lemonade?

NELL: Thank you dear.

LILY: There will be no bickering tonight . . . and no talk of the war. Is that clear? This is a Christmas party.

McNAIR: I'll drink to that.

NELL: You would.

McNAIR: And where is your better half tonight Nell?

NELL: At a patriotic drive.

McNAIR: And yours, Lill?

LILL *(reticent):* At an anti-conscription rally.

McNAIR: Well, I'm glad some of us are doing something irresponsible tonight.
(Awkward silence.)

McNAIR: I heard a funny story the other day. In the spring, they're going to build a roof garden on the legislative building. To supply fresh cut flowers for the politicians.

FRAN: The cabinet ministers can go up and take some air on their roof farm!

LILY: It will be quite inspiring to see Premier Norris in overalls doing his agricultural duty.
(They laugh. Another awkward silence.)

FRAN: There's a new play at the Walker I want to see.

LILY: What's it called?

FRAN: It's called The Guns of . . . . oh, we'll talk about it another time.
(Another awkward silence.)

LILY: I hear Sadie Vaugh is expecting!

FRAN: That didn't take long.

NELL: I think that's called war-risk insurance.

McNAIR: More lemonade, Nell?

NELL: Please.

McNAIR: I don't hear much about suffrage now that you've got the vote, I guess you can't blame every social ill in Manitoba any longer on your political disability.

NELL: Well we still haven't got the federal vote. But it's coming.

McNAIR: Yes, so I hear. But when it does, you'll find the privilege as empty as last year's birdsnest.

NELL: We'll see.

McNAIR: You'll end up choosing between two scoundrels, one not much better than the other. I've often felt when I vote, that I'm not exercising much more political influence than the horses that haul me to the polling station.

NELL: Nor probably much more intelligence.

McNAIR: You're being rude, Nell.

NELL: And you're being patronizing.

FRAN: You're both being . . .

LILY *(to FRANCIS):* Themselves!

McNAIR: I'm simply telling your friend not to feel badly that she hasn't turned the world around.

NELL: We closed the bars.

McNAIR: Aye, that you did. Deprived many a young lad one last good belt before going off to the slaughter.

NELL *(angry):* Don't talk like that about our boys!

LILY: Please don't fight, you two.

McNAIR: It would have done them no harm . . . the odd nip! You should try it yourself sometime!

FRAN: The music is starting up, why don't we dance?

NELL: You're disgusting!

McNAIR: And you are a hypocrite!

NELL: I am not!

McNAIR: Oh no? Then tell us why you told the Prime Minister to exclude foreign women from the upcoming federal election. So much for women's suffrage!

FRAN: That's not true!

McNAIR: I read it in the Free Press.

LILY: Nell, you didn't tell me.

NELL: There wasn't time. He was only in town for a couple of hours.

LILY: But you could have called . . . .

NELL: Well I didn't. And it's done. McNair likes to sensationalize. I simply suggested that the foreign women be excluded as a temporary war measure. A war measure. It's not a new idea. It's been bandied about for over a year. Let's not ruin our evening.

LILY: McNair, will you dance with me? I need to some time to clear my head.

McNAIR: Of course, Lily.
(McNAIR and LILY exit. FRANCIS, NELLIE left in stunned silence.)

FRAN: There was a speech you made once about leaving a word behind to shine in a dark place. It was years ago. Do you remember?

NELL: There've been so many, they kind of float together.

FRAN: It was at the William Avenue Library. It was a summer night. Lily and I walked there from our suite on Arlington. I smelled lilacs; the man next door was out watering his lawn . . . his wife was sitting on the verandah, watching, rocking . . .
  You said that night . . . I want to leave some word behind to shine in a dark place . . . and I want that word to be Democracy.

NELL: You have a good memory.

FRAN: I was so moved by that statement, I would have jumped off a cliff that night, if you'd asked me.

NELL: You've been a hard worker.

FRAN: I don't understand anything anymore, Nellie. Help me!

NELL: Oh Francis, there was a reason for this. I suggested excluding the foreign women only until the war is over.

FRAN: But what does the war have to do with it?

NELL: Francis, there are districts where almost every single English speaking man has enlisted. Do you realize what that means?

FRAN: No, I don't.

NELL: It means the moral tone of the electorate has drastically changed. The only way to protect our traditions is to limit the vote to the Empire women.

FRAN: But don't the foreign women have the same traditions? Justice, love, equality? How can you turn your backs on them . . . if you truly believe in women?

NELL *(with difficulty):* It's not that simple. The foreign community . . . does not view conscription favourably.

FRAN: Oh, I see! How efficient you are! If one doesn't view conscription favourably, then lop off their vote or their heads, whichever is easiest!

NELL: You make me tired, Francis. You were a raw green girl from the country when I first met you, too scared to open your mouth without your sister's prompting. It was Lily and I who brought you out, who filled you with every ideal you have today. And you dare to sit there and question me on what's right and wrong!

FRAN: But this is wrong! What you're doing is a total contradiction!

NELL: Oh don't tell me about contradictions. You have no right. You have nothing to lose in this war. You know nothing of the pain and nausea I feel when I read the casualty lists. You moon around over that drunken torie who'd rather have a woman strapped to the sink than marching in a suffrage parade. You have no right! It is I who is paying every minute this war continues. We have to end it, don't you understand? We have to win this wretched horrid war!

(FRANCIS stunned into silence. NELLIE shaking. Music stops. McNAIR and LILY return.)

FRAN: What about Women For Peace, Nell?

NELL: Stop it.

FRAN: Was that just another phrase that flowed off your tongue . . . glib, effortless and meaningless?

LILY: Fanny, don't talk like this! Please!

FRAN: Did you ever really believe we could stop the war or change the world or anything at all?

NELL: Of course I did! I do!

LILY: Stop this!

McNAIR: Francis, calm down!

FRAN: Why are you all trying to shut me up?

McNAIR: There's nothing anyone can do about the war now! Germany declared war on Britain. We couldn't have stayed out of it, without resorting to cowardice. We have a responsibility to our allies.

FRAN: Don't we have a responsibility to our children . . . to build a peaceful world? isn't that what we've always talked about, Nell?

McNAIR: You're not talking sense, Francis. When war is already in progress, the season for peace has passed.

NELL: This war will be the end of all wars, Francis. This war will do more for the cause of peace than ten years of peaceful propoganda.

FRAN: Do you really believe that?

NELL: I believe that Freedom still have to be paid for. It's like a farm that has to be kept up. Another installment of the debt has fallen due. That's what I believe. There's a Private in the Princess Pats who carries my picture in his cap, Francis. There are times when the doubter is intolerable!

(FRANCIS looks from one to the other, then walks out.)

————————•————————

SCENE 3

FRANCIS is at her desk at the paper.

FRANCIS *(editorial):* When a coincidence of engagements brought Sir Robert Borden and Mrs. Nellie L. McClung to Winnipeg together recently, McClung made use of the opportunity to ask the Prime Minister to grant the federal franchise to all British and Canadian born women, excluding the foreign women.

In this, Mrs. McClung was speaking for herself alone, and not for the organized women of the suffrage provinces. I hope that the majority of the women who fought and won the suffrage fight, on the ground that democracy is right, still believe in democracy.

Personally, if I had a religious faith or a political conviction which wouldn't stand the test of a great crisis, and which had to be discarded whenever an emergency arose, I would rise up and take it out and bury it in a nice deep grave and pray that it might have no resurrection day!

For my part, I believe in democracy just as invincibly today as I did in the yesterday of my own political minority, and if a serious attempt is made to exclude these new women citizens from the franchise, my tongue and pen will do their little best by way of protest.

F.M.B.

(FRANCIS opens her mail.)

DEAR MISS BEYNON
You say that Mrs. McClung was speaking for herself alone, but I say her instincts as a patriot told her the right thing. My husband Jake and our three sons are in the war now and they're all of voting age. Yet their voices won't be heard. The foreign women have their husbands safe and sound by their sides and we all envy them. They may think differently and they may not, but how can we be sure? I think perhaps we should not take the chance.

SINCERELY . . . LONELY AT HOME

DEAR MISS BEYNON:
I think that LONELY AT HOME should have five votes, not just one! One for herself and four for the manhood she has sent off to war! And I say, more power to Mrs. McClung's elbow! You say you believe in democracy. Well democracy means government by the people. In this crisis, I say British People! Shall our men go and fight the Hun across the sea while their country is being turned over to a foreign power? A thousand times NO!

FIERCELY . . . WOLFWILLOW

(FRANCIS puts down the letters, gets up and puts on her coat.)

————————— • —————————

SCENE 4

Train station. Sounds of train sighing and hissing. FRANCIS is helping LILY with her suitcases.

LILY: Vernon took the two big suitcases when he left last week. I've got my hatboxes. I guess that's everything. That's all I guess. *(Looks lost.)*

FRAN *(hands her a book):*   I've brought you a book. Carl Sandburg.

LILY: Thank you.

FRAN: Have you eaten? They probably won't serve lunch til one.

LILY: I've just had breakfast. I couldn't eat another thing.

FRAN: I made you some cookies to have with tea.

LILY: Thank you.

FRAN: Did you write mother and give her your new address in New York?

LILY: No. Could you do that Fanny?

FRAN: Oh Lily!

LILY: Fanny please!

FRAN: What should I tell her?

LILY: Tell her Vernon's been offered a good job in New York and couldn't pass it up. Do you think she'd believe that? Tell her I'm going to be the new editor of The New York Times. Oh, I don't know what to tell her!

FRAN: Well why don't I tell her the truth? That Vernon walked onto the floor of the Legislature to shake hands with the only politician with enough courage to make an anti-conscription speech.

LILY: Don't tell her that.

FRAN: Why not? And for that he was fired! So you decided to go to a country where Democracy still means something.

LILY: Oh, I should have done it myself.
(NELLIE arrives. Looks from one to another.)

NELL: Hello, Francis. *(To LILY)* Lily, I wanted to say goodbye.

LILY: Oh, I'm glad you came. *(They hug.)*

NELL: Here's a book for the train.

LILY: Kipling! Fanny brought me Sandburg. *(Looks from one to the other)*

NELL: Have you had anything to eat? It takes forever for them to serve lunch. Here's some biscuits.

LILY: Fanny brought me some cookies! The two of you will have me rolling off the train in New York. *(Looks from one to the other)* Well, here we are. The carefree sisters of the typewriter and interrogation mark. Any parting shots? *(Grabs both of their hands)*

FRAN: I still don't know the difference between baking soda and baking powder. I'm going to send the hard questions on to you in New York.

NELL: I'll never forgive Vernon for taking you away.

LILY: Vernon had no choice, Nell. No one will hire him here now . . . nor probably anywhere else in Canada with his views. At least in New York, he can write about what he believes.

NELL: You mean he can make a mockery of what our boys are fighting for!

FRAN: That's not what he's doing!

LILY: Please, please, let's not talk about Vernon. Let's talk about ourselves. Can we? I feel so helpless right now. It used to be we'd talk about love and sisterhood . . . now we only talk about death and destruction. Will you take care of Fanny while I'm gone, Nell?

NELL: Of course I will.

FRAN: I'll be fine on my own.

NELL: You're very hard on people, Francis. When the war is over, we'll get the suffrage issue straightened out and there'll be a vote for everyone. Believe me, just like we've always dreamed. When the war is over.

CONDUCTOR *(offstage):* All aboard!

FRAN: Have you got everything Lily?

NELL: I have to go. I've got two meetings before lunch. It never ends. Write big long letters. Goodbye Lily. *(LILY, NELL hug)*
(NELLIE exits.)

LILY: She was apologizing to you and you wouldn't accept it. I understand how Nellie feels, although I don't agree with it. She supports the war because her son is fighting in it. She has no choice. But that's no reason to turn your back on her, your best friend, your teacher, just because she didn't meet your high standards. How arrogant you are!

FRAN: But she gave up her dream.

LILY: No she didn't. She just lost sight of it for a while. It happens to all of us, and it will happen to you. You'll marry McNair and have children, and you won't be so eager to pick up a banner or lead a parade. And the dream won't seem so crystal clear anymore and you'll be glad that there's someone who loves you and won't judge you for your every weakness.

FRAN: I don't know whether I can do that. I want to be free, Lily. I don't know what more to say than that.

LILY: Fanny, you're never really free. You can frame a declaration of independence every day, but you won't be free. We're bound by our affections more than any legal contracts, or governments or causes. We're all trapped by something. The heart doesn't choose wisely, it just chooses.
(Train whistle)

FRAN: Oh don't leave. I don't know what I'll do without you.

LILY: I've got to. It's time.

FRAN: I love you, Lily.

LILY: Fanny, you're a brick. *(They hug, LILY leaves.)*

———————————— • ————————————

SCENE 5

FRANCIS enters office. McNAIR is there. She takes off her hat, and coat.

FRAN: I've got four typewriters now — mine, Lily's and two of Vernon's — and none of them work very well. Have you ever been to New York McNair?

McNAIR: I landed there when I first came over. I read a different paper every day for two weeks, and never found the same opinion twice. Don't worry, Francis. They'll find work.

FRAN: I guess so. McNair, do you think I'm . . . hard on people?

McNAIR: Very! You're like a terrier worrying a bone.

FRAN: Why do you think that is?

McNAIR: Because you've got a vision of the world that's clearer than most.

FRAN: Then why do I feel so frightened all the time . . . frightened that I'm wrong, or that I'm right, that I'm not doing enough, or that I'm doing too much . . . that I'll end up alone. When I was given a mind that questioned everything, why wasn't I given a spirit that feared nothing? I used to think that everything was possible, but I just don't know anymore.

McNAIR: You're just tired, Francis, and you miss Lily. Why don't you open your mail? That will put the fight back into you.
   (FRANCIS opens her letters.)

DEAR MISS BEYNON:
I say hurray for Borden and Conscription. Let's round up those slackers who are hanging around the city poolrooms and get them into uniform. The time has come to send more than socks and tobacco to our heroes in the fighting line. What we need is Men Men and more Men!

WESTERN SISTER

FRAN: DEAR WESTERN SISTER, It is easy for us to be brave with other peoples' lives, but I don't believe in their hearts that the people of Canada want compulsory enlistment. Let's have a referendum to ask Canadians whether they want conscription!

DEAR MISS BEYNON:
Referendum? Referendum now? For three years our boys have fought for us and our cause. Referendum now, while our enemy prepares destruction for our ba-tered heroes? Surely not referendum now but reinforcements! And quickly to our waiting sons!

DEAR MISS BEYNON:
What we are fighting here is a holy war against the very Prince of darkness, and therefore every man owes it to God to support conscription. And if there is any man out there who says his conscience won't allow him to slay his fellow man, then he's laying down too strict a rule for his conscience.

FRAN: That is not God's plan! I believe that God is Democracy, the only true Democracy. He filled the world with human beings, no two of whom are alike and I'm sure he meant them to be left free to develop their differences and to report on life as they see it. War has never been in God's plan — the Lord of Peace — only that of man.

DEAR MISS KNOW IT ALL
"There shall be wars and rumours of war, but the end is not yet"
   Do not go taking the name of the Lord in vain and putting your half-cooked ideas on him.

You used to be alright when you talked about votes for women, but you're a disgrace to the female race the way you go on about peace. Anyone who talks like that is a traitor and probably has foreign friends.

(FRANCIS takes over the reading of the letter from the woman who has written it. She reads it aloud as McNAIR comes into the room.)

My husband told me to say that he's proud of his country and proud to fight for it, and if you don't keep your mouth shut, you might find someone will shut it for you.

McNAIR *(takes letter from FRANCIS):* This is a threat! Who wrote this?

FRAN: Would you sign a letter like this?

McNAIR: This has got to stop. You've gone too far!

FRAN: I've gone too far?

McNAIR: When it gets to the point that people are sending you hate mail, like this, yes! People who write letters like this are unbalanced. You might get hurt, Francis.

FRAN: It was you who told me that if I believe in something, I should have the courage to write about it.

McNAIR: But this is different. The war is making people crazy. A man was beaten up at an anti-conscription rally the other night. These are dangerous times. Where are you going?

(FRANCIS has risen, puts on hat and coat.)

FRAN: To a meeting.

McNAIR: What meeting?

FRAN: A women's meeting, McNair. At the library. It seems that Nellie McClung is giving a talk. I would like to hear what she has to say.

McNAIR: I'll walk you there.

FRAN: Thank you. That would be nice.

———————————•———————————

SCENE 6

Women's meeting. NELLIE McCLUNG is addressing audience.

NELL: The Wartime Elections Act has just given us Dominion women the vote, and I think we should use it to vote for Conscription. I've heard some people say that we need a referendum to find out whether Canadians want conscription. Yesterday, I received a letter from my son in France asking when we're going to send more troops. He says they're holding on as best they can, but they're getting weaker. Are we backing our boys or not? A thousand voices chatter reasons for delay, but across the seas comes one voice loud and clear. Who calls Canada? Our boys are calling us!

Tonight is the beginning of the federal election campaign and the issue is conscription. This is our chance to work for the candidates that are going to help our boys. We have no time to lose. The more women we can get out the better . . . .

FRAN: Mrs. McClung, I have a question?

NELL: We don't have much time.

FRAN: I won't be long. How can our boys be fighting for freedom if we are not giving them the freedom to decide whether or not they'll give their lives?

NELL: That's not an easy question to answer. I've struggled with it in my heart. But sometimes, individual freedom has to be sacrificed for collective freedom. Peace can only be achieved when we band together and let the enemy know that we will not budge.

FRAN: I have another question.

NELL: We have a lot of work to do.

FRAN: How can peace be achieved, how can we get any nearer to peace when a lot more people are being sacrificed?

NELL: I think you're trying to be disruptive, Miss Beynon. Your views on the war are well known. I don't know whether there's any point in taking up more time.

FRAN: Please, I'd jut like to make one suggestion. *(FRANCIS goes up to the front)* Why don't we tell the politicians that we women, the mothers, wives and sisters of Canada, want to bring this war to a peaceful conclusion right now, before any more blood is shed!

NELL: If there aren't any more questions, we should get down to forming committees. We have six candidates to start working for . . .

FRAN: Can I talk for a minute please . . . just a minute! The real issue of this war is not conscription or the war over there. The real issue is being fought right here in halls like these.

The real issue is whether militarism shall grow and prosper or whether it shall decline and fall. We, as women, in our first chance to use our franchise, are being asked to vote for War! To vote for sending more sons and husbands away to fight and be killed.

Let's use our vote to say NO to war!

And let's not exclude our sisters because they speak another language . . . .

WOMAN IN AUDIENCE: Shut up. Just shut up! You don't know what you're talking about! You've got nothing to lose! Just get out of here! GET OUT!

NELL: Please, can we have order. Miss Beynon, I believe you have your answer. Now, let's get back to business.
(FRANCIS anguished. Leaves)

———————————•———————————

SCENE 7

Newspaper office. McNAIR is seated. FRANCIS storms into office.

FRAN: I just received a call from the Censorship Board. Those scoundrels told me not to write anything about the conscription bill which might "arouse" opposition!

McNAIR: Sit down Francis.

FRAN: Since when have British citizens relinquished the right to discuss unmade legislation?

McNAIR: Sit down Francis.

FRAN: Is this Canada or is this Prussia. Has everyone gone war mad?

McNAIR *(shouts):* Sit down Francis!
(FRANCIS finally sits.)

McNAIR: I want to talk to you. I've been getting calls all week from readers. About you. One woman said she'd seen you handing out anti-war pamphlets at Portage and Main on two occasions, and that you were haranguing passers-by.

FRAN *(jumps up):* I was not haranguing them. I was trying to engage them in conversation.

McNAIR: The publisher called me awhile ago. He's running for parliament on the conscription issue. He wants me to . . . he wants your resignation. I told him I would talk to you.

FRAN *(disbelief):* He wants me to resign from my job.

McNAIR: Yes.

FRAN: No! I won't! He can't get away with something like that! We can get my readers to back me!

McNAIR: Francis, your readers haven't been very supportive lately. *(Slams letters down on desk)* Haven't you noticed?

FRAN: What about you?

McNAIR: Don't you ever get tired of rowing upstream?

FRAN: McNair, what about you? The paper has a role to play in presenting all sides of the war issue. We've got to get people thinking! Really thinking! Really questioning!

McNAIR: All of the issues have been discussed to death. Everybody out there has already made up their minds. Borden has granted Nellie and the Empire women the vote and they're going to use it to ram conscription down our throats!

FRAN: No! No!

McNAIR: Yes! And there's nothing you can do about it. Or should do about it!

FRAN: So you simply suspend freedom of the press . . . freedom to express opinions?

McNAIR: Nobody gives a damn about your opinions, or my opinions either! We've just got to win the war and then you can hold any damned opinion you like. Just swallow hard and hold on.

FRAN: Do you want me to resign?

McNAIR: Yes. No. I have no choice.
(FRANCIS turns to leave.)

McNAIR: Francis, wait. Look at me. Will you look at me. *(FRANCIS turns.)* You've got lines on your face now that don't go away when you stop smiling. I can see a hint of grey in your hair along the temples. You're not a young girl anymore. Francis, I love you. I want to marry you. I want to take care of you. I want you to stop worrying about what you can't change. Let me take care of you now. Don't say anything. Let me talk. I've saved enough money to buy a house. Leave the paper. You won't have to put up with any more abusive letters, you won't have to turn yourself inside out with issues. I know how it tortures you. Just let it all go! You can just settle into our new house and wait for our first baby.

FRAN: McNair, I love my work.

McNAIR: I know you do, Francis, but I'm asking you to marry me! You can forget about everything else.
(FRANCIS shivers, moves away.)

FRAN: It's cold in here suddenly. *(Slowly, with difficulty)* I remember you told me once that I was like a bird which you caught and could feel it straining to get free. Do you remember?
(McNAIR nods.)

FRAN: I remember thinking even as you spoke, even as I looked at you, that the bird probably loved the warmth of your hand. McNair, I love you. I love your warmth. But I . . . *(voice breaking)* can't . . . do what you want. It would be too much like a closed hand. And I'd always be struggling to get free. Do you understand?
(McNAIR searches her face, almost speaks, then thinks better of it. McNAIR leaves.)

SCENE 8

FRANCIS stands alone, shaken. She goes over to her desk, begins to collect her belongings.

FRAN: Every once in a while, one comes to a parting of the ways. I have come to that today. It is with deep feelings of regret that I am severing my connection with The Rural Review. I had hoped through this page, that we women of the Prairies could help advance the cause of women, and I believe that in some small ways, we have done that.

It would have been a much bigger thing if we could have claimed to have erased tyranny and war and intolerance. I now think that that is a work to be measured in generations.

But someday, when we who are here now are dead and gone, and the little acorns that were planted on our graves have grown into flourishing trees and fallen into decay, it will come to be recognized that there is no crime in being different, in doing one's own thinking.

It may even be that in that dim and shadowy future, the world will have sense enough to value Peace, and we will be able to live free of the fear of war. This, in the end, is the only thing that really matters.

By the time this reaches print, I will have left for the Mecca of all writers on this continent, the city of New York. There, I will continue to work towards that Future. One can only follow "The Gleam" as one sees it, and hope that it does not prove to be a will-o-the-wisp.

And that is all.

F.M.B.

THE END

Consider the Play

1. As *The Fighting Days* opens, Francis and Lily discuss their memories of their father. How do you think their memories affect the way in which they look upon themselves as adults and as women? Discuss.

2. In Act 1, Scene 2, Fran says to Nellie, "I always wanted to write. . . just like you and Lily! I thought if I could write things down, they'd be clear to everyone. . . all the things I felt inside. I would be clear to everyone and I wouldn't feel so alone." Later, Fran is able to "write things down". Does she, in fact, become "clear to everyone" and does she feel less alone? Discuss.

3. Nellie's speech, which opens Act 1, Scene 3, is very successful with the audience. Does Nellie remain faithful to the tenets of her speech as the years roll by? Give reasons for your answer.

4. McNair and Nellie dislike each other intensely. Why? With which character do you sympathize? Give reasons for your answer.

5. In Act 1, Scene 7, Nellie's attitude towards Fran seems to have changed. Why? With which character do you agree? Why?

6. Act 2, like Act 1, opens with Fran and Lily talking. Six years have passed, however. What has changed in each sister's outlook on life? Discuss.

7. Why are there so many awkward silences in Act 2, Scene 2?

8. Both Fran and Nellie believe that they are fighting for "Freedom" although they are on opposite sides of the conscription issue. With which character do you sympathize most? Give reasons for your answer.

9. In 1916, Nellie McClung tells the Prime Minister of Canada to exclude foreign women from the right to vote in the upcoming federal election. Do you agree with her reasoning? Give reasons to support your answer.

10. In Act 2, Scene 4, Fran and Nellie say good-bye to Lily, who is about to board a train to New York. Both women bring Lily presents. What are the presents? Comment on the significance of each gift.

11. The prairie women, especially those living on farms, face many problems, one of which is the very hard work they have to do. Yet, according to the letters Fran Beynon receives, these women do not feel that hard work is their biggest problem. In your opinion, what does their biggest problem seem to be? Discuss.

12. Add a scene to the end of *The Fighting Days*. Begin with Fran making a first visit to Lily and her husband in New York. Write the scene in script form.

13. What is conscription? Define and discuss it. Would you be for or against conscription in wartime? Give reasons for your position.

14. As early as 1892, Nellie McClung was involved with the WCTU. Temperance means "moderation". The WCTU, however, defined temperance as "abstinence", that is, giving up all alcoholic beverages. The WCTU still exists today. Obtain some pamphlets from the organization. Do you believe that the WCTU's views on the problems caused by alcohol are valid today? Give reasons to support your answer.

15. Canada's suffragists were supported by some men who were not chilled by the prospect of women having the vote. Comment on the tone of this poem, written by L. Case Russell and published in the *Toronto Globe* on September 28, 1912.

You may be our close companion
Share our troubles, ease our pain,
You may bear the servant's burden
(But without a servant's gain)
You may scrub and work and iron
Sew buttons on our coat
But as men we must protect you —
You are far too frail to vote.

16. By 1914, the suffrage movement was gaining strength in Manitoba. But many people were still against giving women the vote, including the Conservative Premier of Manitoba, Sir Rodmond Roblin, who said, "I don't want a hyena in petticoats talking politics at me. I want a nice gentle creature to bring me my slippers." He also told a delegation of women, who came to the legislature on January 27, 1914, to present the case for female suffrage that ". . .woman suffrage is illogical and absurd as far as Manitoba is concerned. . . . The majority of women are emotional and very often guided by misdirected enthusiasms, and if possessed of the franchise would be a menace rather than an aid." In your opinion, are women more emotional than men? Give reasons for your answer.

17. Suffragists were often criticized for neglecting their families in favour of their other activities. When asked if she didn't believe women's place was in the home, Nellie McClung answered, "Yes, I do and so is father's — but not twenty-four hours a day for either of them. Women's duty lies not only in rearing children but also in the world into which those children must some day enter." What is your opinion? Do you think that married women with children should be employed outside the home? Give reasons for your answer.

18. Although *The Fighting Days* is a fictional account, many of its characters and events were taken from life. Nellie McClung, Francis Beynon, and Lillian Beynon Thomas were all active in the suffrage movement, for example. In 1912, they formed the Political Equality League, which was devoted to female suffrage. Do historical research on one of these women or on the League they formed. Report to the class on your findings.

19. "Although *The Fighting Days* deals specifically with Canada during the second decade of the 20th century, it has relevance for Canadians today." Do you agree or disagree with this statement? Discuss, giving reasons to support your position.

20. Discuss the changes that have taken place in the rights and roles of women since the 1800s. Why do you think women had so few rights a hundred years ago? Do you think that they have enough rights today? Give reasons for your answer.

———————————— • ————————————

A Thousand Clowns

by Herb Gardner

The Playwright

Herb Gardner was born in Brooklyn, New York, in 1934. While attending New York's High School of the Performing Arts, he wrote his first play, *The Elevator*. This one-act effort earned him the grand sum of $32 in royalties over the next 12 years. But Gardner was not discouraged. Over the next few years, he earned his living doing commercial art, selling orange drinks in Broadway theatres, and drawing the "in between" parts of television commercials. All the while, he continued his playwriting.

Gardner's first big break came when he created a group of cartoon characters called the Nebbishes. This earned him enough money to quit cartooning and devote all his time to playwriting. He was already at work on *A Thousand Clowns*.

Gardner had developed the seeds of this play as early as 1956, when he wrote a short story called "The Man Who Thought He Was Winston Churchill". Other seeds came from his own life. For example, when Murray shouts out the window, he is doing things which Gardner himself has done.

A Thousand Clowns was nearly three years in the making. During that time, Gardner wrote several versions. (One was a tragedy in which Murray is completely defeated by society.) Even after its successful opening night, Gardner continued to revise it.

As for what might happen to the characters after the final curtain, Gardner has his own theory. He has said that his private belief is that Murray will stick somehow to his television writing job, but he won't necessarily stick to Sandra.

The Play

Comedy is as old as laughter and as modern as life today. Comedy deals with that most interesting of all topics — life itself. The main objective of comedy is to hold up a critical mirror to life and to reflect life with humour — and no person, place, or subject is sacred.

A Thousand Clowns is an optimistic play. It deals with one basic idea — that every person is a unique and fascinating personality just waiting to break out and discover the world and be discovered by the world. It also explores the dark side in its treatment of what the playwright saw as a society which was doing its best to stifle that individualism, to make everyone fit into the same mold.

Critics praised both the stage play and its movie version for its freshness and sharp humour. It was equally popular with audiences, perhaps because it was very much a play of its time.

It was first staged just as the confused decade of the 1960s was getting underway. Many people were questioning the values which had been accepted for generations. It was a time when television situation comedies began to change from gentle humour to satires based on the conflicts that can result when different lifestyles come face to face. (An example is *All in the Family*.) It was a time when John Lennon of The Beatles could say, "We're more popular than Christ."

A Thousand Clowns was a huge success for the 28-year-old Gardner then, and it remains a successful play today.

Herb Gardner

From *A Thousand Clowns,* by Herb Gardner. Copyright © 1961, 1962 by Herb Gardner and Irwin A. Cantor, Trustee. Reprinted by permission of Random House, Inc.

A Thousand Clowns

Herb Gardner

The First Production Was Staged
On April 5, 1962
At the Eugene O'Neill Theatre
In New York City, New York

With This Cast

Murray Burns ....Jason Robards, Jr.
Nick Burns ....Barry Gordon
Albert Amundson ....William Daniels
Sandra Markowitz............................Sandy Dennis
Arnold Burns...................................A. Larry Haines
Leo Herman ....Gene Saks

Time
The present

Place
Murray Burns' apartment and Arnold Burns' office in Manhattan

Staged by Fred Coe and Arthur Cantor
Settings and lightings by George Jenkins
Costumes by Ruth Morley
Production Stage Manager: Porter Van Zandt
Stage Manager: Tom Porter
Press: Gertrude Kirschner, Tony Geiss, and Violet Welles

In complete darkness, before the curtain goes up, we hear the voice of Chuckles the Chipmunk.

---•---

CHUCKLES' VOICE *(Intimately, softly):* Goshes and gollygoods, kid-deroonies; now what're all us Chippermunkies gonna play first this fine mornin'?

CHORUS OF KIDS: Gonna play Chuckle-Chip Dancing.

CHUCKLES' VOICE: And with who?

CHORUS OF KIDS: With you!

CHUCKLES' VOICE *(Louder):* And who is me?

CHORUS OF KIDS *(Screaming):* Chuckles the Chippermunkie! Rayyyyyyyyyyyyyyy.

(The curtain goes up on this last screaming syllable, revealling MURRAY BURNS' one-room apartment. The voices of Chuckles and the kids continue but are now coming from an ancient table-model T.V. set at the left. The set is facing away from the audience and is being watched by NICHOLAS BURNS, a twelve-year-old. The apartment is on the second floor of a brownstone on the lower West Side of Manhattan. It consists of one large, high-ceilinged room in which borrowed furniture rambles in no meaningful arrangement — some gaudy, some impractical, no matching pieces. It is obvious from MURRAY BURNS' apartment that he is a collector, though it is not entirely clear just what he is a collector of. All about the room, on the floor, on the coffee table, on dresser tops, is MURRAY's collection: eighteen broken radios, some with interesting cathedral-style cabinets; over two dozen elaborately disabled clocks of different sizes, some of them on the wall; parts of eight Victrolas, mostly cabinets; a variety of hats, including a Prussian helmet and a deerstalker; a pirate pistol; a bugle; a megaphone; and stacks of magazines and books. It is somehow, though, a very comfortable-looking apartment. There is an alcove at the left, with a small bed, a child's desk and some bookshelves. This is NICK's part of the place and it is very neat, ordered, organized, seeming almost to have nothing to do with the main room. There is a bathroom door at left below the small alcove. Right of the alcove are three large windows and a built-in window seat. A closed venetian blind covers all three windows. At centre is a large, comfortable rumpled bed with an elaborate wooden headboard running up the wall almost to the ceiling. The headboard is loaded with clocks, radios, and two lamps. At right is the entrance door to the apartment. To the left of the door are two large office-style filing cabinets in which MURRAY keeps some of his clothes, and to the right is a bureau covered with knickknacks on which MURRAY's hats are hung. Downstage right is the kitchen door; to the left of it is a desk buried under papers, and built-in bookshelves stuffed with a jumble of books and nonsense. There is a closet to the left of the desk. A Morris chair and an armless swivel chair are on either side of a small table at right and there is a brightly coloured beach chair at left in front of the windows.

AT RISE: It is eight-thirty on a Monday morning; it is rather dark, the only real light is a scattered haze from the television set. The chorus of kids is now singing the "Chuckles Song." NICK watches expressionlessly.

CHORUS OF KIDS *(Singing):* Who's whitcha at — eight-thirty?
Whose face is so — so dirty?
Who's sparky — who's spunky?
Chip, Chip, Chip, Chip — Chippermunkie!

NICK *(Quietly):* Oh, this is terrible. This is rotten.

CHORUS OF KIDS: Who's always good — for funnin'? Whose scooter-bike — keeps runnin'?
(MURRAY enters from the kitchen carrying a cup of coffee; he is in his mid-thirties. He is wearing shorts and an undershirt and is not quite awake yet.)

MURRAY *(Walking across to the bed):* Get those kids outa here. *(Sits on the bed.)* Nick, what'd I tell you about bringing your friends in here this early in the morning?

NICK: It's not my friends; it's the T.V.

MURRAY: Play with your friends outside. Get those kids out of here. *(NICK turns the set off. MURRAY looks over at the front door, waves at it and shouts.)* Good. And none of you kids come back here till this afternoon.

NICK: It wasn't my friends. It was Chuckles the Chipmunk.

MURRAY *(Sleepily):* That's very comforting.

NICK *(Brings a pack of cigarettes to MURRAY):* Boy, it's a terrible program now. It was a much better show when you were writing it.

MURRAY: When Sandburg and Faulkner quit, I quit. What kind of a day is it outside?

NICK *(Going to the kitchen):* It's a Monday.

MURRAY: I mean warm or cold or sunny is what I mean.

NICK: I haven't been outside yet.

MURRAY *(He pulls the blind up revealing the windows; there is no change whatever in the lighting, the room remains dark. The windows have no view other than the gray blank wall of the building a few feet opposite):* Ah, light. *(He leans out of the window, cranes his head around to look up at the sky.)* Can't see a thing. Not a thing. *(Pulls his head back in.)* No matter what time of day or what season, we got a permanent fixture out there; twilight in February.

NICK *(Bringing the coffee pot out of the kitchen and filling MURRAY's cup):* You better call the weather record like always.

MURRAY: One morning I'll wake up and that damn building'll have fallen down into Seventh Avenue so I can see the weather. *(Picks up the phone; dialling.)* Using a machine to call up another machine. I do not enjoy the company of ghosts. *(Into the phone)* Hello, Weather Lady! Well, I'm just fine, and how is your nasal little self this morning? What's the weather? Uh-huh. That high? And the wind, which way does the wind blow this morning? Ah, good. Uh-huh, all the way to East Point and Block Island. Humidity? Very decent. Whoops, oh, there you go again. You simply *must* learn not to repeat yourself. I keep telling you every morning that once is enough. You'll never learn. *(Hangs up.)* Women seldom sense when they have become boring. *(Goes to the window again, leans out, raises his voice, shouting out of the window)* Neighbours, I have an announcement for you. I have *never seen* such a collection of dirty windows. Now I want to see you all out there on the fire escape with your Mr. Clean bottles, and let's snap it up . . .

NICK: Gee, Murray, you gotta shout like that every morning?

MURRAY: It clears my head. *(After glancing around clock-filled apartment)* What time is it?

NICK: It's eight-forty.

MURRAY: Well, what're you doing here? Why aren't you in school?

NICK: It's a holiday. It's Irving R. Feldman's birthday, like you said.

MURRAY: Irving R. Feldman's birthday is my own personal national holiday. I did not open it up for the public. He is proprietor of perhaps the most distinguished kosher delicatessen in this neighbourhood and as such I hold the day of his birth in reverence.

NICK: You said you weren't going to look for work today because it was Irving R. Feldman's birthday, so I figured I would celebrate too, a little.

MURRAY: Don't kid *me*, Nick, you know you're supposed to be in school. I thought you *liked* that damn genius' school — why the hell —

NICK: Well, I figured I'd better stay home today till you got up. *(Hesitantly)* There's something I gotta discuss with you. See, because it's this special school for big brains they watch you and take notes and make reports and smile at you a lot. And there's this psychologist who talks to you every week, each kid separately. He's the biggest smiler they got up there.

MURRAY: Because you got brains they figure you're nuts.

NICK: Anyway, we had Show and Tell time in Mrs. Zimmerman's class on Monday, and each kid in the class is supposed to tell about some trip he took and show pictures. Well, y'remember when I made you take me with you to the El Bambino Club over on Fifty-second?

MURRAY: Nick . . . you showed and you told.

NICK: Well, it turned out they're very square up at the Revere School. And sometimes in class, when we have our Wednesday Free-Association-Talk Period, I sometimes quote you on different opinions . . .

MURRAY: That wasn't a good idea.

NICK: Well, I didn't know they were such nervous people there. Murray, they're very nervous there. And then there was this composition I wrote in Creative Writing about the advantages of Unemployment Insurance.

MURRAY: Why did you write about that?

NICK: It was just on my mind. Then once they got my record out they started to notice what they call "significant data." Turns out they've been keeping this file on me for a long time, and checking with that Child Welfare place; same place you got those letters from.

MURRAY: I never answer letters from large organizations.

NICK: So, Murray . . . when they come over, I figure we'd better . . .

MURRAY: When they come over here?

NICK: Yeah, this Child Welfare crowd, they want to take a look at our environment here.

MURRAY: Oh, that's charming. Why didn't you tell me about this before, Nick?

NICK: Well, y'know, the past coupla nights we couldn't get together.

MURRAY: That was unavoidable. You know when I have a lot of work you stay up at Mrs. Myers'.

NICK *(Pointing at the dresser):* Murray; your work forgot her gloves last night.

MURRAY: That's very bright.

NICK: Anyway, for this Child Welfare crowd, I figure we better set up some kind of story before they get here.

MURRAY: You make it sound like a vice raid.

NICK: I mean, for one thing, you don't even have a job right now.

MURRAY: Look, you want me to put up some kind of front when they get here? O.K., I will. Don't worry, kid. I'll snow 'em good.

NICK: I thought maybe you could at least look in the papers for a job, this morning before they get here. So we could tell them about your possibilities.

MURRAY *(Without much conviction):* I look every day.

NICK: Couldn't I just read you from the *Times* again like last week? While you get dressed?

MURRAY: O.K., read me from the paper. *(He starts to get dressed.)*

NICK: And then, maybe, you'll take a shave?

MURRAY: All right, all right.

NICK *(Picking up the* Times *from the swivel chair):* This paper is three days old.

MURRAY: So what do you want me to do, bury it? Is it starting to rot or something? Read me from the paper.

NICK: But most of these jobs, somebody must have taken them. Look, I'll go down and get a newer —

MURRAY: We do *not* need a newer paper. All the really important jobs stay forever. Now start on the first page of Help-Wanted-Male and read me from the paper.

NICK: O.K. *(Puts on his glasses; reads aloud.)* "Administ, Exoppty. To ninety dollars." What's that?

MURRAY: "Administrative Assistant, excellent opportunity. Nothing. Keep reading.

NICK: But ninety dollars would be ninety dollars more than nothing. Nothing is what you make now.

MURRAY: Have you ever considered being the first twelve-year-old boy in space?

NICK: But, ninety dollars . . .

MURRAY: *You* go be an Administ, Exoppty. They *need* men like you. Read further.

NICK *(Reading from the paper):* "Versatile Junior, traffic manager, industrial representative organization. One hundred to one hundred twenty-five dollars. Call Mr. Shiffman."

MURRAY *(Picks up the cardboard from his shirt collar and talks into it):* Hello, Mr. Shiffman? I read your name in the New York *Times*, so I know you must be real. My name is Mandrake the Magician. I am a versatile Junior and I would like to manage your traffic for you. You see, sir, it has long been my ambition to work in a pointless job, with no future and a cretin like you as my boss . . .

NICK: But, Murray, it says "one hundred twenty-five dollars," that's a lot of . . .

MURRAY: Just read the ads. No editorial comment or personal recommendations. When I need your advice, I'll ask for it. Out of the mouths of babes comes drooling.

NICK: You said that last week. Murray, you don't want a job is the whole thing.

MURRAY: Would you just concentrate on being a child? Because I find your imitation of an adult hopelessly inadequate.

NICK: You want to be your own boss, but the trouble with that is you don't pay yourself anything. *(NICK decides that what he has just said is very funny. He laughs.)* Hey — you don't pay yourself anything — that's a good line — I gotta remember that.

MURRAY: That's what *you* said last week.

NICK: Look, Murray. *(He puts the paper down and stands up.)* Can I speak to you man to man?

MURRAY: That was cute about a year ago, buddy, but that line has got to go.

NICK *(Takes off his glasses):* Murray, I am upset. For me as an actual child the way you live in this house and we live is a dangerous thing for my later life when I become an actual person. An unemployed person like you are for so many months is bad for you as the person involved and is definitely bad for me who he lives with you in the same house where the rent isn't paid for months sometimes. And I wish you would get a job, Murray. Please.
> *(MURRAY tries to control himself but cannot hide his laughter; he sees that NICK is offended by this and tries to stop. NICK walks away from him, goes to his alcove.)*

MURRAY *(Goes to NICK in the alcove):* Kid, I know. I'm sorry. You're right. You are. This *is* terrible.

NICK: You're not kidding.

MURRAY: Nick.

NICK: Yeah?

MURRAY: Nick, y'know when I said I was looking for work last week? *(Somewhat ashamed)* Well, I went to the movies. Every day. In the afternoon.

NICK: *Murray,* you mean you really . . .

MURRAY: Now don't give me any of that indignant crap. I happen to be admitting something to you, and it is bad enough I should have to discuss my adult problems with a grotesque cherub, without you giving me dirty looks on top of it. Swell crowd in the movies on a weekday working afternoon. Nobody sits next to anybody, everybody there figures that everybody else is a creep; and *all* of them are right. *(Suddenly smiling, taking NICK's arm, trying to change the subject)* Have you ever been to the top of the Empire State Building?

NICK: Yes. Six times. With you. In November.

MURRAY: Oh, really? Have you ever been to the Statue of Liberty?

NICK: No.

MURRAY: Today is Irving R. Feldman's birthday. We will go to the top of the Statue of Liberty and watch the *Queen Elizabeth* come in, full of those tired, poor, huddled masses yearning to breathe free.

NICK: Murray, why did you go to the movies in the middle of the afternoon when you said you were looking for work?

MURRAY: There's a window right in her navel, we will look out and see . . .

NICK: What is it? Were you very tired, or what?

MURRAY *(Sits down in his chair):* See, last week I was going to check with Uncle Arnie and some of the other agents about writing for some of the new T.V. shows. I was on the subway, on my way there, and I got off at Forty-second Street and went to the movies. *(He leans back in his chair, lights a cigarette; NICK sits opposite him on the bed.)* There are eleven movie houses on that street, Nick. It is Movieland. It breathes that seductive, carpety, minty air of the inside of movie houses. Almost as irresistible for me as pastrami. Now, there is the big question as you approach the box office, with the sun shining right down the middle of a working day, whether everybody going in is as embarrassed as you are. But once you are past the awkward stage, and have gotten your ticket torn by the old man inside, all doubts just go away. Because it is dark. And inside it is such a scene as to fracture the imagination of even a nut like yourself, Nick, because inside it is lovely and a little damp and nobody can see you, and the dialogue is falling like rain on a roof and you are sitting deep in front of a roaring, colour, Cinemascope, stereophonic, nerve-cooling, heart-warming, spine-softening, perfect-happy-ending picture show and it is Peacefulville, U.S.A. There are men there with neat mustaches who have shaved, and shined their shoes and put on a tie even, to come and sit alone in the movies. And there are near-sighted cute pink ladies who eat secret caramels; and very old men who sleep; and the *ushers;* buddy, you are not kidding *these* boys. They know you are not there because you are waiting for a train, or you are on a vacation, or you work a night job. They know you are there to see the *movie.* It is the business and the purpose of your day, and these boys give you their sneaky smile to show you that they know. *(Depressed by his own words; quietly, almost to himself)* Now the moral question for me here, is this: When one is faced with life in the bare-assed, job-hunting raw on the one hand, and eleven fifty-cent double features on the other, what is the mature, sensible, and mentally healthy step to take? *(He is slumped in his chair now.)*

NICK *(Seeing MURRAY's depression; softly, with concern):* What's wrong, Murray?

MURRAY *(Walks slowly to the window, leans against the wall, looks sadly out of the window; speaks quietly):* I don't know. I'm not sure.

NICK: Hey, Murray, you all right . . .? *(He goes to MURRAY, touches his arm. Then smiling suddenly in an attempt to cheer him)* Murray, let's go to the Statue of Liberty.
(MURRAY turns, laughs in agreement, and NICK starts for his jacket while MURRAY puts his binoculars around his neck and begins putting on his jacket. The doorbell rings. NICK looks at MURRAY, then goes to answer it. NICK is holding the front door only part-way open, hesitating to let in two people we now see standing outside in the hall. They are ALBERT AMUND-SON and SANDRA MARKOWITZ. ALBERT, graduate of N.Y.U.'s School of Social Work, is a middle-aged man of twenty-eight; SANDRA, though a pretty girl of twenty-five, wears clothes obviously more suited to a much older woman. ALBERT carries a small briefcase and SANDRA carries two manila file envelopes and a gigantic handbag.)

ALBERT: Hello, young man, I am Mr. Amundson, this is Miss Markowitz. We would like to speak to your uncle.

NICK *(Still not opening the door all the way):* Well, I don't know if . . .

ALBERT: Isn't he in?

MURRAY: Hello.

ALBERT: How do you do, Mr. Burns. Miss Markowitz and I are a Social Service unit assigned to the New York Bureau of Child Welfare. We had been asked by the Bureau to — May we come in?

MURRAY: Certainly.
(NICK opens the door all the way, letting them both into the main room.)

ALBERT: We, Miss Markowitz and I, have been asked by the B.C.W. to investigate and examine certain pupils of the Revere School. There is certain information which the school and the city would like to have, regarding young Nicholas.

MURRAY: Sit down, Miss Markowitz, please. Mr. Amundson. I'll just get rid of these things.
(MURRAY takes pants, shirts, a bugle, a clock, a yoyo, a half-empty bag of peanuts and an ashtray off the chairs, and with one sweeping movement puts all of them on the bed. The three of them take seats around the coffee table, NICK standing nervously off to one side.)

ALBERT: I'd like to explain just why we are here, Mr. Burns . . .

NICK: Would anybody like some coffee?

ALBERT: Why, thank you, Nicholas. Miss Markowitz?

SANDRA: Yes, thank you.

NICK *(Whispering to MURRAY on his way to the kitchen):*   Watch it.

ALBERT *(Smiling politely):*   It might be best, Mr. Burns, for the child if perhaps you sent him downstairs to play or something, while we have our discussion. Your case is . . .

MURRAY: Our "case." I had no idea we were a "case."

ALBERT: We do have a file on certain students at Revere.

MURRAY: So we're on file somewhere. Are we a great big, fat file, or a li'l teeny file?

ALBERT: Due to the fact that you have chosen not to answer our letters and several of our phone calls, there are many areas in which the file is incomplete, several questions — Mr. Burns, it might be better if the child went outside . . .

MURRAY: You gonna talk dirty?

ALBERT: It would be more advisable for the child not to be present, since Miss Markowitz, who will be discussing the psychological area . . . that is, we will be discussing certain matters which . . .

NICK *(From the kitchen):*   Cream and sugar for everybody?

ALBERT *(To the kitchen):*   Yes, Nicholas. *(To MURRAY again.)* Mr. Burns, it's going to be awkward, with the child present, to . . .

MURRAY *(To SANDRA):*   Miss Markowitz, may I know your first name?

SANDRA: Sandra.

MURRAY: And you are the psychologist part of this team, Sandy?

SANDRA: That's right, Mr. Burns.

MURRAY *(To ALBERT):*   And you, I take it, are the brawn of the outfit?

ALBERT: Perhaps I should explain, Mr. Burns, that the Social Service teams which serve Revere School are a carefully planned balance of Social Case Worker, such as myself, and Psychological Social Worker, such as Miss Markowitz, or, actually, *Dr.* Markowitz. *(NICK enters from the kitchen with four cups, gives one each to ALBERT, SANDRA, MURRAY; keeps one for himself.)* Mr. Burns, it is not easy to define those elements, those influences and problems which go into the make-up of a young boy.

MURRAY: I thought it was just frogs and snails and puppy dogs' tails.

ALBERT *(Using once again his polite smile):*   I appreciate the informality with which you approach this meeting, Mr. Burns, but on the more serious side, if I may, Miss Markowitz and I have a few matters . . .

NICK: Is the coffee any good?

ALBERT: Yes, very good. Thank you, Nicholas.

SANDRA: Very nice, Nicholas. *(She sees the cup in NICK's hand, speaks with professional interest.)* Are you drinking coffee, Nicholas? Don't you think it would be better if . . .

NICK: No. Milk. I like to drink it from a cup.

MURRAY *(To SANDRA, smiling):*   Now aren't you ashamed of yourself?

ALBERT *(Taking a rather large file out of his briefcase):*   Now, to plunge right in here . . .

MURRAY: Sometimes I put his milk in a shot glass. Better for getting him to drink it than adding chocolate syrup.

SANDRA *(Firmly):*   Mr. Burns, Mr. Amundson and I have several cases to examine today, and we would appreciate a certain amount of cooperation . . .

MURRAY *(To NICK):*   East Bronx, Mosholu Parkway.

NICK *(Looks at SANDRA, then to MURRAY):*   With a couple of years in maybe Massachusetts.

MURRAY: No Massachusetts at all. Complete Bronx.

SANDRA: I don't understand what . . .

MURRAY *(Sitting on the beach chair):*   Oh, excuse me. Nick and I are merely testing our sense of voice and accent. Nick insists he's better at it than I am.

SANDRA *(Smiling):*   As a matter of fact, the Bronx is right, but it's Grand Concourse.

MURRAY: The Massachusetts thing, way off, right?

SANDRA: Actually I took my graduate work with a professor, a man with a very strong New England accent, who could very well've influenced my speech. Nick is quite right.

NICK *(Proudly):*   Thank you, lady.

SANDRA: You certainly have a fine ear for sound, Nick. Do you and your uncle play many of these sorts of games together?

NICK: Oh, yes. We play many wholesome and constructive-type games together.

MURRAY: You're a big phony, Nick. Miss Markowitz has beautiful hazel eyes that have read many case histories and are ever watchful, and even clever little boys are not going to snow her. The lady is here for the facts.

ALBERT: Quite so, Mr. Burns. But facts alone cannot complete our examination. *(He takes out a pen, opens to a blank page in the file.)* We wish to understand . . .

NICK *(To SANDRA, showing off for her):*   Jersey City, maybe Newark. And . . . a little bit of Chicago.

MURRAY: Uh-huh. Think you've hit it, Nick.

SANDRA: That's really quite remarkable. Albert — Mr. Amundson *is* from New Jersey, and he went to Chicago University for several . . .

ALBERT *(Firmly):*   This is really quite beside the point, Sandra . . .

SANDRA: I just think it's quite remarkable, Albert, the boy's ability to . . .

ALBERT *(Purposely interrupting her):*   Suppose I just plunge right in here, before Dr. Markowitz begins her part of the interview . . .

(There is a noise at the front door and ARNOLD BURNS enters. He is carrying a medium-sized grocery delivery carton filled with a variety of fruit. He makes a rather incongruous delivery boy in that he is in his early forties and dressed in expensive, distinguished clothes, top coat, and hat. He is MURRAY's older brother, and his agent. It is obvious in the way he enters and automatically sets the delivery carton down on the desk that this is a daily ritual enacted at this same time every day and in this same manner. MURRAY does not even look up to greet him and NICK makes some casually mumbled greeting in his direction.)

ARNOLD: The honeydew melon's in season again but not really ripe yet so . . . *(He turns, sees that there are strangers there.)* Oh, sorry. Didn't you know had company . . . *(Turns, goes to the door.)* See you, Nick.

NICK: Yeah, see you, Uncle Arnie. *(ARNOLD exits.)*

ALBERT *(Looking at the door.)* There is somebody else living here with you?

MURRAY: No. That's just my brother, Arnold. He brings fruit every morning on his way to the office. He's a fruit nut.

ALBERT: I see here in the file that our research team spoke to your brother; your agent, I believe. We also called the people at your last business address, N.B.C. . . .

MURRAY *(Rising):*   You really do a lot of that stuff, calling people, going into my personal . . .

ALBERT: You've refused for quite some time, Mr. Burns, to answer any of our regular inquiries. We understand that you have been unemployed at this point for nearly five months.

NICK *(To ALBERT):*   He has an excellent opportunity to be an administrative assistant . . .

ALBERT *(Pressing forward):*   Other than your activities as free-lance script writer, I understand that you wrote regularly for an N.B.C. program for several years.

MURRAY: I was chief writer for Leo Herman, better known as Chuckles the Chipmunk, friend of the young'uns, and seller of Chuckle-Chips, the potato chips your friend Chuckles the Chipmunk eats and chuckles over.

ALBERT: And the circumstances under which you left the employ of . . .

MURRAY: I quit.

ALBERT: You felt that this was not the work you . . .

MURRAY: I felt that I was not reaching all the boys and girls out there in Televisionland. Actually it was not so much that I wasn't reaching the boys and girls, but the boys and girls were starting to reach *me*. Six months ago, a perfectly adult bartender asked me if I wanted an onion in my martini, and I said, "Gosh n'gollies, you betcha." I knew it was time to quit.

ALBERT: May I ask if this is a pattern; that is, in the past, has there been much shifting of position?

MURRAY: I *always* take an onion in my martini. This is a constant and unswerving . . .

(NICK, concerned with MURRAY's behaviour, goes toward him in an attempt to quiet him down.)

SANDRA *(Firmly, standing):*   Mr. Burns. Perhaps you are not aware of just how serious your situation is. This entire matter is a subject of intense interest to the B.C.W. The circumstances of this child's environment, the danger of . . .

ALBERT: Our investigation, Mr. Burns, is the result of what the Bureau considers to be almost an emergency case.

NICK: He just likes to kid around, lady. But, see, we really got a great environment here . . .

MURRAY *(To NICK):*   Relax, kid. *(To ALBERT and SANDRA)* Look, people, I'm sorry. Let's get back to the questions.

SANDRA: Fine. Nick, suppose you and I have a little chat right here.

NICK *(As he sits down next to her):*   Fine. I was gonna suggest that myself.

SANDRA: Nick, I bet you love to come home when you've been out playing and you get tired. You say to yourself, "Gee, I'd like to go home now."

NICK: Sure, right. And I'm happy here. Boy, if you think I'm happy now, you should see me when I'm *really* happy.

MURRAY *(To SANDRA, sympathetically):*   He's on to you, honey. You're gonna have to be a lot foxier than that . . .

SANDRA: And I'm sure that you and your uncle have a great deal of fun together.

NICK: It's not *all* laughs.

SANDRA: Oh, I'm sure there are times when the fun stops and you have nice talks and your uncles teaches you things, helps you to . . .

NICK: I can do a great Peter Lorre imitation. Murray taught me.

ALBERT: Nicky, what Miss Markowitz means, is that you and your uncle must sometimes . . .

NICK *(In the voice of Peter Lorre, a rather good imitation):*   You can't hang me . . . I didn't do it, I tell you . . . that's my knife . . . I am innocent . . . it's all a mistake . . .
   (MURRAY beams, smiles proudly during imitation.)

ALBERT: Nicky, that's not what we meant, we . . .

MURRAY: What's the trouble? That happens to be a very good imitation.

ALBERT: Perhaps; but we are trying to . . .

MURRAY: Can *you* imitate Peter Lorre?

NICK *(Confidentially, to SANDRA):*   I can do a pretty good James Cagney; I mean it's not fantastic like my Peter Lorre, but it . . .

ALBERT *(Raising his voice a bit, somewhat commanding):*   Nicholas, please. Try to pay attention. Now if I may proceed to . . .

SANDRA *(Aside, to ALBERT, somewhat annoyed with him):* Albert, if you'll just let me handle this area. *(Then, to NICK)* Nick, let's talk about games. O.K.?

NICK: O.K.

SANDRA: Now, what kind of games do you like the best?

NICK: Mostly I like educational games and things like that. Murray gets me to develop my natural inquiring mind.

SANDRA: I wonder, do you have any favourite games or toys you'd like to show me? Some playing that is just the most favourite one of all?

NICK: I just now threw away my collection of *National Geographics* and other educational-type magazines I had a whole collection of . . .

ALBERT: Nicky, Miss Markowitz is very interested in you and cares about you and everything. And if you brought out some of your favourite toys and playthings for her to see, I'm sure that she'd love them just as much as you do.

NICK: Well, there's Bubbles . . . *(He gets up to get it for them.)*

MURRAY: I don't think you'd be interested in seeing Bubbles . . .
(NICK goes to a cardboard carton at the bureau, opens it, and takes out a twenty-four-inch-high plastic statue of a bare-chested hula girl. The statue is in bright colours and has an electric switch as its pedestal. NICK places the statue on the table between ALBERT and SANDRA and turns it on.)

NICK: Bubbles is what you'd call an electric statue. *(The breasts of the statue light up and continue to blink on and off in spectacular fashion for the next part of the scene. ALBERT looks at the statue, begins busily going through the file on his lap. SANDRA regards the statue scientifically, professionally. NICK smiles proudly over his possession.)* It's got an electric battery timer in there that makes it go on and off like that.

SANDRA: Nick, is this your favourite toy?

NICK: Well, after a while it gets pretty boring. But it's a swell gimmick. There was another one in the store that was even better . . .

MURRAY: Anybody want orange juice or toast or anything?

SANDRA: Nick, tell me . . . do you like best the fact that the chest of the lady lights up?

NICK: Well, you got to admit, you don't see boobies like that every day. You want to see the effect when the lights are out? When the room is dark?

SANDRA: Tell me, Nick, is *that* what you like best about it, that you can be alone in the dark with it?

NICK: Well, I don't know. But in the dark they really knock your eyes out.
(ALBERT is blinking nervously at the blinking lights of the statue.)

ALBERT *(With strenuous calm):* Perhaps, don't you think we ought to switch it off, turn off the . . .

SANDRA: Nick, does Bubbles, does she in any way, does her face remind you at all of, oh, let me see, your mother, for example?

NICK *(He looks at the face of the statue):*   No. I mean, it's just a doll, it's not a statue of anybody I know. I got it in this store downtown.

SANDRA: Her chest, is that something which . . .

NICK *(Smiling broadly):*   It's *something* all right, isn't it?

SANDRA: When you think of your mother, do you . . .

NICK: I don't think about her much.

SANDRA: But when you *do* think of her, do you remember her face best, or her *hands*, or . . .

NICK: I remember she has this terrific laugh. The kind of laugh that when she laughs it makes you laugh too. Of course, she overdoes that a lot.

SANDRA: I mean, physically, when you think of her, do you, well, when you see Bubbles, and Bubbles goes on and off like that . . .

MURRAY: Sandra, his mother's chest did not light up. Let's get that settled right now; mark it down in the file.

ALBERT *(Nervously; pointing at the blinking statue):*   Nicky, I wonder if you would turn those off . . . I mean, turn *it* off, turn her off, unplug it . . .
(MURRAY turns the statue off, puts it back into the box.)

SANDRA: Nicky, when you bought this doll . . .

MURRAY: Sandy, why don't I save you a lot of time. Nick is a fairly bright kid and he knows that girls are *not* boys. Other than that his interest in ladies is confined right now to ones that light up or don't light up.

NICK: I mostly like to read books that are healthy, constructive, and extremely educational for a person.

MURRAY: Don't push it, Nick. He does not have any unusual fixations, Sandy. He is no more abnormally interested in your bust than Mr. Amundson is.

ALBERT: Mr. Burns, it is not necessary to . . .

MURRAY: Of course, I might be wrong about that.

ALBERT: Our interest in that doll . . .

MURRAY: You really *are* interested in that doll, Albert.

ALBERT: Our interest . . .

NICK *(To ALBERT):*   I'll sell it to you for two dollars. That's fifty cents less than I paid for it.
(SANDRA is unable to suppress her amusement and laughs happily.)

ALBERT *(Quite annoyed with her):*   Sandra, I fail to see . . .

SANDRA *(Controlling herself again, but still smiling):*   It's just that it was funny, Albert.

ALBERT *(Taking command):*   Suppose *I* pursue, then, the psychological part of . . .

SANDRA *(Bristling at him):*   Excuse me, Albert, I really do feel it would be better if *I* were to . . .

MURRAY: Albert, the lady was just laughing because something funny happened. That's actually the best thing to do under the circumstances.

ALBERT: Mr. Burns . . .

MURRAY: How would you all like to go to the Statue of Liberty? I have it on good authority from the Weather Lady that today is a beautiful day.

ALBERT: Is it at all possible, Mr. Burns, for you to stick to the point?

MURRAY: Albert, I bet you'd make Sandy a lot happier if you took her off somewhere once in a while. Doesn't have to be the Statue of Liberty; actually any . . .

ALBERT: My relationship with Dr. Markowitz is of no . . .

MURRAY: Well, there's obviously some relationship. When Nick asked you if you'd have sugar in your coffee before, Albert, you answered for Sandy.

ALBERT: Mr. Burns, this entire interview has reached a point . . .

NICK: I'm going to get my educational books. I left them out on the street. *(He leaves the apartment, his exit unnoticed by the others.)*

ALBERT: This entire interview, Mr. Burns, has . . .

SANDRA: Mr. Burns, I . . .

ALBERT: Damn it, Sandra, don't interrupt me!

SANDRA: Albert, for goodness sakes, you . . .

ALBERT *(Stands up):* Sandra, perhaps we . . . *(To MURRAY)* Would you excuse us for just a moment, Mr. Burns? *(She gets up. ALBERT and SANDRA walk over to the alcove, where MURRAY cannot hear them. MURRAY starts to peer at them through his binoculars until ALBERT turns and looks at him; he then goes to desk and tinkers with clock. Now alone with SANDRA, ALBERT's manner changes somewhat. He speaks more softly and with more warmth, a departure from the stiff, professional manner he uses in dealing with MURRAY.)* Sandra, what are you *doing*, have we lost all control?

SANDRA: Are you seriously talking to *me* about control?

ALBERT: Dear, I told *you* and I told Dr. Malko. It's much too soon for you to go out on cases. You need another year in the office, behind the lines, I told both of you. You're simply *not* ready.

SANDRA: Really, Albert, you hardly let me get started. I was attempting to deal with the whole child.

ALBERT: Three months out of grad school and you want to go right into the front lines. Not advisable.

SANDRA *(Whispering angrily):* Don't you think that this is rather stupid and unprofessional? Right here in front of him you decide to have a conference.

ALBERT: A necessity. I am supposedly the leader of our examining team . . .

SANDRA: Oh, *really* . . .

ALBERT: You get too *involved*, Sandra. Each case, you get much too emotionally involved. This is an exploratory visit, we are *scientists*, dear, you lose sight of the . . .

SANDRA: You make me sick today, Albert. This is no way to approach this man's problem. We . . .

ALBERT *(sighing):* Oh, fine. That's fine. Well . . . fine . . .
(MURRAY, at the other side of the room, picks up a megaphone.)

MURRAY *(Through the megaphone):* How are we doing? *(Puts the megaphone down, comes over to them in the alcove, sits between them; speaks sympathetically.)* I personally don't feel that you're gonna work out your problems with each other. But I'm glad you came to me because I think I can help you. Al, Sandy is not going to respect you because you threaten her. Respect will have to come gradually, naturally, a maturing process . . .

ALBERT: Mr. Burns . . .

MURRAY: Sandy, I bet he's got a file on you.

ALBERT: Mr. Burns, according to the B.C.W., the child's continuance in your home is in serious and immediate doubt. I am trying to encourage your cooperation . . . *(He is making a genuine attempt to speak warmly, understandingly.)* Aren't you at all willing to answer some questions, to give some evidence in your favour for our report, some evidence to support your competency as a guardian? The Board is thoroughly aware that Nicholas is not legally adopted.

MURRAY: He's my nephew. He's staying with me for a while. He's visiting.

ALBERT: How long has he been here?

MURRAY: Seven years.

ALBERT: So you see, the Child Welfare Board has, I assure you, the right to question . . .

MURRAY *(Rises, faces ALBERT angrily):* You don't assure me of *any*thing, buddy, you make me damn nervous. Do you mean to tell me that four years at N.Y.U. has made you my judge? *(ALBERT shrugs, defeated; crosses to Morris chair for his coat, signals SANDRA that they are leaving. MURRAY goes toward them; speaks quietly, apologetically.)* O.K., all right. What do you want to know? I'll be cooperative.
(SANDRA and ALBERT sit down again.)

ALBERT: Nicholas' father, where is he?

MURRAY: That's not a *where* question. That's a *who* question.

ALBERT: I don't quite . . .

MURRAY: Nick's mother, she didn't quite either.

SANDRA: She is still living . . .

MURRAY: My sister is unquestionably alive.

SANDRA: But her responsibility to the child.

MURRAY: For five years she did everything she could for Nick . . . but get married. Now that's not easy to understand since she used to get married to *everybody*. But, somehow, having Nick matured her, she felt a responsibility not to get married to just *any*body any more, so she didn't marry Nick's father, nor was she married at the time he was born. You might call Nick a bastard, or "little bastard," depending on how whimsical you feel at the time. Is that the sort of information you wanted? . . . Ah, this situation is the social workers' paradise. What a case history, huh? . . . My sister Elaine showed up here one day with two suitcases, a hatbox, a blue parakeet, a dead gold fish, and a five-year-old child. Three days later she went downstairs to buy a pack of filter-tip cigarettes . . . *(MURRAY shrugs.)* Six years later she returned for the suitcases and the hatbox . . . the parakeet I had given away, the gold fish I had long since flushed down the toilet, and the five year-old-child had, with very little effort, become six years older. When Elaine returned for her luggage I reminded her of the child and the pack of filter-tip cigarettes and suggested that this was perhaps the longest running practical joke in recent history. She was accompanied by a tall chap with sunglasses who was born to be her fifth divorce and who tried to start a small conversation with me. At this point I slapped my sister, Fifth Divorce slugged me, Sister cried, stopped quite suddenly, and then proceeded to explain to me, briefly, her well-practiced theory on the meaning of life, a philosophy falling somewhere to the left of Whoopie. At which point, I remember, I started laughing and then we all laughed and said "good-bye" like people at the end of a long party. That was almost a year ago. And I've still got Nick.

(SANDRA is obviously sympathetic to this situation, emotionally involved in the story; ALBERT continues his cool professionalism, here and there jotting notes in the file.)

SANDRA: But . . . but I'm sure she must have had *some* concern about Nicholas . . . about the child . . .

MURRAY: His name is not Nicholas. I will admit that he has stayed with that name much longer than the others . . . no, actually he was "Bill" for almost eight months . . .

SANDRA: I'm sure, on his birth certificate . . .

MURRAY: Certainly an elusive document. Not having given him a last name, Elaine felt reticent about assigning him a first one. When Nick first came here this presented a real difficulty. Nick answered to nothing whatsoever. Even the parakeet recognized its own name. Nick only knew I was calling him when he was positive there was no one else in the room.

SANDRA *(Very much emotionally involved in this now):* Well, how did you communicate with . . .

MURRAY: I made a deal with him when he was six, up to which time he was known rather casually as Chubby, that he could try out any name he wished, for however long he wished, until his thirteenth birthday, at which point he'd have to decide on a name he liked permanently. He went through a long period of dogs' names when he was still little, Rover and King having a real vogue there for a while. For three months he referred to himself as Big Sam, then there was Little Max, Snoopy, Chip, Rock, Rex, Mike, Marty, Lamont, Chevrolet, Wyatt, Yancy, Fred, Phil, Woodrow, Lefty, The Phantom . . . He received his library card last year in the name of Raphael Sabatini, his Cub Scout membership lists him as Barry Fitzgerald, and only last week a friend of his called asking if Toulouse could come over to his house for dinner. Nick seems to be the one that'll stick, though.

SANDRA: His mother . . .?

MURRAY: His mother, when last heard, was studying mime in Paris, having been given a sort of scholarship by a twenty-two-year-old handbag heir named Myron, who seems to believe strongly in the development of talent and student exchange. Well, I don't believe I've left anything out.

ALBERT: I was not aware that Nick was an O.W. child.

MURRAY: O.W.?

ALBERT: Out of wedlock.

MURRAY: For a moment I thought you meant Prisoner of War. I think it's that natural warmth of yours that leads me to misunderstand.

ALBERT: But as concerns the child . . . *(Looks around the room)* Where is the child?

SANDRA: You preferred not having him here anyway, Albert.

ALBERT *(Sharply):* I am perfectly aware, Sandra, of what I *prefer*, and what I do *not* prefer.

SANDRA *(Sharply):* I don't care for that tone of voice at *all*, Albert.

ALBERT *(Rises, begins to put on his coat; calmly):* Sandra, I understand perfectly what has happened. We have allowed this man to disturb us and we have *both* gotten a bit upset. Now, I really do feel that it's time we got over to that family problem in Queens. It's there in your file, the Ledbetters, the introverted child. We've really given an unreasonable amount of time to this case. This interview, I'm afraid, Mr. Burns, has reached a point . . .

SANDRA *(Attempting to sound authoritative):* Albert, I personally feel that it would not be advisable to leave this particular case, at this point.

ALBERT: Sandra, we have done here this morning all we . . .

SANDRA: I feel that we have not really given Mr. Burns a chance to . . .

ALBERT: Sandra, it's really time we left for Queens . . .

SANDRA *(Hands ALBERT one of her two file envelopes):* Here's the Ledbetter file, I'm staying here.

ALBERT *(Raising his voice a little):* Sandra.

SANDRA: I have decided to pursue this case.

ALBERT *(Almost shouting):* Sandra, have we lost all professional control?

SANDRA *(Angry, flustered):* You just . . . you just go yourself to the Leadbellies . . . you go on to Queens.

ALBERT *(Takes her by the arm, gently, but firmly):* May I just talk to you for a moment?
  (ALBERT leads SANDRA over to the alcove.)

MURRAY: Time out for signals again?

ALBERT *(Away from MURRAY, now he speaks, softly, less stiffly, though still* *angry):* What *is* this, dear? What has happened to you today? What are you doing?

SANDRA: I'm doing what I think is right.

ALBERT: I know how you feel, Sandra, but there is no more we can do here.

SANDRA *(Emotionally):* I just . . . I just don't understand your behaviour when you're on a case. We're supposed to be of some help, he . . .

ALBERT: Of course I want to help. But don't forget that the child is the one who needs protection, who needs . . .

SANDRA: Are you really going to leave that man here like that? You're not going to even try to help him or tell him what to do about the Board separating him from the child . . . I mean . . . just so cold.

ALBERT *(Takes her hand):* Dear, you spent much too much time at that graduate school and not enough time in the field. That's your whole trouble. You've got to learn your job, Sandra . . .

SANDRA *(Angry, frustrated):* Oh *really*, is that so? Albert Amundson, don't give me any of that nonsense.

ALBERT *(Glancing over at MURRAY):* Please, Sandra . . . dear, this is not the time or the place for . . .

SANDRA *(Shouting):* Graduate school wouldn't have done *you* any harm, Albert, believe *me*! Oh, this is the most terrible thing . . . *(Very close to tears)* You mean . . . you're just going to leave . . .? Do you know what you are . . .? you're a . . . I don't know; . . . but I'll think of something . . .
(ALBERT walks away, leaving her in the alcove, goes into the main room, calmly picks up his briefcase.)

ALBERT *(Retaining his control, but just a little shaken. To MURRAY):* Mr. Burns . . . You can assume at this point that Miss Markowitz is no longer involved with your case. The Board will be informed that she is no longer involved with this particular case. Her continuing here, to discuss your case . . . at this point . . . is entirely unofficial. You can dismiss any conference . . . that may resume after I leave . . . when I leave here, from your mind. And, regardless of what you think of me . . .

MURRAY: I think you're a dirty O.W.
(Some of SANDRA's file papers slip from her hand and fall to the floor.)

ALBERT: And . . . and do you know what *you* are? *(Readying himself to deliver a crushing insult to MURRAY)* Maladjusted! *(Goes to the door, opens it.)* Good afternoon, Mr. Burns. Good afternoon, Sandra.

MURRAY: Good afternoon, Mr. Amundson. Watch out crossing the street.
(ALBERT exits, closing door sharply behind him. SANDRA stands for a moment in the alcove, then begins to pick up the papers she had dropped on the floor.)

SANDRA: Mr. Burns . . . *(She is making a very strong attempt to control herself, but she is obviously on the verge of tears. She goes into the main room, begins to collect her things to leave.)* Mr. Burns, I must apologize to you. We . . . we have put you . . . you have been put at a disadvantage this morning. You have been involved in a personal problem that has nothing to do whatsoever with your particular case. It is entirely wrong for me to give you this impression of our . . . of our profession. *(She can no longer control herself and becomes, suddenly, a sort of child. She stands quite still, with her hands at her sides, and cries. It is not loud, hysterical crying, but intermittent and disorganized sobs, squeaks, whines, sniffles and assorted feminine noises which punctuate her speech.)* Do you know what? I just lost my job. This is awful. He's right, you know. I'm not suited to my work. I get too involved. That's what he said and he's right. *(Rummaging through her purse for Kleenex.)* Please don't look at me. Do you *have* to stand there? Please go away. Still, he didn't have to talk to me like that. This is the first *week* we've ever gone on cases together. I didn't think he'd behave that way. That was no way. Why don't I ever have any Kleenex? *(He gives her the closest thing at hand to blow her nose in, his undershirt from the bed.)* Thank you. *(She sits down on the bed.)* Do you know that even with two fellowships it still cost me, I mean my parents mostly, it cost them seven thousand two hundred and forty-five dollars for me to go through school. I was the eighth youngest person to graduate in New York State last year and I can't stop crying. Maybe if I hurry, if I took a cab, I could still meet him in Queens.

MURRAY: You can't. Queens is closed. It's closed for the season.

SANDRA: Do you know what? *(Her crying lets up a bit.)*

MURRAY: What?

SANDRA *(With a new burst of sobs):*   I hate the Ledbetters.

MURRAY: Then I'm sure once I got to know them I'd hate them too.

SANDRA: Mr. Burns, you don't understand. Some of the cases I love and some of them I hate, and that's all wrong for my work, but I can't help it. I hate Raymond Ledbetter and he's only nine years old and he makes me sick and I don't give a damn about him.

MURRAY *(Pointing to the file on her lap):*   You can't like everybody in your portfolio.

SANDRA: But some of them I like too much and worry about them all day . . . *(She is making an attempt to control her tears.)* It is an obvious conflict against all professional standards. I didn't like Raymond Ledbetter so I tried to understand him, and now that I understand him I hate him.

MURRAY: I think that's wonderful. Can I get you a cup of coffee?

SANDRA *(She turns to MURRAY as if to answer him, but instead bursts into fresh tears):*   He's gone to Queens and I'll never hear from him again. I wrote out what my married name would be after dinner last night on a paper napkin, Mrs. Albert Amundson, to see how it would look. You know what I think I am, I think I'm crazy.

MURRAY: Well, then, I can talk to you.

SANDRA: We were going to get married. It was all planned, Mrs. Albert Amundson on a napkin. You have to understand Albert. He's really a very nice person when he's not on cases. He's a very intelligent man but last month I fell asleep twice while he was talking. I've known him for so long. *(She tries once again to stop crying but the effort only increases her sobs.)* Mr. Burns, don't look at me. Why don't you go away?

MURRAY: But I live here.

SANDRA: I would like everybody to go away.

MURRAY *(Attempting to comfort her):*   Can I get you a pastrami sandwich?

SANDRA: Oh, I don't know you and I'm crying right in front of you. Go away.

MURRAY: Couldn't you just think of this as Show-and-Tell time?

SANDRA *(Turning away again, still seated on the bed):*   The minute I got out of school I wanted to go right back inside. *(with a great sob.)* Albert is gone and I just lost my job.

MURRAY *(He walks over to her):*   Now, you're really going to have to stop crying, because I am going out of my mind.

SANDRA: I cry all the time and I laugh in the wrong places in the movies. I am unsuited to my profession and I can't do anything right. Last night I burned an entire chicken and after seven years of school I can't work and I've got no place to go. An entire chicken.

MURRAY: If I do my Peter Lorre imitation, will you stop crying?

SANDRA *(She pokes the file-envelope in her lap):*   Look what I've done, I've cried on one of my files. The ink is running all over the Grumbacher twins . . .

MURRAY *(In the voice of Peter Lorre, a decent imitation):*   It was all a mistake, I didn't stab Mrs. Marmalade . . . it was my knife, but someone else did it, I tell you . . .

SANDRA: That's an awful imitation, Mr. Burns . . .
(She turns away from him and sobs into the bedclothes. He takes the Bubbles statue out of the box, switches it on, places it on the floor near the bed; it starts to blink on and off. Her face peeks out, she sees the blinking statue and puts her face back into the bedclothes, but we hear some giggles mixing with her sobs now, and then overtaking them, until she finally lifts her face and we see that she is laughing.)

MURRAY *(Smiling):*   There. Progress. *(He turns off the statue.)* Would you like a cup of coffee, or a pastrami sandwich or something?

SANDRA: No, thank you. *(SANDRA begins to compose herself, she has stopped crying completely and is wiping her eyes with the undershirt he gave her. Then she begins to fold the undershirt neatly, smoothing it out into a nice little square on her lap.)* This is absolutely the most unprofessional experience I have ever had.

MURRAY: People fall into two distinct categories, Miss Markowitz; people who like delicatessen, and people who don't like delicatessen. A man who is not touched by the earthy lyricism of hot pastrami, the pungent fantasy of corned beef, pickles, frankfurters, the great lusty impertinence of good mustard . . . is a man of stone and without heart. Now, Albert is obviously not a lover of delicatessen and you are well rid of him.
(SANDRA is still sitting on the bed, her hands folded neatly in her lap on top of her files and his undershirt.)

SANDRA: What am I going to do? This is an awful day.

MURRAY *(He sits on the swivel chair next to the bed):*   Miss Markowitz, this is a beautiful day and I'll tell you why. My dear, you are really a jolly old girl and you are well rid of Albert. You have been given a rare opportunity to return the unused portion and have your money refunded.

SANDRA: But . . . my work . . . what am I going to . . .

MURRAY: You are a lover, Dr. Markowitz, you are a lover of things and people so you took up work where you could get as many of them as possible; and it just turned out that there were too many of them and too much that moves you. Damn it, please be glad that it turned out you are not reasonable and sensible. Have all the gratitude you can, that you are capable of embarrassment and joy and are a marathon crier.

SANDRA *(Looking directly at him):*   There is a kind of relief that it's gone . . . the job, and even Albert. But I know what it is, it's just irresponsible . . . I don't have the vaguest idea who I am . . .

MURRAY *(He takes her hand):*   It's just there's all these Sandras running around who you never met before, and it's confusing at first, fantastic, like a Chinese fire drill. But god *damn*, isn't it great to find out how many Sandras there are? Like those little cars in the circus, this tiny red car comes out and putters around, suddenly its doors open and out come a thousand clowns, whooping and hollering and raising hell.

SANDRA *(She lets go of his hand in order to pick up the undershirt in her lap):*   What's this?

MURRAY: That's my undershirt. How's about going to the Empire State Building with me?

SANDRA: I'll have that coffee now.

MURRAY: You didn't answer my question. Would you like to visit the Empire State Building?

SANDRA: No, not really.

MURRAY: Well, then how about the zoo?

SANDRA: Not just now.

MURRAY: Well, then will you marry me?

SANDRA: What?

MURRAY: Just a bit of shock treatment there. I have found after long experience that it's the quickest way to get a woman's attention when her mind wanders. Always works.

SANDRA: Mr. Burns . . .

MURRAY: Now that you've cried you can't call me Mr. Burns. Same rule applies to laughing. My name is Murray.

SANDRA: Well, Murray, to sort of return to reality for a minute . . .

MURRAY: I will only go as a tourist.

SANDRA: Murray, you know, you're in trouble with the Child Welfare Board.

They could really take Nick away. Murray, there's some things you could try to do . . . to make your case a little stronger . . .

MURRAY: Sandra, do you realize that you are not wearing your shoes?

SANDRA *(She looks down at her bare feet):* Oh.
(The front door opens and NICK bursts into the room, laden with books.)

NICK: Well, here I am with all my favourite books, *Fun in the Rain, The Young Railroader, Great Philosophers, Science for Youth,* a Spanish dictionary. What I did was I left them out in the street when I was playing, and I went down to . . .

MURRAY: Nick, you just killed a month's allowance for nothing. Miss Markowitz isn't even on our case any more.

NICK: I shouldn't have left. You got angry and insulted everybody.

MURRAY: Don't worry about it, Nick, we'll work it out. *(He goes over to the closet for something.)*

NICK *(Dropping his books regretfully on the chair):* Four dollars right out the window. *(To SANDRA)* Y'know, I really do read educational books and am encouraged in my home to think.

SANDRA: I'm sure that's true, Nicholas, but I'm not in a position to do you much official good any more.

NICK: We're in real trouble now, right? *(He turns to MURRAY who has taken two ukuleles from the closet and is coming toward NICK.)* I figured it would happen; you got angry and hollered at everybody.

MURRAY: Nick, we have a guest, a music lover. . . . *(He hands the smaller of the two ukuleles to NICK.)* We've got to do our song. I am sure it will be requested.

NICK *(Protesting, gesturing with his ukulele):* Murray, stop it . . . we — this is no time to sing songs, Murray . . . .

MURRAY *(Striking a downbeat on his ukulele):* Come on, where's your professional attitude?
(MURRAY starts playing "Yes, Sir, That's My Baby" on the ukulele, then sings the first line. NICK turns away at first, shaking his head solemnly at MURRAY's behaviour. MURRAY goes on with the second line of the song. Reluctantly, NICK begins to pick out the melody on his ukulele, then he smiles in spite of himself and sings the third line along with MURRAY.
They really go into the song now, singing and playing "Yes, Sir, That's My Baby," doing their routine for SANDRA. She sits in front of them on the bed, smiling, enjoying their act. NICK is in the spirit of it now and having a good time. In the middle of the song NICK and MURRAY do some elaborate soft-shoe dance steps for a few lines, ukuleles held aloft. This is followed by some very fast and intricate two-part ukulele harmony on the last few lines of the song for a big finish.
SANDRA applauds.
MURRAY and NICK, singing and strumming ukes, go into a reprise of the song, MURRAY moving forward and sitting down on the bed next to

SANDRA. *NICK, left apart from them now, does a line or two more of the song along with MURRAY, then gradually stops. NICK considers them both for a moment as MURRAY goes on doing the song alone now for SANDRA. NICK nods to himself, circles around in front of them and, unnoticed by them, puts his uke down on the window seat, goes to his alcove, gets school briefcase and pajamas from his bed. MURRAY is still playing the uke and singing the song to SANDRA as NICK goes past them on his way to the front door, carrying his stuff.)*

NICK *(Pleasantly, to SANDRA):*   Nice to meet you, lady, I'll see you around.

MURRAY *(Stops singing, turns to NICK):*   Where you off to, Nick?

NICK: Gonna leave my stuff up at Mrs. Myers'. *(Opens the door.)* I figure I'll be staying over there tonight.
(NICK exits, waving a pleasant good-bye to SANDRA. SANDRA looks at the front door, puzzled; then she looks at MURRAY, who resumes the song, singing and strumming the uke.)

CURTAIN

Scene: MURRAY's apartment, eight A.M. the following morning.

At rise: The phone is ringing loudly on the window seat. MURRAY enters from the bathroom with his toothbrush in his mouth, grabs the phone. The room is as it was at the end of Act One except that there is a six-foot-high folding screen placed around the bed, hiding it from view, and the shades are drawn again on the windows.

MURRAY *(Speaks immediately into the phone):*   Is this somebody with good news or money? No? Good-bye. *(He hangs up.)* It's always voices like that you hear at eight A.M. Maniacs. *(He pulls up the shade to see what kind of a day it is outside. As usual the lighting of the room changes not at all with the shade up, as before he sees nothing but the blank, grayish wall opposite.)* Crap. *(With a sign of resignation, he picks up the phone, dials, listens.)* Hello, Weather Lady. I am fine, how are you? What is the weather? Uh-huh . . . uh-huh . . . uh-huh . . . very nice. Only a *chance* of showers? Well, what exactly does that . . . Aw, there she goes again . . . *(He hangs up.)* Chance of showers. *(The phone rings. He picks it up, speaks immediately into it.)* United States Weather Bureau forecast for New York City and vicinity: eight A.M. temperature, sixty-five degrees, somewhat cooler in the suburbs, cloudy later today with a chance of . . . *(Looks incredulously at the phone.)* He hung up. Fool. Probably the most informative phone call he'll make all day. *(He stands, opens the window, leans out, raising his voice, shouting out the window.)* This is your neighbour speaking! Something must be done about your garbage cans in the alley here. It is definitely second-rate garbage! By next week I want to see a better class of garbage, more empty champagne bottles and caviar cans! So let's *snap* it up and get on the *ball!*

(SANDRA's head appears at the top of the screen, like a puppet's head. She is staring blankly at MURRAY. MURRAY steps toward her, she continues to stare blankly at him. Her head suddenly disappears again behind the screen. The screen masks the entire bed and SANDRA from his view, and the view of audience. We hear a rustle of sheets and blankets, silence for a couple of seconds, and then SANDRA's voice; she speaks in a cold, dignified, ladylike voice, only slightly tinged with sleep, impersonal, polite, and distant, like one unintroduced party guest to another.)

SANDRA: Good morning.

MURRAY: Good morning.

SANDRA: How are you this morning?

MURRAY: I am fine this morning. How are you?

SANDRA: I am fine also. Do you have a bathrobe?

MURRAY: Yes, I have a bathrobe.

SANDRA: May I have your bathrobe, please?

MURRAY: I'll give you Nick's. It'll fit you better.

SANDRA: That seems like a good idea. *(He takes NICK's bathrobe from the hook in the alcove, tosses it over the top of the screen.)*

MURRAY: There you go.

SANDRA *(Her voice from behind the screen is getting even colder):* Thank you. What time is it?

MURRAY: It is eight-fifteen and there is a chance of showers. Did you sleep well?

SANDRA: Yes. How long have you been up?

MURRAY: Little while.

SANDRA: Why didn't you wake me?

MURRAY: Because you were smiling. *(Silence for a moment)* How does the bathrobe fit?

SANDRA: This bathrobe fits fine. *(After a moment.)* Did you happen to see my clothes?

MURRAY *(Starts for the bathroom):* They're in the bathroom. Shall I get them?

SANDRA: No, thank you. *(She suddenly pops out from behind the screen and races across the room into the kitchen at right, slamming the kitchen door behind her. We hear her voice from behind the door.)* This isn't the bathroom. This is the kitchen.

MURRAY: If it *was* the bathroom then this would be a very extreme version of an efficiency apartment. *(He goes to the bathroom to get her clothes, brings them with him to the kitchen door. He knocks on the door.)* Here are your clothes. Also toothpaste and toothbrush.

(The kitchen door opens slightly, her hand comes out. He puts the stuff in it, her hand goes back, the door closes again.)

SANDRA: Thank you.

MURRAY: Sandy, is everything all right?

SANDRA: What?

MURRAY: I said, is everything all right?

SANDRA: Yes. I'm using the last of your toothpaste.

MURRAY: That's all right. There's soap by the sink.

SANDRA: I know. I found it.

MURRAY: That's good.

SANDRA: It was right by the sink.

MURRAY: Suppose we broaden this discussion to other matters . . .

SANDRA: I saw the soap when I came in.
(The front door opens and ARNOLD BURNS enters as he did before, carrying a grocery carton filled with varieties of fruit. He sets it down on the desk.)

ARNOLD: Morning, Murray.

MURRAY *(Without turning to look at him):* Morning, Arnold.

ARNOLD: Murray, Chuckles called again yesterday. I told him I'd talk to you. And Jimmy Sloan is in from the coast; he's putting a new panel-show package together . . .

MURRAY: Arnold, you have many successful clients . . .

ARNOLD: Murray . . .

MURRAY: With all these successful people around, where are all of our new young failures going to come from?

ARNOLD: Murray, those people I saw here yesterday; they were from the Welfare Board, right? I tried to warn you . . .

MURRAY: Nothing to worry about.

ARNOLD: These Welfare people don't kid around.

MURRAY: Arnold, I don't mind you coming with fruit if you keep quiet, but you bring a word with every apple . . . Everything's fine. You'll be late for the office.

ARNOLD: Is Nick all right?

MURRAY: Fine.

ARNOLD: O.K., good-bye, Murray.

MURRAY: Good-bye, Arnold. *(ARNOLD exits. MURRAY talks to the closed kitchen door again.)* There's coffee still in the pot from last night, if you want to heat it up.

SANDRA: I already lit the flame.

MURRAY: Good. The cups are right over the sink. Will you be coming out soon?

SANDRA: Yes, I think so. Cream and sugar in your coffee?

MURRAY: Yes, thank you.

SANDRA: Murray.

MURRAY: Yes.

SANDRA: I'm coming out now.

MURRAY: That's good.

SANDRA: I'm all finished in here so I'm coming out now.

MURRAY: That's very good.
(The kitchen door opens. SANDRA, dressed neatly, comes out of the kitchen, carrying two cups of coffee and NICK's bathrobe.)

SANDRA *(Pausing at kitchen doorway, smiles politely):* Well, here I am. *(She goes to MURRAY, gives him a cup, sits on swivel chair. He sits next to her, on the stool. She takes a sip of coffee, straightens her hair. She is quite reserved, though pleasant; she behaves as though at a tea social.)* You know, yesterday was the first time I've ever been to the Statue of Liberty. It's funny how you can live in a city for so long and not visit one of its most fascinating sights.

MURRAY: That is funny. *(He sips his coffee.)* This coffee isn't bad, for yesterday's coffee.

SANDRA: I think it's very good, for yesterday's coffee. *(Takes another sip.)* What kind of coffee is it?

MURRAY: I believe it's Chase and Sanborn coffee.

SANDRA: "Good to the last drop," isn't that what they say?

MURRAY: I think that's Maxwell House.

SANDRA: Oh yes. Maxwell House coffee. "Good to the last drop."

MURRAY: It's Chase and Sanborn that used to have the ad about the ingredients: "Monizalles for mellowness" was one.

SANDRA: They used to sponsor Edgar Bergen and Charle McCarthy on the radio.

MURRAY: Yes. You're right.

SANDRA: "Monizalles for mellowness." I remember. That's right. *(She finishes her coffee, puts her cup down on the table. Then, after a moment)* I have to leave now.

MURRAY: Oh?

SANDRA: Yes. I'll have to be on my way. *(She stands, takes her pocketbook, puts on her shoes and starts to exit.)*

MURRAY *(Takes her files from the floor, hands them to her):* Don't forget your files.

SANDRA: Oh yes. My files. *(She takes them from him, stands looking at him.)* Well, good-bye.

MURRAY: Good-bye, Sandra.

SANDRA: Good-bye. *(She walks out of the apartment, and closes the door behind her. Alone in the apartment now, MURRAY stands for a moment looking at the door. He then runs to open the door; she has had her hand on the outside knob and is dragged into the room as he does so.)*

MURRAY *(laughing, relieved):*   You nut. I was ready to kill you.

SANDRA *(Throws her arms around him, drops her bag and files on floor):* What happened? You didn't say anything. I was waiting for you to say something. Why didn't you say something or kiss me or . . .

MURRAY: I was waiting for *you*, for God's sake. *(He kisses her.)*

SANDRA: I didn't know *what* was going on. *(She kisses him, their arms around each other; he leans away from her for a moment to put his coffee cup on the table.)* Don't let me go . . .

MURRAY: I was just putting my coffee cup down . . .

SANDRA: Don't let me go. *(He holds her tightly again.)* Murray, I thought about it, and I probably love you.

MURRAY: That's very romantic. I probably love you too. You have very small feet. For a minute yesterday, it looked like you only had four toes, and I thought you were a freak. I woke up in the middle of the night and counted them. There are five.

SANDRA: I could have told you that.

MURRAY *(He sits in the swivel chair; she is on his lap):*   You knocked down maybe seven boxes of Crackerjacks yesterday. You are twelve years old. You sleep with the blanket under your chin like a napkin. When you started to talk about the coffee before, I was going to throw you out the window except there'd be no place for you to land but the trash can from the Chinese restaurant.

SANDRA: You mean that you live above a Chinese restaurant?

MURRAY: Yes. It's been closed for months, though.

SANDRA: Do you mean that you live above an abandoned Chinese restaurant?

MURRAY: Yes, I do.

SANDRA: That's wonderful. *(She kisses him; jumps up from his lap happily excited about what she has to say. Takes off her jacket and hangs it on the back of the Morris chair.)* I didn't go to work this morning and I simply can't tell you how fantastic that makes me feel. I'm not going to do a *lot* of things any more. *(Picks at the material of her blouse.)* This blouse I'm wearing, my mother picked it out, everybody picks out things for me. She gets all her clothes directly from Louisa May Alcott. *(Picks up the stool, changes its position in the room.)* Well, we've all seen the last of this blouse anyway. Do you realize that I feel more at home here after twenty-four hours than I do in my parents' house after twenty-five years? Of course, we'll have to do something about curtains . . . and I hope you didn't mind about the screen around the bed, I just think it gives such a nice, separate bedroomy effect to that part of the room . . . *(Picks up her bag and files from the floor where she dropped them, puts them in the closet. She is moving in.)* Oh, there are so many wonderful tricks you can try with a one-room apartment, really, if you're willing to use your imagination . . . *(He watches helplessly as she moves happily about the apartment judging it with a decorator's eye.)* I don't care if it sounds silly, Murray, but I was projecting a personality identification with the Statue of Liberty yesterday . . . courageous and free and solid metal . . . *(She kisses him, then continues pacing happily.)* I was here with you last night and I don't give a damn who knows it or what anybody thinks, and that goes for Dr. Malko, Albert, my mother, Aunt Blanche . . . Oh, I'm going to do so many things I've always wanted to do.

MURRAY: For example.

SANDRA: Well . . . I'm not sure right now. And that's marvelous too, I am thoroughly enjoying the idea that I don't know what I'm going to do next. *(Stops pacing.)* Do you have an extra key?

MURRAY: What?

SANDRA: An extra key. Altman's has this terrific curtain sale, thought I'd go and . . .

MURRAY: Well, then I'd better give you some money . . .

SANDRA: No, that's all right. *(Holds out her hand.)* Just the key.

MURRAY: Oh. *(He looks at her blankly for a moment, then reaches into his pocket slowly, finds the key, slowly hands it to her.)*

SANDRA *(Snatches up the key, goes on delightedly pacing up and down):* Murray, did we bring back any Crackerjacks?

MURRAY *(Pointing to some packages on the desk):*   Only stuff we brought back was that cleaning equipment. I'll admit this place is a little dirty, but all that stuff just for . . .
(The doorbell rings. SANDRA flinches for a moment, but then smiles and stands firmly.)

SANDRA: You'd better answer it, Murray.

MURRAY: Sandra, would you prefer to . . .
(He indicates the kitchen as a hiding place, but she stands right where she is, refusing to move.)

SANDRA: I've got no reason to hide from anybody.
(MURRAY goes to the front door and opens it halfway, but enough for us to see the visitor, ALBERT AMUNDSON. ALBERT cannot see beyond the door to where SANDRA is standing.)

ALBERT: Good morning, Mr. Burns.

MURRAY: Albert, how are you?
(SANDRA, hearing ALBERT's voice, and realizing who it is, goes immediately into the closet, closing the door behind her.)

ALBERT: May I come in?

MURRAY: Sure.

(MURRAY opens the front door all the way, allowing ALBERT into the main room. MURRAY closes the door, then follows ALBERT into the room. MURRAY smiles to himself when he sees that SANDRA is not there and then glances at the closet door.)

ALBERT: I called you twice this morning, Mr. Burns.

MURRAY: That was you.

ALBERT: That was me. Miss Markowitz did not show up in Queens yesterday.

MURRAY: So?

ALBERT: Her parents are quite upset. I am quite upset. Where is she?

MURRAY: She's hiding in the closet.

ALBERT: We're really all quite anxious to know where she is.

MURRAY: I'm not kidding. She's in the closet.
(ALBERT goes to the closet, opens the door, sees SANDRA, then closes the door. ALBERT comes back to MURRAY.)

ALBERT: She *is* in the closet.

MURRAY: I wouldn't lie to you, Albert.

ALBERT: Why is she in the closet?

MURRAY: I don't know. She's got this thing about closets.

ALBERT: That's a very silly thing for her to be in the closet.

MURRAY: Don't knock it till you've tried it. Now, what else can I do for you?

ALBERT: That's a difficult thing for me to believe. I mean, that she's right there in the closet. You are not a person, Mr. Burns, you are an experience.

MURRAY *(Goes into the kitchen):* That's very nice, Albert, I'll have to remember that.

ALBERT: Actually, Dr. Markowitz is not the reason for my visit today. I came here in an official capacity.

MURRAY *(From the kitchen):* You don't wear an official capacity well, Albert. Coffee?

ALBERT: No, thank you.
(MURRAY brings the pot out, fills the two cups on the table; brings one of the cups of coffee to the closet and hands it through the partly open door.)

MURRAY *(Returns to the table, sits opposite ALBERT):* What have you got on your mind, Albert?

ALBERT *(Sits; begins hesitantly):* Burns, late yesterday afternoon the Child Welfare Board made a decision on your case. Their decision is based on three months of a thorough study; our interview yesterday is only a small part of the . . . I want you to understand that I am not responsible, personally, for the decision they've reached, I . . .

MURRAY: Relax, Albert, I won't even hold you responsible for the shadow you're throwing on my rug.

ALBERT: For eleven months you have avoided contact with the Board, made a farce of their inquiries. You are not employed, show no inclination to gain employment, have absolutely no financial stability . . .

MURRAY: Look, Albert, I . . .

ALBERT: Months of research by the Board and reports by the Revere School show a severe domestic instability, a libertine self-indulgence, a whole range of circumstances severely detrimental to the child's welfare . . .

MURRAY: Look, stop the tap-dancing for a second, Albert; what's going on, what . . .

ALBERT: It is the Board's decision that you are unfit to be the guardian of your nephew, and that action be taken this Friday to remove the child from this home and the deprivation you cause him.

MURRAY: You mean they can really . . . *(Sips his coffee, putting on an elaborate display of calm, showing no emotion.)* Where'd they get this routine from, Charles Dickens?

ALBERT: The Board is prepared to find a more stable, permanent home for your nephew, a family with whom he will live a more wholesome, normal . . .

MURRAY: Look, Albert, there must be some kind of a hearing or something, where I'll have a chance to . . .

ALBERT: You will have the opportunity Thursday to state your case to the Board. If there is some substantial change in your circumstances, some evidence they're not aware of; if you can demonstrate that you are a responsible member of society . . .

MURRAY: It's Tuesday; what the hell am I supposed to do in two days, win the Nobel Peace Prize? They sent you here to tell me this?

ALBERT: No, you were to be informed by the court. But in view of the confusion which took place here yesterday, for which I consider myself responsible, I felt it my duty to come here and explain . . .

MURRAY: Buddy, you speak like you write everything down before you say it.

ALBERT: Yes, I do speak that way, Mr. Burns. I wish that I spoke more spontaneously. I realize that I lack warmth. I will always appear foolish in a conversation with a person of your imagination. Please understand, there is no vengeance in my activities here. I love my work, Mr. Burns. I believe that you are a danger to this child. I wish this were not true, because it is obvious that you have considerable affection for your nephew. It is in your face, this feeling. I admire you for your warmth, Mr. Burns, and for the affection the child feels for you. I admire this because I am one for whom children do not easily feel affection. I am not one of the warm people. But your feeling for the child does not mollify the genuinely dangerous emotional climate you have made for him. *(He moves toward MURRAY.)* I wish you could understand this, I would so much rather you understood, could really hear what I have to say. For yours is, I believe, a distorted picture of this world.

MURRAY: Then why don't you send *me* to a foster home?

ALBERT: I was right. You really can't listen to me. You are so sure of your sight. Your villains and heroes are all so terribly clear to you, and I am obviously one of the villains. *(Picks up his briefcase.)* God save you from your vision, Mr. Burns. *(Goes to the front door, opens it.)* Good-bye. *(ALBERT exits.)*

MURRAY *(Stands at the window with his coffee cup in his hand, looking out at gray, blank wall of the building opposite):* Hey, courageous, free one, you can come out now.

(SANDRA comes out of closet carrying her coffee cup; MURRAY does not look at her.)

SANDRA: I'm sorry, Murray. I'm really very embarrassed. I don't know what happened. I just ran into the closet. And . . . and once I was in there, I just didn't want to come out. I'm sorry, Murray . . .

MURRAY: Don't be nervous, lady, you're just going through an awkward stage. You're between closets. *(Quietly, calmly)* Look, if Nick has to leave, if he goes, he goes, and my life stays about the same. But it's no good for *him*, see, not for a couple of years, anyway. Right now he's still ashamed of being sharper than everybody else, he could easily turn into another peeled and boiled potato. Are you listening to me?

SANDRA: Yes, of course . . .

MURRAY: Well, make some kind of listening noise then, will you? Wink or nod your head or something.

SANDRA: But, I'm . . .

MURRAY *(Casually; gesturing with his coffee cup):* Tell you the truth, it's even a little better for me if he goes. I mean, he's a middle-aged kid. When I signed with the network he sat up all night figuring out the fringe benefits and the pension plan. And he started to make *lists* this year. Lists of everything; subway stops, underwear, what he's gonna do next week. If somebody doesn't watch out he'll start making lists of what he's gonna do next year and the next ten years. Hey, suppose they put him in with a whole family of listmakers? *(Angrily)* I didn't spend six years with him so he should turn into a listmaker. He'll learn to know everything before it happens, he'll learn to plan, he'll learn how to be one of the nice dead people. Are you listening?

SANDRA: Of course, I told you, Murray, I . . .

MURRAY: Then stamp your feet or mutter so I'll know you're there, huh? *(Still speaking quite calmly)* I just want him to stay with me till I can be sure he won't turn into Norman Nothing. I want to be sure he'll know when he's chickening out on himself. I want him to get to know exactly the special thing he is or else he won't notice it when it starts to go. I want him to stay awake and know who the phonies are, I want him to know how to holler and put up an argument, I want a little guts to show before I can let him go. I want to be sure he sees all the wild possibilities. I want him to know it's worth all the trouble just to give the world a little goosing when you get the chance. And I want him to know the subtle, sneaky, important reason why he was born a human being and not a chair. *(Pause)* I will be very sorry to see him go. That kid was the best straight man I ever had. He is a laugher, and laughers are rare. I mean, you tell that kid something funny . . . not just any piece of corn, but something funny, and he'll give you your money's worth. It's not just funny jokes he reads, or I tell him, that he laughs at. Not just set-up funny stuff. He sees street jokes, he has the good eye, he sees subway farce and crosstown-bus humour and all the cartoons that people make by being alive. He has a good eye. And I don't want him to leave until I'm certain he'll never be ashamed of it. *(Still quite calmly, unemotionally)* And in addition to that . . . besides that . . . see *(Suddenly; loudly)* Sandy, I don't want him to go. I like having him around here. What should I do, Sandy? Help me out. *(Suddenly slumps forward in his chair, covers his face with his hands; very quietly)* I like when he reads me from the want ads.

SANDRA *(Taking his hands):* Murray, don't worry, we'll do something. I know the Board, their procedure, there's things you can do . . .

MURRAY *(Quietly, thoughtfully):* What I'll do is I'll buy a new suit. The first thing is to get a dignified suit.

SANDRA: If you could get some kind of a job, get your brother to help you.

MURRAY: Right. Right.

SANDRA: Is there something you can get in a hurry?

MURRAY: Sure, one of those suits with the ready-made cuffs . . .

SANDRA: No, I mean a job. If we could just bring some proof of employment to the hearing, Murray, show them how anxious you are to change. We'll show them you want to be reliable.

MURRAY *(Brightening):* Yeah, reliable . . . *(Rises; going toward the phone)* Sandy, we will put on a God-damned show for them. Spectacular reliability; a reliability parade; bands, floats, everything. *(Starts to dial.)* Sandy, go to the files and pick me out a tie that is quiet but at the same time projects a mood of inner strength. *(Into the phone)* Arnold Burns' office, please.

SANDRA *(On her way to the file cabinet):* One quiet tie with a mood of inner strength.

MURRAY *(Into the phone):* Hello, Margot? It's Murray. Oh, well, when Arnie comes in here's what you do. First you tell him to sit down. Then you tell him I want to get a job. When he has recovered suffiently from that shock, tell him . . . *(SANDRA comes to him with a tie.)* Excuse me a second, Margot . . . *(To SANDRA, indicating the tie)* Yes, quiet but with strength. *(SANDRA laughs.)* Sandy, that is the greatest happy laugh I ever heard on a lady. Do that again. *(She laughs again.)* Great. Keep that laugh. I'll need it later. *(Into the phone)* Margot, tell him I'm going downtown to pick up a new suit for myself and a beautiful pineapple for him, call him back in about an hour, O.K.? Thanks, Margot. *(Puts the phone down, goes to get his jacket.)*

SANDRA: Can I come with you? I'd love to buy a suit with you.

MURRAY *(Putting on his jacket):* Better not, Sandy. Gotta move fast. These shoes look O.K.? *(She nods, he takes her hand.)* Look, don't go away.

SANDRA: I won't. *(She kisses him.)*

MURRAY *(Goes to the front door; turns to her, smiles):* Say "Good luck."

SANDRA: Good luck.

MURRAY *(Opening the door):* Now say "You are a magnificent human being."

SANDRA: You are a magnificent human being.

A Thousand Clowns

MURRAY *(As he exits):* I *thought* you'd notice.
(She stands in door and watches him go as the lights fade out quickly. Immediately, as the lights fade, we hear the voice of Chuckles the Chipmunk (LEO HERMAN)

LEO'S VOICE: Hi there, kidderoonies; there's nothin' more lonelier than a lonely, little looney Chippermunk. So won't ya please come on along with me fer a fun hour, 'cuz that loneliest, littlest, looniest Chippermunk, is *me* . . . Chuckles. *(Lights come up now in ARNOLD BURNS' office, later that afternoon. The office is part of a large theatrical agency of which ARNOLD is a rather successful member; modern, wood panelling, nonobjective paintings and framed photographs of his clients on the wall, a spectacularly large window behind the desk with a twenty-second-floor skyline view. A large bowl of fruit is on an end table near the door. One of the two phones on ARNOLD's desk is a special speaker-phone, consisting of a small loudspeaker box on the desk which amplifies clearly the voice of whoever is calling. It can also be spoken into from almost any point in the room if one is facing it. As the following scene progresses the speaker-phone is treated by those present as if it were a person in the room, they gesture to it, smile at it. ARNOLD is alone in his office, leaning against the desk, listening to the speaker-phone, from which we continue to hear the voice of LEO HERMAN.)* God damn it, Arn; that's the intro Murray wrote for me two years ago; and it's still lovely, still warm. It's the way the kids know me, the way I say "Hello, kids"; he is a sweetie of a writer.

ARNOLD: That was *last* year he won the sweetie award, Leo.

LEO'S VOICE *(Laughs good-naturedly):* Please excuse my little words. They slip out of my face once in a while. Arn, you got my voice comin' out of that speaker-phone in your office, huh? Comes out like the biggest phony you ever met, right? That's how I sound, don't I? Big phony.

ARNOLD: No, Leo.

LEO'S VOICE: I'm getting sick of myself. Hey, Arn, you figure there's a good chance of Murray comin' back with me on the show?

ARNOLD: Can't guarantee it, Leo; I've sent him to one other appointment today, fairly good offer . . .

LEO'S VOICE: Well, I'm hopin' he comes back with *me*, Arn. Funny bit you being the agent for your own brother — what d'ya call that?

ARNOLD: It's called incest. *(The intercom buzzes; ARNOLD picks it up.)* O.K., send him in. *(Into the speaker-phone)* Got a call, fellah; check back with you when Murray shows.

LEO'S VOICE: Right, 'bye now.
(MURRAY enters wearing a new suit and carrying a beautiful pineapple.)

MURRAY: Good afternoon, Mr. Burns.

ARNOLD: Good afternoon, Mr. Burns. Hey, you really did get a new suit, didn't you? How'd the appointment go with . . .

MURRAY *(Putting the pineapple on the desk, gestures around at the office):* Arnold, every time I see you, the agency's put you on a higher floor. I swear, next time I come you'll be up in a balloon.

On Stage 1

ARNOLD: Murray, the appointment . . .

MURRAY: Can't get over this office, Arnie. *(Goes to the window, looks out.)* Twenty-second floor. You can see everything. *(Shocked by something he sees out of the window.)* My God. I don't believe it: it's King Kong. He's sitting on top of the Time-Life Building. He . . . he seems to be crying. Poor gorilla bastard, they should told him they don't make those buildings the way they used to . . .

ARNOLD *(Raising his hand in the air):* Hello, Murray, hello there . . . here we are in my office. Welcome to Tuesday. Now, come *on*, how'd it go with Jimmy Sloan?

MURRAY: He took me to lunch at Stefanos, East Fifty-third. Christ, it's been a coupla years since I hustled around lunchland. There is this crazy hum that I haven't heard for so long, Arnie; eight square yards of idea men, busily having ideas, eating away at their chef's salad like it's Crackerjacks and there's a prize at the bottom.

ARNOLD: And Sloan . . .?

MURRAY *(Sitting on the sofa):* Sloan lunches beautifully, can out-lunch anybody. He used to be a Yes-man but he got himself some guts and now he goes around bravely saying "maybe" to everybody. And a killer, this one, Arnie; notches on his attaché case. Told me this idea he had where I'd be a lovable eccentric on his panel show. This somehow led him very logically to his conception of God, who he says is "probably a really fun guy."

ARNOLD: What'd you tell him about the offer?

MURRAY: I told him good-bye. I don't think he noticed when I left; he focuses slightly to the right of you when he talks, just over your shoulder, so if you stay out of range he can't tell that you're gone. Probably thinks I'm still there.

ARNOLD: Murray, you told me this morning to get any job I could; Sloan's offer wasn't so bad . . .

MURRAY: Sloan is an idiot.

ARNOLD *(Sitting next to him on the sofa; angrily, firmly):* Listen, cookie, I got *news* for you, right now you *need* idiots. You got a bad reputation for quitting jobs; I even had trouble grabbing Sloan for you. Why did you have to go and build your own personal blacklist; why couldn't you just be blacklisted as a Communist like everybody else?

MURRAY: Don't worry, Arnie; I figured I'd go back with Chuckles. He's ready to take me back, isn't he?

ARNOLD: Yea, he's ready. I just spoke to him. *(Solemnly)* Hey, Murray, Leo says he came up to your place last January, a week after you quit him, to talk you into coming back with the show. And right in the middle you went into the kitchen and started singing "Yes, Sir, That's My Baby." Just left him standing there. Your way of saying "good-bye."

MURRAY: Well, that was five months ago, Arnie . . .

ARNOLD *(Attempts to conceal his amusement, then turns to MURRAY, smiling):* So, what'd you do with him, just left him standing there? *(He laughs.)* Like to have been there, seen that, must have been great.

MURRAY: Arnie, it was beautiful.

ARNOLD *(Still laughing):*   It's about time somebody left Leo Herman standing around talking to himself. *(Rubbing his head)* I wish to God I didn't enjoy you so much. Crap, I don't do you any good at all. *(Then, solemnly again.)* Murray, no fun and games with Leo today, understand? He is absolutely *all* we got left before the hearing Thursday.

MURRAY: Yes, I understand.

ARNOLD *(Goes to pick up the phone on the desk):*   I wish we coulda got something better for you, kid, but there just wasn't any time.

MURRAY: Well, Chuckles won't be so bad for a while . . .

ARNOLD: No, Murray. *(Puts phone down firmly.)* Not just for a while. You'll really have to stick with Chuckles. I had our agency lawyer check the facts for me. Most the Board'll give you is a probationary year with Nick; a trial period. The Board's investigators will be checking on you every week . . .

MURRAY: That's charming.

ARNOLD: . . . checking to see if you've still got the job, checking with Leo on your stability, checking up on the change in your home environment.

MURRAY: Sounds like a parole board.

ARNOLD *(Into the intercom phone):*   Margot; get me Leo Herman on the speaker-phone here, his home number. Thanks. *(Puts the phone down.)* He's waiting for our call. Look, Murray, maybe he's not the greatest guy in the world; but y'know, he really *likes* you, Murray, he . . .

MURRAY: Yeah. I have a way with animals.

ARNOLD *(Pointing at MURRAY):*   That was your last joke for today. *(A click is heard from speaker-phone; ARNOLD turns it on.)* You there, Leo?

LEO'S VOICE: Right, Arn. I'm done here in the basement, in my gymnasium; lot of echoing. Am I coming through, am I coming through O.K.?

ARNOLD: Clearly, Leo. Murray's here.

LEO'S VOICE: Murray! Murray the wonderful wild man; fellah, how are ya?

MURRAY *(Takes his hat off, waves hello to the speaker-phone):*   O.K., Leo, how're you doing?

LEO'S VOICE: Oh, you crazy bastard, it's damn good to hear that voice again. You're an old monkey, aren't ya?

MURRAY: You sound about the same too, Leo.

LEO'S VOICE: Not the same. I'm *more impossible* than I used to be. Can you imagine that?

MURRAY: Not easily, Leo; no.

LEO'S VOICE: Murray, I need you, fellah; I need you back with the show. Murr', we'll talk a while now, and then I'll come over to your place tonight, go over some ideas for next week's shows. It'll be great, sweetie . . . Oh, there's that word again. "Sweetie," I said that word again. Oh, am I getting *sick* of myself.

Big phony. The truth, fellah, I'm the biggest phony you ever met, right?

MURRAY: Probably, Leo.

LEO'S VOICE *(After a pause; coldly):* Probably, he says. There he goes, there goes Murray the old joker, right? You're a jester, right? Some fooler. You can't fool with a scheduled show, Murray; a scheduled show with a tight budget. *(Softly, whispering)* Murray, come closer, tell you a secret . . . (MURRAY comes closer to the box.) You're gonna hate me, Murray; I gotta tell you something and I know you're gonna hate me for it, but we can't have the same Murray we used to have on the show. Who appreciates a good joke more than anybody? *Me.* But who jokes too much? *(Suddenly louder) You!*

MURRAY: Leo, couldn't we talk about this tonight when we get together . . .

LEO'S VOICE *(Softly again):* It hurt me, Murr', it hurt me what you used to do. When all those thousands of kids wrote in asking for the definition of a chipmunk and you sent back that form letter sayin' a chipmunk was a . . . was a what?

MURRAY: A cute rat.

LEO'S VOICE *(Still soft):* A cute rat; yeah. I remember my skin broke out somethin' terrible. Some jester you are, foolin' around at the script conferences, foolin' around at the studio. Now, we're not gonna have any more of that, are we?

MURRAY *(Subservient, apologetic):* No, we won't, I'm sorry, Leo.

LEO'S VOICE: Because we can't fool with the innocence of children, can we? My God, they believe in the little Chipmunk, don't ask me why; I'm nothing; God, I know that. I've been damned lucky. A person like me should get a grand and a half a week for doin' nothin'. I mean, I'm one of the big no-talents of all time, right?

MURRAY: Right . . . I mean, no, Leo, no.

LEO'S VOICE: Oh, I know it's the truth and I don't kid myself about it. But there'll be no more jokin'; right, Murr'? Because I'll tell you the truth, I can't stand it.

MURRAY: Right, Leo.

LEO'S VOICE *(Softly):* Good. Glad we cleared that up. Because my skin breaks out somethin' terrible. *(Up again)* You're the best, Murray, such talent, you know I love ya, don't ya? You old monkey.

MURRAY *(To ARNOLD):* Please, tell him we'll talk further tonight, too much of him all at once . . .

ARNOLD: Say, Leo, suppose we . . .

LEO'S VOICE: Murray, I want you to put some fifteen-minute fairy tales into the show. You've got your Hans Christian Andersens there, your Grimm Brothers, your Goldilocks, your Sleepin' Beauties, your Gingerbread Men, your Foxy-Loxies, your legends, your folk tales . . . do I reach ya, Murr'?

MURRAY *(Quietly):* Yeah, Leo . . .

A Thousand Clowns

LEO'S VOICE: Now, what I want in those scripts is this, Murray, I want you to give 'em five minutes a action, five minutes a poignancy and then five minutes of the moral message; race-relations thing; world-peace thing; understanding-brings-love thing. I don't know. Shake 'em up a little. Controversy. Angry letters from parents. Kid's show with something to say, get some excitement in the industry, wild . . .

MURRAY *(He leans over very close to speaker-phone; whispers into it):* Hey, Leo, I might show up one day with eleven minutes of poignancy, no action and a twelve-second moral message . . .

ARNOLD: Murray, stop it . . .

MURRAY *(Shouting into the speaker-phone):* And then were would we be? *(There is a pause. No sound comes from the speaker-phone. Then:)*

LEO'S VOICE: See how he mocks me? Well, I guess there's plenty to mock. Plenty mocking. Sometimes I try to take a cold look at what I am. *(Very soft)* Sweaty Leo jumping around in a funny costume trying to make a buck out of being a chipmunk. The Abominable Snowman in a cute suit. But I'll tell you something, Murray . . . sit down for a minute. *(MURRAY is standing; LEO'S VOICE is still fairly pleasant.)* Are ya sitting down, Murray? *(MURRAY remains standing; LEO'S VOICE is suddenly loud, sharp, commanding.)* Murray, sit down! *(MURRAY sits down.)* Good. Now I'm gonna tell you a story . . .

MURRAY *(Softly, painfully):* Arnold, he's gonna do it again . . . the story . . .

LEO'S VOICE: Murray . . .

MURRAY *(Softly, miserably):* The story I got tattooed to my skull . . .

LEO'S VOICE: On June the third . . .

MURRAY *(Hunching over in his chair, looking down at the floor):* Story number twelve . . . the "Laughter of Children" story . . . again . . .

LEO'S VOICE: I will be forty-two years old . . .

MURRAY *(To ARNOLD; painfully pleading):* Arnie . . .

LEO'S VOICE: And maybe it's the silliest, phoniest, cop-out thing . . .

LEO'S VOICE and MURRAY *(in unison):* . . . you ever heard, but the Chipmunk, Chuckles, the little guy I pretend to be, is real to me . . .

LEO'S VOICE: . . . as real to me as . . . as this phone in my hand; those children, don't ask me why, God I don't know, but they believe in that little fellah . . . *(MURRAY looks up from the floor now and over at the speaker-phone, which is on the other side of the room; his eyes are fixed on it.)* Look, Murr', I do what I can for the cash-monies; but also, and I say it without embarrassment, I just love kids, the laughter of children, and we can't have you foolin' with that, Murr', can't have you jokin' . . . *(MURRAY stands up, still looking at the speaker-phone.)* because it's this whole, bright, wild sorta child kinda thing . . . *(MURRAY is walking slowly toward the speaker-phone now; ARNOLD, watching MURRAY, starts to rise from his chair.)* it's this very up feeling, it's all young, and you can't joke with it; the laughter of children; those warm waves, that fresh, open, spontaneous laughter, you can feel it on your face . . .

MURRAY *(Picking the speaker-phone up off the desk):* Like a sunburn . . .

LEO'S VOICE: Like a sunburn . . .

ARNOLD *(Coming toward MURRAY as if to stop him):* Murray . . . wait . . .

LEO'S VOICE: And it's a pride thing . . . *(MURRAY turns with the speaker-phone held in his hands and drops it into the wastepaper basket next to the desk. He does this calmly. ARNOLD, too late to stop him, stands watching, dumbly paralyzed. LEO, unaware, goes right on talking, his voice somewhat garbled and echoing from the bottom of the wastepaper basket.)* . . . so then how lovely, how enchanting it is, that I should be paid so well for something I love so much . . . *(Pause)* Say, there's this noise . . . there's this . . . I'm getting this crackling noise on my end here . . . What's happened to the phone?

ARNOLD *(Sadly, solemnly; looking down into the basket):* Leo, you're in a wastepaper basket.

LEO'S VOICE: That you, Murray? . . . There's this crackling noise . . . I can't hear you . . . Hello? . . . What's going on? . . .

ARNOLD: Leo, hold it just a minute, I'll get you.

LEO'S VOICE: There's this funny noise . . . Where'd everybody go? Where is everybody? . . . Hello, Murray . . . hello . . . come back . . . come back . . .

ARNOLD *(Fishing amongst the papers in basket for the speaker-phone):* I'll find you, Leo, I'll find you. . . . *(Finally lifts the speaker out of the basket, holds it gently, tenderly in his hands like a child, speaks soothingly to it.)* Look, Leo . . . Leo, we had a little . . . some trouble with the phone, we . . . *(Realizes that he is getting no reaction from the box.)* Leo? . . . Leo? . . . *(As though the box were a friend whom he thinks might have died, shaking the box tenderly to revive it)* Leo . . . Leo, are you there? . . . Are you there? . . . It's dead. *(Turning to look at MURRAY, as though announcing the demise of a dear one.)* He's gone.

MURRAY: Well, don't look at me like that, Arnie; I didn't *kill* him. He doesn't *live* in that box . . . Or maybe he does.

ARNOLD: A man has a job for you so you drop him in a basket.

MURRAY: Arnie, I quit that nonsense five months ago . . .

ARNOLD: Murray, you're a *nut*, a man has a job for you, there's a hearing on Thursday . . .

MURRAY: A fool in a box telling me what's funny, a Welfare board checking my underwear every week because I don't look good in their files . . . and *I'm* the nut, right? *I'm* the crazy one.

ARNOLD: Murray, you float like a balloon and everybody's waitin' for ya with a pin. I'm trying to put you in *touch*, Murray . . . with *real things*; with . . .

MURRAY *(Angrily, taking in the office with a sweep of his hand):* You mean like this office, *real* things, like this office? The world could come to an end and you'd find out about it on the phone. *(Pointing at two framed photographs on ARNOLD's desk)* Pictures of your wife six years ago when she was still a piece, and your kids at their cutest four years ago when they looked best for the office . . . Oh, you're in *touch* all right, Arnie.

ARNOLD *(Softly, soothing):* Murray, you're just a little excited, that's all, just relax, everything's gonna be fine . . .

MURRAY *(Shouting):* Damn it . . . get angry; I just insulted you, personally, about your wife, your kids; I just said lousy things to you. Raise your voice, at least your eyebrows . . . *(Pleading painfully)* Please, have an argument with me . . .

ARNOLD *(Coaxing):* We'll call Leo back, we'll apologize to him . . . *(MURRAY goes to the end table, picks up an apple from the bowl of fruit.)* Everything's gonna be just fine, Murray, you'll see . . . just fine.

MURRAY: Arnie?

ARNOLD: Huh?

MURRAY: Catch. *(Tosses the apple underhand across the room. ARNOLD catches it. MURRAY exits.)*

ARNOLD *(His hand out from catching the apple):* Aw, Murray . . . *(Lowers his hand to his side; speaks quietly, alone now in the office.)* Murray, I swear to you, King Kong is *not* on top of the Time-Life Building . . .
   (ARNOLD discovers the apple in his hand; bites into it. The lights fade quickly. As they dim, we hear NICK humming and whistling "Yes, Sir, That's My Baby." The lights go up on MURRAY's apartment. NICK's humming and whistling fades back so that it is coming from outside the window; the humming grows louder again after a second or two as, it would seem, he descends the fire-escape ladder from Mrs. Myers' apartment. It is early evening. No one is onstage. The apartment has been rather spectacularly rehabilitated by SANDRA since we saw it last. The great clutter of MURRAY's nonsense collection, clocks, radios, knickknacks, has been cleared away, the books have been neatly arranged in the bookcases, a hat rack has been placed above the bureau and MURRAY's hats are placed neatly on it. There are bright new bedspreads and brightly coloured throw pillows, one new curtain is already up at the windows and a piece of matching material is over the Morris chair. The beach chair and swivel chair are gone and the wicker chair has been painted gold, the table has a bright new cloth over it. Pots of flowers are on the table, the bookshelves, the file cabinets, headboard and desk; and geraniums are in a holder hanging from the window molding. The whole place has been dusted and polished and gives off a bright glow. After two lines or so of the song. NICK enters through the window from the fire escape, carrying his pajamas and school books. NICK sees the new curtain first, and then, from his position on the window seat, sees the other changes in the apartment and smiles appreciatively. SANDRA enters from the kitchen, carrying a mixing bowl and a spoon. She smiles, glad to see NICK.)

SANDRA: Hello, Nick . . .

NICK: Hello, lady. I came in from the fire escape. Mrs. Myers lives right upstairs. I went there after school, I . . . *(Indicating her work on the apartment)* Did . . . did you do all this?

SANDRA: Yes, Nick; do you like it?

NICK *(Goes to her, smiling):* I think it's superb. I mean, imagine my surprise when I saw it. *(Pause)* Where's Murray?

SANDRA *(Happily telling him the good news):* Nick . . . Murray went downtown to see your Uncle Arnold. He's going to get a job.

NICK: That's terrific. Hey, that's just terrific. *(SANDRA goes to the folded new curtains on the bed, sits down on the bed, unfolds one of the curtains, begins attaching curtain hooks and rings to it; NICK sits next to her, helping her as they talk together.)* See, lady, he was developing into a bum. You don't want to see somebody you like developing into a bum, and doing nutty things, right? You know what he does? He hollers. Like we were on Park Avenue last Sunday, it's early in the morning and nobody is in the street, see, there's just all those big quiet apartment houses; and he hollers "Rich people, I want to see you all out on the street for volley ball! Let's snap it up!" And sometimes, if we're in a crowded elevator some place, he turns to me and yells "Max, there'll be no *more* of this self-pity! You're forty, it's time you got *used* to being a midget!" And everybody stares. And he has a wonderful time. What do you do with somebody who hollers like that? Last week in Macy's he did that. *(He laughs.)* If you want to know the truth, it was pretty funny. *(SANDRA smiles.)* I think you're a very nice lady.

SANDRA: Thank you, Nick.

NICK: What do you think of me?

SANDRA: I think you're very nice also.

NICK: A very nice quality you have is that you are a good listener, which is important to me because of how much I talk. *(She laughs, enjoying him.)* Hey, you're some laugher, aren't you, lady?

SANDRA: I guess so, Nick.

NICK *(Trying to make her feel at home):* Would you like some fruit? An orange maybe?

SANDRA: No thank you, Nick.

NICK: If you want to call your mother or something, I mean, feel free to use the telephone . . . or my desk if you want to read a book or something . . . or *any* of the chairs . . .

SANDRA: I will, Nick, thank you.

NICK: O.K. *(Pause)* Are you going to be staying around here for a while?

SANDRA: I might, yes.

NICK *(He rises, picks up the pajamas and books he brought in with him; indicates apartment):* Has . . . has Murray seen . . . all this?

SANDRA: No, not yet.

NICK *(Nods):* Not yet. Well . . . *(Goes to the window, steps up on window seat.)* Good luck, lady. *(He exits through the window, carrying his pajamas and school books, goes back up the fire escape. SANDRA crosses to window seat, smiling to herself. MURRAY enters, unnoticed by her.)*

MURRAY *(Standing still at the front door, glancing around at the apartment; to himself):* Oh God, I've been attacked by the *Ladies' Home Journal.*
   (SANDRA hears him, goes to him happily.)

SANDRA: Murray, what a nice suit you bought. How is everything, which job did . . .

MURRAY *(Looking around at her work on the apartment):* Hey look at this. You've started to get rid of the Edgar Allan Poe atmosphere.

SANDRA: Don't you like it?

MURRAY *(Looking around, noticing his knicknacks are missing):* Sure. Sure. Lotta work. Place has an unusual quality now. Kind of Fun Gothic.

SANDRA: Well, of course I'm really not done yet, the curtains aren't all up, and this chair won't look so bad if we reupholster . . . Come on, Murray, don't keep me in suspense, which one of the jobs did you . . .

MURRAY *(Takes her arm, smiles, seats her on the chair in front of him):* I shall now leave you breathless with the strange and wondrous tale of this sturdy lad's adventures today in downtown Oz. *(She is cheered by his manner and ready to listen.)* Picture, if you will, me. I am walking on East Fifty-first Street an hour ago and I decided to construct and develop a really decorative, general-all-purpose apology. Not complicated, just the words "I am sorry," said with a little style.

SANDRA: Sorry for what?

MURRAY: Anything. For being late, early, stupid, asleep, silly, alive . . . *(He moves about now, acting out the scene on the street for her.)* Well, y'know when you're walking down the street talking to yourself how sometimes you suddenly say a coupla words out loud? So I said, "I'm sorry," and this fella, complete stranger, he looks up a second and says, "That's all right, Mac," and goes right on. *(MURRAY and SANDRA laugh.)* He automatically forgave me. I communicated. Five-o'clock rush-hour in midtown you say, "Sir, I believe your hair is on fire," and they wouldn't hear you. So I decided to test the whole thing out scientifically, I stayed right there on the corner of Fifty-first and Lex for a while, just saying "I'm sorry" to everybody that went by. *(Abjectly* "Oh, I'm so sorry, sir . . ." *(Slowly, quaveringly)* "I'm terribly sorry, madam . . ." *(Warmly)* "Say there, miss, I'm sorry." Of course, some people just gave me a funny look, but Sandy, I swear, seventy-five percent of them *forgave* me. *(Acting out the people for her)* "Forget it, buddy" . . . "That's O.K., really." Two ladies forgave me in unison, one fella forgave me from a passing car, and one guy forgave me for his dog. "Poofer forgives the nice man, don't you, Poofer?" Oh, Sandy, it was fabulous. I had tapped some vast reservoir. Something had happened to all of them for which they felt *some*body should apologize. If you went up to people on the street and offered them money, they'd refuse it. But everybody accepts apology immediately. It is the most negotiable currency. I said to them, "I am sorry." And they were all so generous, so kind. You could give 'em love and it wouldn't be accepted half as graciously, as unquestioningly . . .

SANDRA *(Suspiciously, her amusement fading):* That's certainly . . . that's very interesting, Murray.

MURRAY: Sandy, I could run up on the roof right now and holler, "I am sorry," and half a million people would holler right back, "That's O.K., just see that you don't do it again!"

SANDRA *(After a pause):* Murray, you didn't take any of the jobs.

MURRAY *(Quietly):* Sandy, I took whatever I am and put a suit on it and gave it a haircut and took it outside and that's what happened. I know what I said this morning, what I promised, and Sandra, I'm sorry, I'm very sorry. *(She just sits* *there before him and stares at him expressionlessly.)* Damn it, lady, that was a beautiful apology. You gotta love a guy who can apologize so nice. I rehearsed for over an hour. *(She just looks at him.)* That's the most you should expect from life, Sandy, a really good apology for all the things you won't get.

SANDRA: Murray, I don't understand. What happens to Nick? What about the Welfare Board?

MURRAY *(He takes her hand):* Sandra . . .

SANDRA: I mean, if you don't like the jobs your brother found you, then take *any* job . . .

MURRAY *(He takes both of her hands and kneels next to her chair):* Oh, Sandy . . . *(Softly, pleading for her to understand)* Nick, he's a wonderful kid, but he's brought the God-damned world in on me. Don't you understand, Sandy, they'd be checking up on me every week; being judged by people I don't know and who don't know me, a committee of ghosts; gimme a month of that and I'd turn into an ashtray, a bowl of corn flakes; I wouldn't know me on the street . . . *(Looks under chair.)* Have you seen Murray? He was here just a minute ago. . . . *(Looks at her, smiles.)* Hey, have you seen Murray? *(Pleading for her to understand)* I wouldn't be of any use to Nick or you or anybody . . .
    (SANDRA moves away from him, goes to the window seat, leaves him kneeling at the chair. She is still holding the curtain she had been working on.)

SANDRA *(Quietly):* I've had no effect on you at all. I've made no difference. You have no idea what it feels like to have no effect on people. I am not a leader. I scored very low in leadership in three different vocational aptitude tests. When I point my finger, people go the other way . . . *(Absently, she begins to fold the curtain neatly in her lap.)*

MURRAY: Sandra . . .

SANDRA: In grad school they put me in charge of the Structured-Childs-Play-Analysis session one day . . . *(She shrugs.)* and all the children fell asleep. I am not a leader.

MURRAY *(Going to her at the window seat; warmly, with love.):* Oh, Sandy, you are a cute, jolly lady . . . please understand.

SANDRA: When you left this morning, I was so sure . . .

MURRAY: This morning . . . *(He sits next to her on the window seat, his arm around her, his free hand gesturing expansively, romantically.)* Oh, Sandy, I saw the most beautiful sailing this morning . . . The *Sklardahl*, Swedish liner, bound for Europe. It's a great thing to do when you're about to start something new; you see a boat off. It's always wonderful; there's a sailing practically every day this time of year. Sandy, you go down and stand at the dock with all the well-wishers and throw confetti and make a racket with them. . . . Hey, bon voyage, Charley, have a wonderful time. . . . It gives you a genuine feeling of the beginning of things. . . . There's another one Friday, big French ship, two stacker . . .
    (SANDRA has been watching him coldly during this speech; she speaks quietly; catching him in mid-air.)

SANDRA: Nick will have to go away now, Murray. *(She looks away from him.)* I bought new bedspreads at Altman's, I haven't spoken to my mother in two days, and you went to see a boat off. *(She pauses; then smiles to herself for a moment.)* My goodness; I'm a listmaker. *(She leaves him alone in the window seat.)* I have to have enough sense to leave you, Murray. I can see why Nick liked it here. I would like it here too if I was twelve years old. *(She puts the folded curtain down on the chair, picks up her jacket.)*

MURRAY *(Coming toward her, warmly):* Come on, stick with me, Dr. Markowitz, anything can happen above an abandoned Chinese restaurant. . . .

SANDRA *(Looking directly at him; quietly):* Maybe you're wonderfully independent, Murray, or maybe, maybe you're the most extraordinarily selfish person I've ever met. *(She picks up her hand bag and starts toward the door.)*

MURRAY *(Tired of begging; angrily, as she walks toward the door):* What're you gonna do now, go back and live in a closet? It's really gonna be quite thrilling, you and Albert, guarding the Lincoln Tunnel together.

SANDRA *(Tuning at the door to look at him):* I think, Murray, that you live in a much, much larger closet than I do.

MURRAY *(Painfully):* Lady, lady, please don't look at me like that . . .

SANDRA *(Looking about the apartment; very quietly):* Oh, there are so many really attractive things you can do with a one-room apartment if you're willing to use your imagination. *(Opens the door.)* Good-bye, Murray. *(She exits. MURRAY stands still for a moment; then rushes forward to the closed door, angrily.)*

MURRAY *(Shouting):* Hey, damn it, you forgot your files! *(Picks up her files from the bureau, opens the door; but she is gone.)* The management is not responsible for personal property! *(Closes the door, puts the files back on the bureau; stands at the door, looking around the apartment.)* And what the hell did you do to my apartment? Where are my clocks? What'd you do with my stuff? Where's my radios? *(His back to the audience, shouting)* What've we got here; God damn Sunnybrook Farm! What happened to my place? *(Suddenly realizing he is still wearing a new suit, he pulls off his suit jacket, rolls it up into a tight ball, and throws it violently across the room. A moment; then he relaxes, walks casually to the window, puts his favourite hat on, sits, leans back comfortably in the window seat and smiles. He talks out of the window in a loud mock-serious voice.)* Campers . . . the entertainment committee was quite disappointed by the really poor turn-out at this morning's community sing. I mean, where's all that old Camp Chickawattamee spirit? Now, I'd like to say that I . . . *(He hesitates; he can't think of anything to say. A pause; then he haltingly tries again.)* I'd like to say right now that I . . . that . . . that I . . . *(His voice is soft, vague; he pulls his knees up, folds his arms around them, his head bent on his knees; quietly)* Campers, I can't think of anything to say . . .

(A moment; then)

CURTAIN

In the darkness, before the curtain goes up, we hear an old recording of a marching band playing "Stars and Stripes Forever." This goes on rather loudly for a few moments. The music diminishes somewhat as the curtain goes up; and we see that the music is coming from an old phonograph on the wicker chair near the bed. It's about thirty minutes later and, though much of SANDRA's work on the apartment is still apparent, it is obvious that MURRAY has been busy putting his place back into its old shape. The curtains are gone, as is the tablecloth and the material on the Morris chair. All the flower pots have been put on top of the file cabinet. The swivel chair and the beach chair are back in view. Cluttered about the room again is much of MURRAY's nonsense collection, clocks, radios, knickknacks and stacks of magazines.

As the curtain goes up, MURRAY has just retrieved a stack of magazines, the megaphone and the pirate pistol from the closet where SANDRA has put them; and we see him now placing them back around the room carefully, as though they were part of some strict design. ARNOLD enters, carrying his attaché case; walks to the beach chair, sits, takes his hat off. The two men do not look at each other. The music continues to play.

———————————— • ————————————

ARNOLD *(After a moment):* I didn't even bring a tangerine with me. That's very courageous if you think about it for a minute. *(Looks over at MURRAY, who is not facing him, points at record player.)* You wanna turn that music off, please? *(No reply from MURRAY.)* Murray, the music; I'm trying to . . . *(No reply from MURRAY, so ARNOLD puts his attaché case and hat on table, goes quickly to the record player and turns the music off; MURRAY turns to look at ARNOLD.)* O.K., I'm a little slow. It takes me an hour to get insulted. Now I'm insulted. You walked out of my office. That wasn't a nice thing to do to me, Murray . . . *(MURRAY does not reply.)* You came into my office like George God; everybody's supposed to come up and audition for Human Being in front of you. *(Comes over closer to him, takes his arm.)* Aw, Murray, today, one day, leave the dragons alone, will ya? And look at the dragons you pick on; Sloan, Leo, me; silly old arthritic dragons, step on a toe and we'll start to cry. Murray, I called Leo back, I apologized, told him my phone broke down; I got him to come over here tonight. He's anxious to see you, everything's O.K. . . . .

MURRAY: Hey, you just never give up, do you, Arnie?

ARNOLD: Listen to me, Murray, do I ever tell you what to do . . .

MURRAY: Yes, all the time.

ARNOLD: If you love this kid, then you gotta take any kinda stupid job to keep him . . .

MURRAY: Now you're an expert on love.

ARNOLD: Not an expert, but I sure as hell value my amateur standing. Murray, about him leaving, have you told him yet?

MURRAY *(Softly, realizing ARNOLD's genuine concern):* Arnie, don't worry, I know how to handle it. I've got a coupla days to tell him. And don't underrate Nick, he's gonna understand this a lot better than you think.

ARNOLD: Murray, I finally figured out your problem. There's only one thing that really bothers you . . . *(With a sweep of his hand)* Other people. *(With a mock-secretive tone)* If it wasn't for them other people, everything would be great, huh, Murray? I mean, you think everything's fine, and then you go out into the street . . . and there they all *are* again, right? The Other People; taking up space, bumping into you, asking for things, making lines to wait on, taking cabs away from ya . . . The Enemy . . . Well, *watch* out, Murray, they're *every*where. . . .

MURRAY: Go ahead, Arnie, give my advice. At thirty thousand a year you can afford it.

ARNOLD: Oh, I get it, if I'm so smart why ain't I poor? You better get a damn good act of your own before you start giving *mine* the razzberry. What's this game you play gonna be like ten years from now, without youth? Murray, Murray, I can't *watch* this, you gotta *shape* up . . .

MURRAY *(Turning quickly to face ARNOLD; in a surprised tone):* Shape *up*? *(Looks directly at ARNOLD; speaks slowly.)* Arnie, what the hell happened to you? You got so old. I don't know you any more. When you quit "Harry the Fur King" on Thirty-eighth Street, remember?

ARNOLD: That's twenty years ago, Murray.

MURRAY: You told me you were going to be in twenty businesses in twenty years if you had to, till you found out what you wanted. Things were always going to change. Harry said you were not behaving maturely enough for a salesman; your clothes didn't match or something . . . *(Laughs in affectionate memory of the event.)* So the next day, you dressed perfectly, homburg, gray suit, cuff links carrying a briefcase and a rolled umbrella . . . and you came into Harry's office on roller skates. You weren't going to take crap from *any*body. So that's the business you finally picked . . . taking crap from *every*body.

ARNOLD: I don't do practical jokes any more, if that's what you mean.

MURRAY *(Grabs both of ARNOLD's arms tensely):* Practical, that's right; a way to stay alive. If most things aren't funny, Arn, then they're only exactly what they are; then it's one long dental appointment interrupted occasionally by something exciting, like waiting or falling asleep. What's the point if I leave everything exactly the way I find it? Then I'm just adding to the noise, then I'm just taking up some more room on the subway.

ARNOLD: Murray, the Welfare Board has these specifications; all you have to do is meet a couple specifications . . .
   (MURRAY releases his grip on ARNOLD's arms; MURRAY's hands drop to his sides.)

MURRAY: Oh, Arnie, you don't understand any more. You got that wide stare that people stick in their eyes so nobody'll know their head's asleep. You got to be a shuffler, a moaner. You want me to come sit and eat fruit with you and watch the clock run out. You start to drag and stumble with the rotten weight of all the people who should have been told off, all the things you should have said, all the specifications that aren't yours. The only thing you got left to reject is your food in a restaurant if they do it wrong and you can send it back and make a big fuss with the waiter . . . *(MURRAY turns away from ARNOLD, goes to the window seat, sits down.)* Arnold, five months ago I forgot what *day* it was. I'm on the subway on my way to work and I didn't know what day it was and it scared the hell out of me. . . . *(Quietly)* I was sitting in the express looking out the window same as every morning watching the local stops go by in the dark with an empty head and my arms folded, not feeling great and not feeling rotten, just not feeling, and for a minute I couldn't remember, I didn't know, unless I really concentrated, whether it was a Tuesday or a Thursday . . . or a . . . for a minute it could have been *any* day, Arnie . . . sitting in the train going through any day . . . in the dark through any year . . . Arnie, it scared the hell out of me. *(Stands up.)* You got to know what day it is. You got to know what's the name of the game and what the rules are with nobody else telling you. You have to own your days and name them, each one of them, every one of them, or else the years go right by and none of them belong to you. *(Turns to look at ARNOLD.)* And that ain't just for weekends, kiddo . . . *(Looks at ARNOLD a moment longer, then speaks in a pleasant tone.)* Here it is, the day after Irving R. Feldman's birthday, for God's sake . . . *(Takes a hat, puts it on.)* And I never even congratulated him . . . *(Starts to walk briskly toward the front door. ARNOLD shouts in a voice stronger than we have ever heard from him.)*

ARNOLD: Murray! *(MURRAY stops, turns, startled to hear this loud a voice from ARNOLD. ARNOLD looks fiercely at MURRAY for a moment, then ARNOLD looks surprised, starts to laugh.)*

MURRAY: What's so funny?

ARNOLD: Wow, I scared myself. You hear that voice? Look at that, I got you to stop, I got your complete, full attention, the floor is mine now . . . *(Chuckles awkwardly.)* And I can't think of a God-damned thing to say . . . *(Shrugs his shoulders; picks up his hat from the table.)* I have long been aware, Murray . . . I have long been aware that you don't respect me much . . . I suppose there are a lot of brothers who don't get along. . . . But in reference . . . to us, considering the factors . . . *(Smiles, embarrassed.)* Sounds like a contract, doesn't it? *(Picks up his briefcase, comes over to MURRAY.)* Unfortunately for you, Murray, you want to be a hero. Maybe, if a fella falls into a lake, you can jump in and save him; there's still that kind of stuff. But who gets opportunities like that in midtown Manhattan, with all that traffic. *(Puts on his hat.)* I am willing to deal with the available world and I do not choose to shake it up but to live with it. There's the people who spill things, and the people who get spilled on; I do not choose to notice the stains, Murray. I have a wife and I have children, and business, like they say, is business. I am not an exceptional man, so it is possible for me to stay with things the way they are. I'm lucky. I'm gifted. I have a talent for surrender. I'm at peace. But you are cursed; and I like you so it makes me sad, you don't have the gift; and I see the torture of it. All I can do is worry for you. But I will not worry for myself; you cannot convince me that I am one of the Bad Guys. I get up, I go, I lie a little, I peddle a little, I watch the rules, I talk the talk. We fellas have those offices high up there so we can catch the wind and go with it, however it blows. But, and I will not apologize for it, I take pride; I am the best possible Arnold Burns. *(Pause.)* Well . . . give my regards to Irving R. Feldman, will ya? *(He starts to leave.)*

MURRAY *(Going toward him):* Arnold . . .

ARNOLD: Please, Murray . . . *(Puts his hand up.)* Allow me once to leave a room before you do.
(ARNOLD snaps on record player as he walks past it to the front door; he

exits. MURRAY goes toward the closed door, the record player has warmed up and we suddenly hear "Stars and Stripes Forever" blaring loudly from the machine again; MURRAY turns at this sound and stands for a long moment looking at the record player as the music comes from it. NICK enters through the window from the fire escape, unnoticed by MURRAY. NICK looks about, sees that the apartment is not quite what it was an hour before.)

NICK: Hey, Murray . . .

MURRAY *(Turns, sees NICK):* Nick . . . *(Turns the record player off, puts the record on the bed.)*

NICK: Hey, where's the lady?

MURRAY: Well, she's not here right now . . .

NICK *(Stepping forward to make an announcement):* Murray, I have decided that since *you* are getting a job today then I made up my mind it is time for *me* also to finish a certain matter which I have been putting off.

MURRAY: Nick, listen, turned out the only job I could get in a hurry was with Chuckles . . .

NICK *(Nodding in approval):* Chuckles, huh? Well, fine. *(Then, grimly)* Just as long as I don't have to watch that terrible program every morning. *(Returning to his announcement)* For many months now I have been concerned with a decision, Murray . . . Murray, you're not listening.

MURRAY *(Distracted):* Sure I'm listening, yeah . . .

NICK: The past couple months I have been thinking about different names and considering different names because in four weeks I'm gonna be thirteen and I gotta pick my permanent name, like we said.

MURRAY: Why don't you just go on calling yourself Nick? You've been using it the longest.

NICK: Nick is a name for a short person. And since I am a short person I do not believe I should put a lot of attention on it.

MURRAY: Whaddya mean, where'd you get the idea you were short?

NICK: From people who are taller than I am.

MURRAY: That's ridiculous.

NICK: Sure, standing up there it's ridiculous, but from down here where I am it's not so ridiculous. And half the girls in my class are taller than me. Especially Susan Bookwalter. *(NICK sits dejectedly in the swivel chair.)*

MURRAY *(Crouching over next to him):* Nick, you happen to be a nice medium height for your age.

NICK *(Pointing at MURRAY):* Yeah, so how is it everybody crouches over a little when I'm around?

MURRAY *(Straightening up):* Because you're a kid. *(Sits next to him.)* Listen, you come from a fairly tall family. Next couple years you're gonna grow like crazy. Really, Nick, every day you're getting bigger.

NICK: So is Susan Bookwalter. *(Stands.)* So for a couple of months I considered various tall names. Last month I considered, for a while, Zachery, but I figured there was a chance Zachery could turn into a short, fat, bald name. Then I thought about Richard, which is not really tall, just very thin with glasses. Then last week I finally, really, decided and I took out a new library card to see how it looks and today I figured I would make it definite and official. *(He takes a library card out of his pocket, hands it to MURRAY.)*

MURRAY *(Looks at the card, confused):* This is *my* library card.

NICK: No, that's the whole thing; it's mine.

MURRAY: But it says "*Murray* Burns" on it . . .

NICK: Right, that's the name I picked. So I took out a new card to see how it looks and make it official.

MURRAY *(Looks at the card, is moved and upset by it, but covers with cool dignity; stands, speaks very formally):* Well, Nick, I'm flattered . . . I want you to know that I'm . . . very flattered by this. *(NICK goes to the alcove to put his school books and pajamas away.)* Well, why the hell did you . . . I mean, damn it, Nick, that's too many Murrays, very confusing . . . *(MURRAY begins to shift the card awkwardly from one hand to the other, speaks haltingly.)* Look, why don't you call yourself George, huh? Very strong name there, George . . .

NICK *(Shaking his head firmly):* No. We made a deal it was up to me to pick which name and that's the name I decided on; "Murray."

MURRAY: Well, what about Jack? What the hell's wrong with Jack? Jack Burns . . . sounds like a promising heavyweight.

NICK: I like the name I picked better.

MURRAY *(Very quietly):* Or Martin . . . or Robert . . .

NICK: Those names are all square.

LEO'S VOICE *(From behind the door, shouting):* Is this it? Is this the Lion's Den, here? Hey, Murr'!

MURRAY *(Softly):* Ah, I heard the voice of a chipmunk.

NICK *(Going into the bathroom):* I better go put on a tie.

MURRAY *(Goes to the door; stands there a moment, looks over to the other side of the room at NICK, who is offstage in the bathroom; smiles, speaks half to himself, very softly.)* You coulda called yourself Charlie. Charlie is a very musical name.
(Then, he opens the door. LEO HERMAN enters. He wears a camel's-hair coat and hat. The coat, like his suit, is a little too big for him. He is carrying a paper bag and a large Chuckles statue — a life-size cardboard cutout of himself in his character of Chuckles the Chipmunk; the statue wears a blindingly ingratiating smile.)

LEO *(With great enthusiasm):* Murray, there he is! There's the old monkey! There's the old joker, right?

MURRAY *(Quietly, smiling politely):* Yeah, Leo, here he is. *(Shakes LEO's hand.)* It's . . . it's very nice to see you again, Leo, after all this time.

LEO *(Turning to see NICK, who has come out of the bathroom wearing his tie):*

There he is! There's the little guy! *(Goes to NICK carrying the statue and the paper bag.)* Looka here, little guy . . . *(Setting the statue up against the wall next to the window.)* I gotta Chuckles statue for you.

NICK *(With his best company manners):*   Thank you, Mr. Herman; imagine how pleased I am to receive it. It's a very artistic statue and very good cardboard too.

LEO *(Taking a Chuckles hat from the paper bag; a replica of the furry, big-eared hat worn by the statue):*   And I gotta Chuckles hat for you too, just like the old Chipmunk wears. *(He puts the hat on NICK's head.)*

NICK: Thank you.

LEO *(Crouching over to NICK's height):*   Now that you've got the Chuckles hat, you've got to say the Chuckles-hello.

NICK *(Confused, but anxious to please):*   The what?

LEO *(Prompting him):*   "Chip-chip, Chippermunkie!" *(He salutes.)*

NICK: Oh, yeah . . . "Chip-chip, Chippermunkie!" *(He salutes too.)*

LEO: May I know your name?

NICK: It's Nick, most of the time.

LEO: Most of the . . . *(Pulling two bags of potato chips from his overcoat pockets)* Say, look what I've got, two big bags of Chuckle-Chip potato chips! How'd ya like to put these crispy chips in some bowls or somethin' for us, huh? *(NICK takes the two bags, goes to the kitchen.)* And take your time, Nick, your uncle'n'me have some grown-up talkin' to do. *(After NICK exits into the kitchen)* The kid hates me. I can tell. Didn't go over very well with him, pushed a little too hard. He's a nice kid, Murray.

MURRAY: How are *your* kids, Leo?

LEO: Fine, fine. But, Murray, I swear, even *they* don't like my show since you stopped writing it. My youngest one . . . my six-year-old . . . *(He can't quite remember.)*

MURRAY: Ralphie.

LEO: Ralphie; he's been watching the Funny Bunny show now every morning instead of me. *(Begins pacing up and down.)* Oh *boy*, have I been bombing out on the show. Murray, do you know what it *feels* like to bomb out in front of children? You flop out in front of kids and, Murray, I swear to God, they're ready to *kill* you. *(Stops pacing.)* Or else, they just stare at you, that's the worst, that hurt, innocent stare like you just killed their pup or raped their turtle or something. *(Goes over to MURRAY.)* Murray, to have you back with me on the show, to see you at the studio again tomorrow, it's gonna be *beautiful*. You're the best.

MURRAY: I appreciate your feeling that way, Leo.

LEO: This afternoon, Murray, on the phone, you hung up on me, didn't you?

MURRAY: I'm sorry Leo, I was just kidding . . . I hope you . . .

LEO *(Sadly):*   Murray, why do you do that to me? Aw, don't tell me, I know, I make people nervous. Who can listen to me for ten minutes? *(Begins pacing up and down again, strokes his tie.)* See *that*? See how I keep touching my suit and my tie? I keep touching myself to make sure I'm still there. Murray, I get this feeling, maybe I vanished when I wasn't looking.

MURRAY: Oh, I'm sure that you're here, Leo.

LEO *(Pointing at MURRAY):*   See how he talks to me? A little nasty. *(Smiles suddenly.)* Well, I like it. It's straight and it's real and I like it. You know what I got around me on the show? Finks, dwarfs, phonies and frogs. No Murrays. The show: boring, boredom, bore . . . *(Cups his hands around his mouth and shouts.)* boring, boring . . .
   (During these last few words, SANDRA has entered through the partly opened door. MURRAY turns, sees her.)

SANDRA *(Staying near the doorway; reserved, official):*   Murray, I believe that I left my files here; I came to get my files; may I have my files, please. I . . . *(She sees LEO, comes a few feet into the room.)* Oh, excuse me . . .

MURRAY *(Cordially, introducing them):*   Chuckles the Chipmunk . . . this is Minnie Mouse.

LEO *(Absently):*   Hi, Minnie . . .

SANDRA *(Looking from one to the other taking in the situation, smiles; to LEO):*   You must be . . . you must be Mr. Herman.

LEO *(Mumbling to himself):*   Yeah, I must be. I must be him; I'd rather not be, but what the hell . . .

SANDRA *(Smiling, as she turns right around and goes to the door):*   Well, I'll be on my way . . . *(She exits. MURRAY picks up her files from the bureau, goes to the door with them.)*

LEO *(Interrupting MURRAY on his way to the door):*   Very attractive girl, that Minnie; what does she do?

MURRAY: She's my decorator.

LEO *(Looking around the apartment):*   Well, she's done a *wonderful* job! *(Indicating the apartment with a sweep of his hand.)* This place is great. It's loose, it's open, it's free. Love it. Wonderful, crazy place. My God . . . you must make out like mad in this place, huh? *(MURRAY closes the door, puts the files back on the bureau; LEO is walking around the apartment.)* How come I never came here before?

MURRAY: You were here last January, Leo.

LEO: Funny thing, work with me for three years and I never saw your apartment.

MURRAY: You were here last January, Leo.

LEO *(Stops pacing, turns to MURRAY):*   Wait a minute, wait a minute, wasn't I here recently, in the winter? Last January, I think . . . *(Goes over to Murray.)* Oh, I came here to get you back on the show and you wouldn't listen, you went into the kitchen, sang "Yes Sir, That's My Baby." I left feeling very foolish, like I had footprints on my face . . . You old monkey. *(Smiles, musses up MURRAY's hair.)* You're an old monkey, aren't ya? *(Starts pacing again.)* You know what I got from that experience? A rash. I broke out something terrible. . . . Minnie Mouse! *(Stops pacing.)* Minnie *Mouse! (Laughs loudly, points at the door.)* You told me her name was Minnie Mouse! I swear to God, Murray, I think my mission in life is to feed you straight-lines . . . *(Taking in the apartment with a sweep of his hand.)* It's kind of a fall-out shelter, that's what you got here, Murr', protection against the idiots in the atmosphere. Free, freer, freest . . . *(Cups his hands around his mouth, shouts.)* Free! Free! *(Takes off his coat.)* Another year and I'm gonna cut loose from the God-damn Chipmunk show. Binds me up, hugs me. Finks, dwarfs, phonies and frogs. . . . *(Following MURRAY to the window seat)* Two of us should do something new, something wild; new kind of kid's show, for adults maybe . . .

MURRAY *(Sitting on the window seat):* You told me the same thing three years ago, Leo.

LEO *(Sits next to MURRAY):* Well, whaddya want from me? I'm a coward; everybody knows that. *(Suddenly seeing the Chuckles statue against the wall next to him.)* Oh God! *(Points at the statue; in anguish)* Did you ever see anything so *immodest*? I bring a big statue of myself as a gift for a child! I mean, the *pure ego* of it. . . *(Covers his face with his hands.)* I am ashamed. Murray, could you throw a sheet over it or something . . . *(Sees NICK, who has just come out of the kitchen with two bowls of potato chips.)* Mmmm, good! Here they are. *(Grabs one bowl from NICK's hand, gives it to MURRAY. Then LEO turns to NICK, assumes the character and the voice of Chuckles the Chipmunk; a great mock-frown on his face, he goes into a routine for NICK.)* Oh, goshes, Kidderoonies, look at your poor Chippermunk friend; he got his mouff stuck. No matter how hard I try I can't get my mouth unstuck. But maybe — if you Chippermunks yell, "Be happy, Chuckles," maybe then it'll get unstuck. . . *(LEO waits. NICK does not react. LEO prompts NICK in a whisper.)* You're supposed to yell, "Be happy, Chuckles."

NICK: Oh yeah . . . sure . . . *(Glances quickly at MURRAY; then, a little embarrassed, he yells.)* Be happy, Chuckles!

LEO: Oh *boy! (His frown changes to a giant smile.)* You *fixed* me! Looka my mouff!! *(He jumps up in the air.)* Now I'm all fixed! *(Gets no reaction from NICK. NICK stands patiently in front of LEO.)*

NICK *(Offering the other bowl of potato chips to LEO, trying to be polite):* Mr. Herman, don't you want your . . .

LEO *(Not accepting the potato chips, speaking in his own voice again, stroking his tie nervously):* That was a bit from tomorrow morning's show. You'll know it ahead of all the kids in the neighbourhood.

NICK: Thank you.

LEO: That . . . that was one of the funny parts there, when I couldn't move my mouth.

NICK: Yeah?

LEO: Didn't you think it was funny?

NICK: Yeah, that was pretty funny.

LEO *(Smiling nervously):* Well, don't you laugh or something when you see something funny?

NICK: It just took me by surprise is all. So I didn't get a chance. *(Offering him the potato chips, politely)* Here's your . . .

LEO: Another funny part was when I jumped up with the smile there, at the end there. That was another one.

NICK: Uh-huh.

LEO *(Pressing on, beginning to get tense):* And the finish on the bit, see, I've got the smile . . . *(NICK, looking trapped, stands there as LEO switches back to his Chipmunk voice and puts a giant smile on his face.)* Now I'm aaaall fixed, Chippermunks! *(Suddenly mock-pathos in his eyes.)* Oooops! *Now* I got stuck the *other* way! Oh, *oh*, now my face is stuck the *other* way! *(Throws up his arms, does a loose-legged slapstick fall back onto the floor. Remains prone, waiting for NICK's reaction. NICK stands there looking at LEO quite solemnly.)*

NICK *(Nods his head up and down approvingly):* That's terrific, Mr. Herman. *(With admiration)* That's all you have to do, you just get up and do that and they pay you and everything.

LEO: You didn't laugh.

NICK: I was waiting for the funny part.

LEO *(Sits up):* That was the funny part.

NICK: Oh, when you fell down on the . . .

LEO: When I fell down on the floor here.

NICK: See, the thing is, I was . . .

LEO *(Gets up from the floor, paces up and down tensely):* I know, waiting for the funny part. Well, you missed another funny part.

NICK: Another one. Hey, I'm really sorry, Mr. Herman, I . . .

LEO: Forget it . . . I just happen to know that that bit is very *funny*. I can prove it to you. *(Takes small booklet from pocket, opens it, shows it to NICK.)* Now, what does that say there, second line there?

NICK *(Reading from the booklet):* "Frown bit; eighty-five percent of audience; outright prolonged laughter on frown bit."

LEO: That's the analysis report the agency did for me on Monday's preview audience. The routine I just did for you, got outright prolonged laughter; eighty-five percent.

MURRAY: You could try him on sad parts, Leo; he's very good on sad parts.

LEO *(Goes to MURRAY at the window seat, shows him another page in the booklet):* Matter fact, there's this poignant-type bit I did at the Preview Theatre: "Sixty percent of audience; noticeably moved."

MURRAY: They left the theatre?

LEO *(Tensely, angrily):* There he is; there's the old joker; Murray the joker, right?

NICK: I do some routines. I can imitate the voice of Alexander Hamilton.

LEO: That's lovely, but I . . .

NICK: I do Alexander Hamilton and Murray does this terrific Thomas Jefferson; we got the voices just right.

MURRAY *(In a dignified voice; to NICK):*   Hello there, Alex, how are you?

NICK *(In a dignified voice; to MURRAY):*   Hello there, Tom; say, you should have been in Congress this morning. My goodness, there was quite a discussion on . . .

LEO: Now, that's *ridiculous*. You . . . you can't *do* an imitation of Alexander Hamilton; nobody knows what he *sounds* like . . .

NICK *(Pointing triumphantly at LEO):*   That's the *funny* part.

MURRAY *(Shaking his head regretfully):*   You missed the funny part, Leo.

LEO *(Walking away from them):*   I'm getting a terrible rash on my neck. *(Turns to them, growing louder and more tense with each word.)* The routine I did for him was *funny*. I was workin' good in front of the kid, I know how to use my Goddamn *warmth*, I don't go over with these odd kids; I mean, here I am right in *front* of him, in *person* for God's sake, and he's *staring* at me . . . *(Moves toward them, on the attack.)* It's oddness here, Murray, *odd*ness. Alexander Hamilton imitations! Jaded jokes for old men. Murray, what you've done to this kid. It's a damn shame, a child can't enjoy little animals, a damn shame . . . *(Really on the attack now; waving at the apartment, shouting)* The way you brought this kid up, Murray, grotesque atmosphere, *unhealthy*, and you're not even guilty about it, women in and out, *decorators*; had he been brought up by a *normal* person and not in this *mad*house . . .

NICK *(Quietly, going toward LEO):*   Hey, don't say that . . .

LEO: A certain kind of freakish way of growing up . . .

NICK *(Quietly):*   Hey, are you calling me a freak? You called me a freak. Take back what you said.

LEO *(Walks away from them, mumbling to himself):*   On June third I will be forty-two years old and I'm standing here arguing with a twelve-year-old kid . . . *(LEO quiets down, turns, comes toward NICK, sits on bed, NICK standing next to him; speaks calmly to NICK.)* See, Nicky, humour is a cloudy, wonderful thing, but simple and clear like the blue, blue sky. All I want is your simple, honest child's opinion of my routine; for children are too honest to be wise . . .

NICK *(Looking directly at LEO, calmly, quietly, slowly):*   My simple, child's reaction to what you did is that you are not funny. Funnier than you is even Stuart Slossman my friend who is eleven and puts walnuts in his mouth and makes noises. What is not funny is to call us names and what is mostly not funny is how sad you are that I would feel sorry for you if it wasn't for how dull you are and those are the worst-tasting potato chips I ever tasted. And that is my opinion from the blue, blue sky.

(NICK and LEO stay in their positions, looking at each other. A moment; then MURRAY throws his head back and laughs uproariously. LEO stands; the bowl of potato chips tips over in his hand, the chips spilling onto the floor.)

LEO *(Seeing MURRAY's laughter, goes to him at the Morris chair; angrily):* Murray the joker, right? You didn't want to come back to work for me, you just got me up here to step on my face again! *(NICK, unnoticed by LEO, has gone quickly into his alcove and comes out now with his ukulele, playing and singing*

"Yes, Sir, That's My Baby" with great spirit. *LEO, hearing him, turns to look at NICK.)* It's the *song*. It's the good-*bye song. (LEO grabs his hat and coat quickly, as NICK goes on playing, starts for front door, shouting.)* Getting *out*, bunch of *nuts* here, *crazy* people . . .

MURRAY: Leo, wait . . . *(Goes to the door to stop LEO.)* Leo, wait . . . I'm sorry . . . wait . . . *(LEO stops at the door; MURRAY goes down toward NICK, who is near the alcove, still playing the song.)* Nick, you better stop now . . .

NICK: Come on, Murray, get your uke, we'll sing to him and he'll go away . . .

MURRAY *(Quietly):* Nick, we can't . . . *(Gently taking the uke from NICK, puts it on the window seat.)* Just put this down, huh?

NICK *(Confused by this; urgently):* Come on, Murray, let him go away, he called us names, we gotta get rid of him . . .

MURRAY: Quiet now, Nick . . . just be quiet for a minute . . . *(Starts to go back toward LEO.)*

NICK *(Shouting):* Murray, please let him go away . . . *(NICK, seeing the Chuckles statue next to him against the wall, grabs it angrily, throws it down on the floor.)* It's a crummy statue . . . that crummy statue . . . *(Begins to kick the statue fiercely, jumping up and down on it, shouting.)* It's a terrible statue, rotten cardboard . . .
  (MURRAY comes quickly back to NICK, holds both of his arms, trying to control him.)

MURRAY: Aw, Nick, please, no more now, stop it . . .
  (There is a great struggle between them; NICK is fighting wildly to free himself from MURRAY's arms.)

NICK *(Near tears, shouting):* We don't want jerks like that around here, Murray, let him go away, we gotta get rid of him, Murray, we gotta get rid of him . . .

MURRAY *(Lifts the struggling NICK up into his arms, hugging him to stop him.):* No, Nick . . . I'm sorry, Nick . . . we can't . . . *(NICK gives up, hangs limply in MURRAY's arms. MURRAY speaks quietly, with love.)* I'm sorry . . . I'm sorry, kid . . . I'm sorry . . . *(He puts NICK down, still holding him.)*

NICK *(After a pause; quietly, in disbelief):* Murray . . .

MURRAY: You better go to your room.

NICK: This is a one-room apartment.

MURRAY: Oh. Then go to your alcove. *(NICK waits a moment, then turns, betrayed, walks over to his alcove, lies down on the bed. MURRAY looks over at LEO, who is standing at the front door. He walks slowly over to LEO, looking down at the floor; humbly)* Leo . . . hope you didn't misunderstand . . . we were just kidding you . . . we . . .

LEO *(Coming toward MURRAY, apologetically):* I, myself, I got carried away there myself.

MURRAY: We all got a little excited, I guess. *(Reaches out to shake LEO's hand.)* So, I'll see you at work in the morning, Leo.

LEO *(Smiling, shaking MURRAY's hand):* Great to have you back, fellah. *(Pause)* You both hate me.

MURRAY: Nobody hates you, Leo.

LEO: I hollered at the kid, I'm sorry. I didn't mean to cause any upset. I don't get along too good with kids . . .

MURRAY: Don't worry about it.

LEO: Wanna come have a drink with me, Murray? We could . . .

MURRAY: No thanks; maybe another night, Leo.

LEO: Look, after I leave, you horse around a little with the kid, he'll feel better.

MURRAY: Right, Leo.

LEO *(Pauses; then comes closer to MURRAY):* Murray . . . that bit I did was funny, wasn't it?

MURRAY *(After a moment):* Yeah, Leo . . . I guess it was just a bad day for you.

LEO *(Pointing at the Chuckles statue on the floor; quietly, but giving a command):* You don't want to leave that statue lying around like that, huh, Murray?

MURRAY: Oh, no. *(Goes to statue obediently, lifts it up off the floor, leans it upright against the wall.)* There.

LEO: Fine.

MURRAY: See you tomorrow, Leo.

LEO *(Smiles):* Yeah, see ya tomorrow at the studio . . . *(Ruffles up MURRAY's hair.)* You old monkey. *(Goes to the door.)* Hey, you're an old monkey, aren't you?
   (LEO exits. MURRAY stays at the door for a moment. NICK is sitting on the alcove step, his back to MURRAY.)

MURRAY *(Walking over to NICK, trying to make peace with him):* Say, I could use a roast-turkey sandwich right now, couldn't you, Nick? On rye, with cold slaw and Russian dressing. . . .
   (NICK does not reply. MURRAY sits down next to him on the alcove step. NICK refuses to look at MURRAY. They are both silent for a moment.)

NICK: Guy calls us names. Guy talks to us like that. Shoulda got rid of that moron. Coulda fooled the Welfare people or something . . . *(SANDRA enters through the partly open door, unnoticed by them; she stays up in the doorway, watching them.)* We coulda gone to Mexico or New Jersey or someplace.

MURRAY: I hear the delicatessen in Mexico is terrible.

NICK *(After a moment):* I'm gonna call myself *Theodore*.

MURRAY: As long as you don't call yourself Beatrice.

NICK: O.K., fool around. Wait'll you see a Theodore running around here. *(Silent for a moment, his back still to MURRAY; then, quietly)* Another coupla seconds he would abeen out the door . . . *(Turns to look at MURRAY.)* Why'd you go chicken on me, Murray? What'd you stop me for?

MURRAY: Because your routines give me outright prolonged laughter, Theodore.

SANDRA *(After a pause):* Four ninety-five for this tablecloth and you leave it around like this . . . *(Picks up the discarded tablecloth from the chair.)* A perfectly new tablecloth and already there are stains on it . . . *(Sits on the Morris chair, starts to dab at the tablecloth with her handkerchief.)* You know, it's very interesting that I left my files here. That I forgot them. I mean, psychologically, if you want to analyze that. Of course, last month I left my handbag in the Automat, and I have no idea what that means at all. *(MURRAY leaves alcove, starts toward her.)* I think that the pattern of our relationship, if we examine it, is very intricate, the different areas of it, especially the whole "good-bye" area of it, and also the "hello" and "how-are-you" area . . . of it.

MURRAY *(Standing next to her chair now, smiles warmly):* Hello, Sandy, and how are you?

SANDRA *(Looks up at him, smiles politely):* Hello, Murray. *(Goes right back to her work, rubbing the tablecloth with her handkerchief.)* You're standing in my light.

MURRAY: Oh. *(He retreats a step.)*

NICK *(Walking over to her):* Hello, lady.

SANDRA: Hello, Nick.

NICK *(Indicating her work on the tablecloth):* Lady, can I help you with any of that?

SANDRA: Matter of fact, Nick . . . *(She stands; her arm around NICK, she goes to centre with him.)* Nick, I don't think the effect, I mean, the overall design of this room, is really helped by all these . . . *(Gesturing to MURRAY's stuff around the bed)* these knicknacks.

NICK: You mean the junk?

SANDRA: Yes.

NICK: Yeah, not too good for the overall design.

SANDRA: If you'd just put them away in that carton there. *(She indicates a carton near the bed.)*

NICK: Sure, lady . . .
(NICK goes quickly to the carton, begins to put MURRAY's junk into it — some radios, a megaphone, some clocks. SANDRA starts pulling the tablecloth on the table.)

MURRAY *(Realizes that they are taking over, moves forward, trying to halt the proceedings):* Hey, Sandy, now wait a minute . . . *(She goes on with her work, putting a piece of material over the Morris chair. He turns at the sound of one of his radio cabinets being dropped into the carton by NICK.)* Listen, Nick, I didn't tell you to . . . Nick . . .

NICK *(Looking up from his work):* Wilbur . . . *(Drops a clock into the carton.)* Wilbur Malcom Burns.

(SANDRA is putting the flowers back around the room, picking up the magazines.)

MURRAY *(Protesting):* Hey, now, both of you, will ya wait a minute here, will ya just wait . . . *(They ignore him, going on with their work. He shrugs, defeated; gives up, goes over to the windows, away from them, sits down sadly in the window seat.)* Wonder what kind of weather we got out there tonight. *(Looks out of window; as usual, he can see nothing but the gray, blank wall of the building a few feet opposite; sadly, to himself)* Never can see the God-damned weather. We got a permanent fixture out there: twilight in February. Some day that damn building'll fall down into Seventh Avenue so I can see the weather. *(Leans over, begins to talk out of the window.)* Everybody onstage for the Hawaiian number, please . . . *(SANDRA, during these last few lines, has gone to the phone, dialed. Listened a few moments and hung up. MURRAY hears her hang up, turns to her.)* What're you doing?

SANDRA: I just spoke to the Weather Lady. She says it's a beautiful day. *(She goes back to her work on the apartment.)*

MURRAY *(He continues to talk out the window, softly at first):* Well, then, if you're not ready, we better work on the Military March number. Now the last time we ran this, let's admit it was pretty ragged. I mean, the whole "Spirit of '76" float was in dis*grace*ful shape yesterday . . . O.K. now, let's go, everybody ready . . . *(As MURRAY continues to talk out the window, NICK looks up from his work, smiles, picks up a record from the bed, puts it on the record player, turns it on.)* Grenadiers ready, Cavalry ready, Cossacks ready, Rough Riders ready, Minute Men ready . . . *(The record player has warmed up now and we hear "Stars and Stripes Forever." MURRAY hears the music, turns from the window, smiling, acknowledges NICK's assistance; turns to the window again, his voice gradually growing in volume.)* O.K. now, let's go . . . ready on the cannons, ready on the floats, ready on the banners, ready on the flags . . . *(The music builds up with MURRAY's voice, NICK humming along with the band and SANDRA laughing as MURRAY shouts.)* Let's go . . . let's go . . . let's go . . . *(His arms are outstretched.)*

CURTAIN

————————— • —————————

Consider the Play

1. Note the stage directions at the beginning of the play. Why does Gardner make the room so cluttered? Does the clutter have any bearing on the plot? Discuss.

2. During much of the first act, Murray avoids Nick's efforts to persuade Murray to go job-hunting. What are three different ways Murray uses to sidestep Nick?

3. Props and costumes are important symbols for characterization.
   (A) What does Albert's small briefcase tells us about Albert?
   (B) What do the clothes Sandra wears tell us about the way she sees herself?

4. Audiences usually laugh when Sandra and Albert go to the alcove for their private conferences. Why do you think they laugh? Were you amused? Explain your point of view.

5. "It's just there's all these Sandras running around who you never met before." What do you think Murray means?

6. An *effective curtain* is a dramatic ending to an act. Do you think that the way Act 1 ends is an effective curtain? Why?

7. When Albert comes back to tell Murray about the Welfare Board's decision, he reveals a great deal about his true character in a long speech. What do we learn about Albert which we didn't know before?

8. Murray keeps making jokes about the people in charge of the Chuckles show. Underneath the jokes, however, he is trying to express his thoughts about the world of children. What are some of Murray's thoughts?

9. To *satirize* means to ridicule individuals, ideas, customs, or situations in order to achieve humour and/or to achieve change. When Murray says, "I've been attacked by the *Ladies Home Journal*!", what is he satirizing? Identify three other points of satire in the play, and explain briefly what is being satirized by each.

10. "Maybe you're wonderfully independent, Murray, or maybe, maybe you're the most extraordinarily selfish person I've ever met." In your opinion, which view of Murray is the right one? Why?

11. In Act 3, Murray and Arnold have a talk. It ends when Arnold sums up the basic difference between himself and Murray with this: "I'm lucky. I'm gifted. I have a talent for surrender. I'm at peace, but you are cursed." Explain what Arnold meant. Do you agree with his view? Why?

12. Leo Herman can be viewed as both a tragic and comic figure. Is he more likely to move the audience to laughter or tears? Why? How did you react to Herman? Why?

13. For the most part, all the characters in the play are quite different from one another. Yet, they all seem to be attracted to each other. Why? Explain your point of view.

14. Jason Robards, who has played the role of Murray, described Murray as "the sidewalk superintendent of the human race". What do you think he meant?

15. Murray has been described as "a nonconformist who worries about getting mothered by the world". What do you think this means?

16. Murray feels that too many people spend their lives in the "rat race". He found a way to avoid this with his own life. What other ways do you think there could be of avoiding the rat race?

17. Herb Gardner has his own idea about what happens to Murray after the final curtain. What do you think is most likely to happen to him? Why?

18. A nonconformist, such as Murray, can cause problems within a social institution or group. What problems can a nonconformist cause? What positive changes can a nonconformist bring about? Discuss.

19. Christopher Fry, a British playwright, has written: "When I set about writing a comedy the idea presents itself to me first of all as a tragedy. . . . If the characters . . . were not qualified for tragedy, there would be no comedy." Discuss *A Thousand Clowns* in the light of this statement. In your opinion, what do the play's characters have in common? Which characters qualify for tragedy? Which have qualities that make the play a comedy? What are these qualities?

20. Get together with three or four other students and brainstorm to come up with topics for humourous writing. Then, as a group or as an individual, do one of the following:

    (A) Recreate an incident from your own experience which was humourous. Specify whether the humour was recognized at the time or not seen until after the event.

    (B) Recreate an incident from your own experience which was *not* humourous when it happened but which becomes humourous when you present it.

    (C) Write a light, clever poem.

    (D) Write a digression.

    (E) Satirize a person, event, or custom which you feel should be changed.

———————— • ————————

The Barretts of Wimpole Street

by Rudolf Besier

The Playwright

Rudolf Besier was born in Java in 1878, the son of Dutch-English parents. He was educated in England and Germany and began his career as a journalist in London. Here he collaborated with such famous authors as Hugh Walpole, H.G. Wells, and May Edington in the work of adapting their novels for the stage.

Besier's first play was produced in 1908 in London. During the next few years, he wrote several plays, which were produced in London and New York, but he did not have a major success until 1930. It was in that year that *The Barretts of Wimpole Street* was first staged, and it brought Besier lasting fame and fortune.

The Play

Rudolf Besier achieved international success with his historical drama, *The Barretts of Wimpole Street*. Part of that success was due to the tense, interesting style Besier used for the play, and part of it was due to the great interest the public had always had in the torrid love affair between Elizabeth Barrett and Robert Browning, two fascinating poets of nineteenth century England.

Elizabeth Barrett Moulton-Barrett was born in 1806, six years before Robert Browning. She was the oldest of the 12 children of Edward Barrett Moulton. (Her father added another Barrett to the family name when he inherited the Jamaican estates of his maternal grandfather.)

Elizabeth was a childhood prodigy. By the age of eight, she could read Greek. She was completely devoted to poetry, reading it in several languages, and while still a child, she began to write poems as well. One of her first major poems was an epic, *Battle of Marathon*. It so pleased her father that he had 50 copies privately printed in 1820 when Elizabeth was only 14.

Elizabeth deserves consideration as one of the leading poets of the 1830s. At that time, many of the most famous names in poetry were gone or soon to be gone. Byron, Keats, and Shelley had died tragically young. Sir Walter Scott and Samuel Taylor Coleridge were nearing death, and William Wordsworth was in decline. Neither Robert Browning nor Alfred, Lord Tennyson, were yet at their peak. Elizabeth began to take her place in the poetic limelight with the publication of *The Seraphim and Other Poems* in 1838 and with her many contributions to the *New Monthly Magazine*.

Although gaining a reputation as a sparkling new talent, Elizabeth rarely left her room in her father's house at 50 Wimpole Street in London. She had been seriously ill in her teens, and in 1838 she became a confirmed invalid. During that year, she was sent off to Torquay in Devon in the hope that a prolonged stay by the sea would help her. Two years later she was still there. It was during that summer of 1840 that her favourite brother, Edward, called "Bro" by Elizabeth, was drowned when his boat capsized. Since Edward had come to Torquay solely to visit her, Elizabeth blamed herself for his death. Her overwhelming sense of guilt greatly increased her physical ailments, which included weakness of the spine, lungs, and blood vessels. She also developed a wide streak of hypochondria (exaggerated worry about one's physical health). In accordance with accepted medical knowledge of the day, Elizabeth was prescribed laudanum, a form of opium. As a result she became drug-dependent, too.

Elizabeth was a recluse, who saw few people outside her family circle of father, brothers, sisters, and cousins. With each passing year, she withdrew still more from society. Despite this, by the 1840s she was a celebrity with a well established reputation as a learned poet, essayist, and translator.

Robert Browning was a complete contrast to the serene, withdrawn Elizabeth Barrett. Robert was tempestuous, out-going, and somewhat unruly as a boy. He did not attend school in a regular way until he was in his late teens, and so his early, formative education was drawn from his random scholarly reading.

Robert was 14 when he discovered the poetry of Percy Bysshe Shelley, and from that time on, he modelled his life on Shelley's. Robert became a vegetarian, an extreme liberal in political matters, and an atheist in religious matters, and he began to write poetry. His early poems were moderately successful, and he began to write plays as well. As a dramatist, however, he was a disaster. For him, the fascination of life lay in the inner drama of human character rather than in the outer interaction between characters. Still, the lessons he learned from his stage failures were useful later when he wrote dramatic monologues.

By 1843, however, fame appeared to be within Robert's grasp. Slim, dark, handsome, dynamic, and charming, Robert seemed to be the very image of everything that a poet should be. He was a prominent figure in London's artistic society, and his poems were attracting favourable attention.

It was the next year, 1844, that Robert and Elizabeth met for the first time. He was entranced by two volumes of her poetry and impulsively wrote to her of his admiration. ("I love your poems, dear Miss Barrett, and I love you too.") His imagination was fired by the romantic image of the beautiful invalid guarded by a tyrannical and jealous father, and he was determined to meet her. The story of the romance that followed is one of the most famous of all time.

Rudolf Besier approached the story as a family chronicle based on two romances — that of Elizabeth Barrett and Robert Browning and that of Elizabeth's sister and a soldier. Elizabeth's father is portrayed as a domestic despot who is determined to keep his vast family unmarried and untainted by the world. Elizabeth is portrayed as a delicate lady, trapped in a house of terror, and Robert is portrayed as a life-giver, the impetuous knight in shining armour who sets out to rescue the fair Elizabeth from her Victorian prison.

Besier's interpretation horrified the Barrett family, which objected to Besier's portrayal of Elizabeth's father. The audiences loved it, however, and it was a smash hit. Two movie versions were made, one in 1934 (with Norma Shearer and Fredric March) and another in 1957 (with Jennifer Jones and Sir John Gielgud). Besier's play and the two films based on it have helped make the romance of Elizabeth Barrett and Robert Browning a legend of literary history.

Rudolf Besier

From *The Barretts of Wimpole Street,* a comedy in five acts, by Rudolf Besier. Copyright 1930 by Rudolf Besier; Copyright renewed © 1958 by Daphne Collinson. Reprinted by permission of Little, Brown and Company.

The Barretts of Wimpole Street

Rudolf Besier

The First Production Was Staged
On August 20, 1930
At the Malvern Festival
In England

With This Cast

Doctor Chambers...............................Aubrey Mallalieu
Elizabeth Barrett Moulton-Barrett..........Gwen Ffrancgon-Davies
Wilson ....Eileen Beldon
Henrietta Moulton-Barrett ....Marjorie Mars
Arabel Moulton-Barrett.......................Susan Richmond
Octavius Moulton-Barrett ....Barry K. Barnes
Septimus Moulton-Barrett....................B.B. Coleman
Alfred Moulton-Barrett ....Hugh Moxley
Charles Moulton-Barrett......................Leonard Bennett
Henry Moulton-Barrett ....Douglas Quayle
George Moulton-Barrett ....Anthony Marshall
Edward Moulton-Barrett ....Cedric Hardwicke
Bella Hedley ....Joan Barry
Henry Bevan....................................Oliver Johnston
Robert Browning ....Scott Sunderland
Doctor Ford-Waterlow........................Wilfrid Caithness
Captain Surtees Cook ....Harry Wilcoxon
Flush ....Tuppenny of Ware

Director: Sir Barry Jackson

Scene
Elizabeth Barrett's bed-sitting-room at 50 Wimpole Street, London

Time
1845

SCENE 1

ELIZABETH BARRETT's bed-sitting room, in Wimpole Street, London.

It is a large square room, comfortably furnished in the English furniture of the period. There is a wide door to the right, with massive iron lock on its inner side, and with brass doorknobs, and large brass key in the lock. A large fireplace with a marble mantel is opposite. At back, the wall is somewhat bowed outward to form a large bay, in which are spaced equally three large, recessed windows, with double-hung, square-paned sash, and panelling in the recesses below the windows. Through door at left is seen the hall with stairway leading up toward back. Through windows at back are seen the small iron balcony railings outside each one of them, and the flowers in the boxes just outside the sills. In the distance can be seen the upper stories of the houses on the opposite sides of the street, and a corner of the outer brick wall of this house, vines are seen climbing up outside the windows. A large wardrobe cabinet with mirror door is against wall at right. A small square tea-table is against back wall. On it are books and pamphlets. The windows at back are fitted with shades, long lace curtains, sash curtains on lower sash, and long drapes with pull cords. At back is a small open-shelved secretary desk filled with books, and with desk top also littered with books and pamphlets. Between windows, before this desk, is a straight walnut chair with upholstered seat. Before the window is a fine mahogany dressing table with swinging oval back. There is a fine mahogany dressing table with swinging oval mirror, on which are a lace cover, and some few pomade jars, toilet bottles, glass tray, tumblers, etc. Against back wall is a round low dog basket on floor with old cushion inside. Beside it a stack of books, also on floor. Against side wall is a large secretary desk with glass doors, filled with books. On mantel are a couple of brass candlesticks and candles in glass chimneys, and a small white marble statuette of a half-open shell. A round gold-framed mirror in black shadow box is on wall above. In fireplace below is a built-in black iron grate with andirons, and low brass fender rail. A brass stand with tongs, shovel, and poker stands above it, and black, brass-mounted scuttle of coal is below. Also above is a small square tabourette or stand of mahogany. A tapestry bell-pull hangs from ceiling below fireplace. To the left is a carved leg stool, with round tapestry-upholstered seat. A walnut straight chair with upholstered seat is before dressing table. On back wall over small desk hangs a square tapestry in gold frame. Over drop-leaf table is a pair of hanging book-shelves filled with books, and on wall beneath them hangs a small plaster plaque of a man's head. Over stool is a duplicate pair of hanging book-shelves with books, and a framed plaster plaque on wall beneath them. On top of wardrobe cabinet, and on top of large desk, are two plaster busts of male heads. A large table desk stands up and down stage at right of center with a green-figured upholstered bench at right of it. In front of this table is a large upholstered armchair, and a little at left of this table is another armchair with carved arms and upholstered seat and back with cushion in it. A large duplicate armchair to that in front of table is at center angled towards couch. Table top is littered with piles of books, a copy of newspaper, large portfolio of leather, with paper and envelopes, a large leather-covered inkwell, green feather quill pen, and a black sand-shaker. There is a large upholstered couch, with low straight back, and sharply upturned head and foot. On this are a number of pillows and couch covers and shawls. *In hall to the right is seen a small oblong table against wall, on which is a lighted candle in glass stand with red tinted glass shade, an old portrait of woman's head in old gold frame is on wall above, and a straight rush-bottom chair with yellow flowered cushion is at either end above and below.*

TIME: *Evening, about 8:30 P.M.*

AT RISE: *Shade on window is down, and drapes on all windows are closely drawn. The books from tea table have been piled on floor. Tea table is in front of couch. On it is a tray with the remains of a light meal, and a glass full of porter. The stand or tabourette near fire-place has been brought forward to head of couch, and on it is a lighted candle in lamp, of painted china with bronze base, and rough globe-shaped blue tinted glass chimney. There are discovered ELIZABETH's dog, FLUSH, a tiny cocker-spaniel, in basket; ELIZABETH, reclining on couch amidst cushions and covers, and DR. CHAMBERS, who is standing behind couch, watch in hand, taking her pulse.*

———————— • ————————

CHAMBERS *(Dropping her wrist and pocketing watch, behind couch.):* H-m-m! Yes! It's this increasingly low vitality of yours that worries me. No life in you — none. What are we going to do about it?

ELIZABETH *(Reclining on couch.):* Well, Doctor, if you shut a person up in one room for years on end, you can't very well expect to find her bursting with life and vigor. Why not prescribe something really exciting for a change?

CHAMBERS: Exciting, eh?

ELIZABETH: A gallop three times around the Park every morning — dumb-bell exercises — a long sea-voyage.

CHAMBERS: How I wish I could, my dear!

ELIZABETH: It's funny to think of it now, but you know, Doctor, as a child I was a regular tomboy.

CHAMBERS: Yes, I've heard all about that — and mentally you're a tomboy still! To tell you the truth, my dear Miss Elizabeth, I'm not at all sure that brain of yours isn't altogether too active. Still hard at Greek?

ELIZABETH: Oh, not more than two or three hours a day.

CHAMBERS: Are you engaged in any literary work at the moment?

ELIZABETH: Only a few articles for the "Athenaeum," and other papers.

CHAMBERS: The "Athenaeum" — dear, dear! Now, why not give all these heavy labors a rest, and turn your mind to something light and easy for a bit? Poetry? You're not neglecting your poetry, I hope?

ELIZABETH *(On couch):* Meaning something light and easy? *(Laughs.)* Oh, Doctor, I shudder to think what my life would be like if I hadn't a turn for scribbling and study.

CHAMBERS: H-m — yes. Quite so. Yes. And this isn't the liveliest house for anyone to live in — let alone an invalid.

ELIZABETH: No, I suppose not. I wish Papa were a happier man! It would make such a world of difference to all of us.

CHAMBERS: Happier, eh? It's no business of mine, but when a man has good health, plenty of money, and a jolly family, I can't see why he should make life a burden to himself and others. Well, as I said, it's no concern of mine. But *you are*, my dear, and a very worrying concern too. Of course the winter has been abominable, and these spring months are always trying. The fact is, you oughtn't to live in England at all. Italy's the place for you.

ELIZABETH: *Italy!* Oh, Doctor, what a heavenly dream!

CHAMBERS: But if only I could prescribe some sort of change for you — something — anything to get you out of these dismal surroundings for a time. Tell me now, Miss Elizabeth, have you ventured on your feet at all lately?

ELIZABETH: No, hardly at all. I rather lost my nerve after that fall I had last Christmas. Papa, or one of my brothers, carries me from my bed to the sofa. Sometimes when I'm feeling venturesome, my maid supports me across the room.

CHAMBERS *(Rising):* Feeling venturesome at the moment?

ELIZABETH *(Reclining on couch):* Not particularly.

CHAMBERS: All the same, I think we'll try a step or two. *(Crossing to take her, takes both her hands.)* Quietly now — slowly — there's no hurry. *(With his help she gets to her feet.)* There we are. *(She sways a little; he supports her.)* Feeling giddy, eh?

ELIZABETH: A little —

CHAMBERS: Close your eyes and lean against me — it will pass in a minute. *(After a moment she raises her head.)* Better?

ELIZABETH: Yes — oh, yes —

CHAMBERS: Take your time now, and step carefully. Don't be nervous — I won't let go your hand. *(She takes a few faltering steps as he walks backward before her, holding her hands.)* No — don't look at the floor. Look straight ahead. That's first rate — that's fine — splendid — splendid — *(After taking half a dozen steps she falters and sways.)*

ELIZABETH: Oh, Doctor! *(He quickly catches her in his arms, and carries her back, placing her on sofa again.)*

CHAMBERS: Feeling faint?

ELIZABETH: No, it's just my knees — they don't seem able to — to support me.

CHAMBERS *(Replacing covers):* Well, if they can't do that, they're a pretty useless pair! *(Walks around back of sofa, pats her shoulder.)* Why, there's no more to you than to a five-year-old. How's your appetite? Just peck at your food, I suppose?

ELIZABETH *(Reclining on sofa):* I always try to eat what I'm given, but I'm never very hungry. *(With sudden animation, half sitting up.)* Oh, Doctor, that reminds me! Do you remember Papa suggesting that a kind of beer called porter might do me good?

CHAMBERS: Yes — and an excellent suggestion, too.

ELIZABETH: Oh, but forgive me — it was nothing of the kind! I have to drink it twice a day, out of a pewter tankard, and my life in consequence has become one long misery.

CHAMBERS: God bless my soul!

ELIZABETH: I am not exaggerating — *one long misery!*

CHAMBERS: But, my dear child —! There's nothing I enjoy more than a pint of porter with my steak or chops at breakfast.

ELIZABETH: With your breakfast! All I can say is that to me porter is entirely horrible! Horrible to look at — more horrible to smell — and most horrible to drink! Surely, something one abominates so intensely can't possibly do one any good! It's no use my appealing to Papa — especially as the dreadful idea originated with him. But if *you*, dear, dear Doctor Chambers, were to suggest to him that something else — anything — I don't mind what it is — might be equally efficacious —?

CHAMBERS *(Laughing):* You poor little lady! But of course I will!

ELIZABETH: Oh, thank you, a thousand times!

CHAMBERS *(Seated on sofa):* What do you say to a couple of glasses of hot milk as a substitute?

ELIZABETH *(On sofa):* I dislike milk, but I'll drink it all day long — if only you'll rescue me from porter! *(There is a knock at door.)* Come in! *(WILSON, ELIZABETH's maid, enters, leaving door open.)* Yes, Wilson?

WILSON: Begging your pardon, Miss — *(Turning to CHAMBERS.)* But the Master wishes most particularly to see you before you leave, sir.

CHAMBERS: Of course — of course. *(Rising, looking at watch.)* And high time I were off — is your Master in his study?

WILSON: Yes, sir. *(Crosses to door, waits there for CHAMBERS.)*

CHAMBERS *(Crossing to ELIZABETH):* Well, good-bye, my dear Miss Elizabeth, good-bye. *(Takes her hand.)*

ELIZABETH: Good-bye, doctor. *(In a low voice.)* And you won't forget?

CHAMBERS: Eh?

ELIZABETH *(Spelling):* P-O-R-T-E-R!

CHAMBERS *(Laughing):* No — no. I'll speak to him about it now.

ELIZABETH *(On sofa):* Thank you — thank you!

CHAMBERS *(Laughing):* Good night — *(To WILSON as he crosses to door.)* You needn't see me downstairs — I know my way.

WILSON: Thank you, sir. *(CHAMBERS exits, leaving door open.)* I am just going to post your letter, Miss Ba — shall I take Flush with me?

ELIZABETH *(Excitedly, ignoring question, points at glass of porter.):* Quick, Wilson — away with it!

WILSON: What, Miss?

ELIZABETH: I hadn't the courage to drink it at dinner. I have been putting off the dreadful moment as long as I could.

WILSON *(Turning to look at porter, then back at ELIZABETH):* Your porter, Miss?

ELIZABETH: And now dear Doctor Chambers says I needn't drink it at all. Take it away. Quick! Quick! And never mention the word porter to me again!

WILSON *(Crossing to her):* Lor, Miss — very good, Miss. But since you 'aven't 'ad your porter, won't you —?

ELIZABETH *(Covering her ears):* I told you never to mention the word again! Take it away, please. Please.

WILSON *(A little alarmed, picks up FLUSH, puts him out of door.):* Very good, Miss Ba. Come, Flush. *(ELIZABETH starts laughing, as HENRIETTA MOULTON-BARRETT runs quickly in. WILSON crosses with FLUSH.)*

HENRIETTA: What are you laughing at, Ba?

ELIZABETH *(On sofa):* Wilson thinks I've gone mad.

WILSON *(Re-entering):* Mad, Miss? What things you do say!

ELIZABETH *(Still laughing):* Will you, or won't you, take away that — that black beer?

WILSON: Very good, Miss Ba. *(Crosses, gets tray, exits with it, closing door.)*

HENRIETTA *(Crosses toward ELIZABETH, stands by chair.):* I don't know why you're laughing, Ba, and you needn't tell me. Only don't stop. Go on laughing till midnight. I'll tickle you if you think you can't keep it up without being helped. Oh, Ba, dinner was awful — awful! *(Sits on foot of sofa facing her.)*

ELIZABETH: Was Papa —?

HENRIETTA: Yes, he was. He was in one of his moods — the worst kind. The nagging mood is bad enough, the shouting mood is worse, but don't you think the dumb mood is the worst of all?

ELIZABETH: Yes, perhaps — but they all frighten me.

HENRIETTA: I don't believe there were more than a dozen remarks all through dinner — and most of them were frozen off at the tips. Papa would just turn his glassy eyes on the speaker. You know? For the last twenty minutes or so the only sound in the room was the discreet clatter of knives and forks. Directly dinner was over he ordered the port to be taken to his study, and thank Heaven he followed it almost at once.

ELIZABETH: Doctor Chambers is with him now.

HENRIETTA: Oh, Ba, I do hope for all our sakes his report of you isn't too good.

ELIZABETH: But, Henrietta —!

HENRIETTA *(All contrition, moves and sits on sofa with ELIZABETH and*

126   *On Stage 1*

takes her hand.):   Forgive me, dearest — it was odious of me to say that. You know I didn't mean it, don't you?

ELIZABETH: Of course I do, you silly child. But what you said makes Papa an inhuman monster. And that's wickedly untrue. In his own way he cares for all his children.

HENRIETTA *(Rises):*   In his own way! No, dear, what I meant was that good news of any kind would be sure to aggravate him in his present mood. *(Sits on sofa again.)* I don't know why it should, but it does. *(ARABEL MOULTON-BARRETT enters, closing door.)*

ARABEL: Oh, you're here, Henrietta. I've been looking for you everywhere. Papa has just sent you this note from his study.

HENRIETTA: Me? Oh, dear! When he starts sending notes from his study, look out for squalls! *(Opens note, reads. ARABEL sits in chair.)* "I have heard this morning that your Aunt and Uncle Hedley, and your cousin Bella have arrived in London earlier than was expected. They are staying at Fenton's Hotel. Your cousin Bella and her fiancé, Mr. Bevan, propose to call on you tomorrow at three o'clock. You and Arabel will, of course, be here to receive them, and if Elizabeth is well enough you will bring them upstairs to see her. I have written to invite your Uncle and Aunt and Cousin to dinner next Thursday — Papa." Well!

ARABEL: I understand now why Papa seemed so — so displeased at dinner.

HENRIETTA: Vile-tempered, you mean!

ARABEL: Is it necessary always to use the ugliest word?

HENRIETTA: Yes, Arabel — when you're describing the ugliest thing! *(To ELIZABETH.)* Oh, but Papa is quite impossible! He got this letter from the Hedleys at breakfast. Why couldn't he have spoken then? Why couldn't he have spoken at dinner? Heaven knows he had time enough!

ARABEL: I'm afraid he was displeased.

HENRIETTA: Displeased! Oh, of course we all know that he hates being ordinarily polite to anyone, and now he's simply bound to show some kind of hospitality to the Hedleys. No wonder he was — displeased! *(Rising.)* What enrages me is that I was expecting a friend tomorrow at three, and now I shall have to put him off somehow. *(Crosses to ARABEL.)*

ARABEL *(Archly, stopping her.):*   Why?

HENRIETTA *(Turning to ARABEL):*   Why what?

ARABEL: Why must you put your friend off? Bella and her fiancé won't eat your friend.

HENRIETTA: What — what business is that of yours?

ARABEL: But, Henrietta —

HENRIETTA *(Rising):*   I hate people prying into my affairs! *(Exits, slamming door.)*

ARABEL *(Distressed, takes a couple of steps after her, then turns back toward ELIZABETH.):*   Oh dear! Oh dear! What can be the matter with her tonight? Usually she quite enjoys being quizzed about Captain Surtees Cook.

ELIZABETH: Perhaps she may have begun to take his attentions seriously.

ARABEL: Oh, Ba, I hope not! *(Sits.)* You remember when young Mr. Palfrey wanted to marry her two years ago — those dreadful scenes with Papa?

ELIZABETH: I should rather forget them.

ARABEL: Oh, why can't Henrietta realize that if there's one thing Papa will never permit, it's marriage in the family! It doesn't worry me at all, as gentlemen never attracted me in that way. Nor you, dear.

ELIZABETH *(With a laugh):* Me?

ARABEL *(Rising, goes to her):* Oh, of course, today, anything of that kind is quite out of the question, my poor darling — Papa or no Papa. But even when you were younger and stronger, I don't ever remember your having had little affairs with gentlemen.

ELIZABETH: Perhaps the gentlemen never gave me the chance!

ARABEL: Oh, but you were quite pretty as a young girl.

ELIZABETH: What is Captain Surtees Cook like? Is he nice?

ARABEL: Yes, I think so. Yes, quite nice. But he never says much. He just sits and looks at Henrietta.

ELIZABETH: She's very lovely.

ARABEL: But Papa would never countenance any kind of understanding between them. You know that as well as I do.

ELIZABETH: Poor Henrietta — *(HENRIETTA re-enters, closing door, crosses quickly to ARABEL and kisses her.)*

HENRIETTA: I'm sorry.

ARABEL: Oh, my dear, I never meant to annoy you. *(Rising, going to meet her.)*

HENRIETTA: You didn't — *(They kiss, then with a laugh.)* — you *displeased* me. Oh, I'm Papa's daughter, all right!

ELIZABETH: Henrietta, when Bella and her fiancé call tomorrow, Arabel will bring them up here to see me, and you can entertain Captain Cook in the drawing-room. *(ARABEL looks distressed.)*

HENRIETTA: What a lovely thing it is to be a genius! You darling!

ELIZABETH: But I must have the room to myself at half-past three, as Mr. Robert Browning is calling then.

HENRIETTA: No!

ARABEL *(Turns, starts to ELIZABETH):* But I thought — } *(Together.)*

HENRIETTA: Of course I know you've been corresponding with Mr. Browning for months. But then you write to so many literary people whom you absolutely refuse to see.

ARABEL: Has Papa given his permission?

ELIZABETH: Of course.

128

HENRIETTA: But why? Why have you made an exception of Mr. Browning? I've heard he's wonderfully handsome, but —

ELIZABETH: Oh, Henrietta, you're incorrigible!

ARABEL: I know he's been most anxious to call. Mr. Kenyon told me so.

HENRIETTA: But you said yourself only a short time ago that you didn't intend to receive him.

ELIZABETH: I didn't — and I don't particularly want to now.

HENRIETTA: But why?

ELIZABETH: Because, my dear, at heart I'm as vain as a peacock! You see, when people admire my work, they are very likely to picture the poetess as stately and beautiful as her verses. And it's dreadfully humiliating to disillusion them.

HENRIETTA: Don't be silly, Ba. You're very interesting and picturesque.

ELIZABETH (*Laughing as ARABEL sits down.*): Isn't that how guide-books usually describe a ruin? As a matter of fact, Mr. Browning has been so insistent that out of sheer weariness I've given way. But I don't want an audience to witness the tragedy of his disillusionment! So mind, Arabel, Bella and her Mr. Bevan must be out of the room before he arrives. (*A knock at door.*) Come in. (*OCTAVIUS MOULTON-BARRETT enters, closing door after him. He stammers slightly.*) Come in, Occy.

OCTAVIUS: I've just come to see how you are, and to wish you g-good night. Doctor satisfied?

ELIZABETH: Oh, yes, I think so.

HENRIETTA (*Handing him PAPA's note*): Read that, Octavius.

ARABEL (*While he is reading.*): Oh dear! I quite forgot that I was to attend a meeting on the Chinese Weslyan Mission at Exeter Hall tomorrow afternoon.

OCTAVIUS (*Flourishing letter*): Well, you can't attend it! This is undoubtedly a Royal d-decree.

HENRIETTA (*To ARABEL*): "Given at our study at 50 Wimpole Street on this nineteenth day of May 1845. God save Papa!"

ARABEL (*Reprovingly*): Henrietta, dear! (*A knock at door.*)

ELIZABETH: Come in. (*SEPTIMUS MOULTON-BARRETT enters. He is a year older than OCTAVIUS.*) Well, Septimus?

SEPTIMUS (*Crossing to ELIZABETH*): How are you, Ba? (*Kisses her.*) I hope the Doctor is satisfied with you?

ELIZABETH: Oh, yes, I think so.

OCTAVIUS: I say, Septimus, the Hedleys are d-dining here in force next Thursday.

SEPTIMUS: By Jove! Not really? (*OCTAVIUS gives him letter. A knock at door.*)

ELIZABETH: Come in. (*ALFRED MOULTON-BARRETT enters. He is older than SEPTIMUS.*) Come in, Alfred.

ALFRED: And how's our dear Ba tonight? I hope the Doctor was happy with you?

ELIZABETH: Oh, yes, I think so. *(Another knock at door.)* Come in. *(CHARLES MOULTON-BARRETT enters.)* Come in, Charles.

CHARLES *(Enters):* How are you feeling tonight, Ba? I hope Doctor Chambers' report was good?

ELIZABETH: Oh, yes, I think so. *(Another knock at door.)* Come in. *(HENRY MOULTON-BARRETT enters. He is slightly older than CHARLES.)* Come in, Henry.

HENRY: Well, Ba? How are you, my dear? *(Kisses her.)* Was the Doctor pleased with his patient?

ELIZABETH: Oh, yes, I think so.

HENRY: That's good. I must say, I think you are looking a little better. What do you say, Charles?

CHARLES: Eh? *(SEPTIMUS goes up to give OCTAVIUS the letter. Tells him in an undertone to take it to HENRIETTA.)*

HENRY: Looking better, don't you know. More herself, what? *(Another knock at door.)*

ELIZABETH: Come in. *(GEORGE MOULTON-BARRETT enters, closing door. He is slightly older than HENRY.)* Come in, George.

GEORGE: Well, and how's Ba tonight? *(Kisses her.)* The Doctor's just been, hasn't he? I'm afraid he wasn't too pleased with you.

ELIZABETH: Oh, yes, I think so — I mean — why?

GEORGE: You're not looking so well. Is she, Henry?

HENRY: On the contrary, I think she's looking considerably better. So does Charles — don't you, Charles?

CHARLES: Eh?

OCTAVIUS: I say, George, the Hedleys have arrived unexpectedly in town. Bella and her swain are c-calling on the girls tomorrow afternoon, and on Thursday, she and her parents are d-dining here, in state.

HENRY: Dining *here!*

ALFRED *(Rising):* Not here! ⎫ *(Together.)*

SEPTIMUS: Not really! ⎭

ALFRED: Well, I hope they'll enjoy their dinner as much as we did ours tonight!

SEPTIMUS: You have met this Mr. Bevan, haven't you, Alfred?

ALFRED: I have.

SEPTIMUS: What is he like?

HENRIETTA: Yes?

ALFRED: Pompous ass. But warm — a very warm fellow. Ten thousand pounds a year, if he has a penny —

HENRIETTA: No!

ALFRED: And ten thousand more when his grandmother dies.

ARABEL: Oh!

HENRIETTA: It's grossly unfair! *(To ARABEL.)* What has Bella done to deserve such luck?

OCTAVIUS: Alfred says he's a pompous ass.

HENRIETTA: Oh, that's jealousy! No man with ten thousand a year can be a pompous ass!

HENRY: I think it's just possible that you'll all be interested to hear that Papa is going to Plymouth on business next week, and — *(Excited exclamations from all but ELIZABETH.)*

HENRIETTA: Go on, Henry, and —?

HENRY: And that he's not expected to return for at least a fortnight. *(Smiles and murmurs of satisfaction.)*

HENRIETTA *(Flings arms around GEORGE's neck, kisses him.):* Oh, George! How wonderful! How glorious! Do you polk, George?

GEORGE: Don't be childish!

HENRIETTA: Well, I polk. *(She dances the polka around room, while humming "Little Brown Jug," all the brothers join in the humming. HENRY moves up to fireplace. Others look on amused, OCTAVIUS claps his hands. Door opens quietly, and EDWARD MOULTON-BARRETT enters.)*

ELIZABETH *(Breathlessly, as she sees him.):* Papa — *(An awkward silence. HENRIETTA stops dead in middle of room. BARRETT stands just inside room with a perfectly expressionless face. ELIZABETH continues.)* Good evening, Papa. *(Without reply BARRETT crosses, stands with his back to fireplace. A pause, no one moves.)*

BARRETT *(Before fireplace, in a cold measured voice looking straight before him.):* I am most displeased! *(A pause.)* It is quite in order that you should visit your sister of an evening, and have a few quiet words with her. But I think I have pointed out, not once, but several times, that in her very precarious state of health it is most inadvisable for more than three of you to be in her room at the same time! My wishes in this matter have been disregarded — as usual! *(A pause.)* You all know very well that your sister must avoid any kind of excitement. Absolute quiet is essential, especially before she retires for the night. And yet I find you romping around her like a lot of disorderly children. I am gravely displeased. *(HENRIETTA gives a nervous little giggle.)* I am not aware that I have said anything amusing, Henrietta.

HENRIETTA: I — I beg your pardon, Papa.

BARRETT: May I ask what you were doing, as I came into the room?

HENRIETTA: I was showing Ba how to polk.

BARRETT: To — polk?

HENRIETTA: How to dance the polka.

BARRETT: I see. *(Long pause.)*

OCTAVIUS *(Nervously, starting toward ELIZABETH.):* Well, B-Ba, I think I'll say g-good night, and —

BARRETT: I should be grateful if you would kindly allow me to finish speaking.

OCTAVIUS *(Stepping back):* Sorry, sir, I thought you'd d-done.

BARRETT *(With frigid anger):* Are you being insolent, sir?

OCTAVIUS: N-no, indeed, sir. I assure you —

BARRETT: Very well.

ELIZABETH: As I am really the cause of your displeasure, Papa, I ought to tell you that I like nothing better than a little noise occasionally. It's delightful having all the family here together, and can't possibly do me any harm.

BARRETT: Perhaps you will forgive my saying, Elizabeth, that you are not the best judge of what is good or bad for you. And that brings me to what I came here to speak to you about. Dr. Chambers told me just now that you had persuaded him to allow you to discontinue drinking porter with your meals.

ELIZABETH: It needed very little persuasion, Papa. I said I detested porter, and he agreed at once that I should take milk instead.

BARRETT: I questioned him closely as to the comparative strength-giving values of porter and milk, and he was forced to admit that porter came decidedly first.

ELIZABETH: That may be, Papa. But when you dislike a thing to loathing, I don't see how it *can* do you any *good*.

BARRETT: I said just now that you are not the best judge of what is good or bad for you, my child. May I add that self-discipline is always beneficial, and self-indulgence invariably harmful! Believe me, Elizabeth, I have nothing but your welfare at heart when I warn you that if you decide to discontinue drinking porter, you will incur my grave displeasure.

ELIZABETH: But when Dr. Chambers himself —

BARRETT: I have told you what Dr. Chambers said!

ELIZABETH: Yes, but —

BARRETT: Did you drink your porter at dinner?

ELIZABETH: No.

BARRETT: Then I hope you will do so before you go to bed.

ELIZABETH: No, Papa, that's asking too much. I can't drink the horrible stuff in cold blood.

BARRETT: Very well. Of course I have no means of coercing you. You are no longer a child. But I intend to give your better nature every chance of asserting itself. A tankard of porter will be left at your bedside, and I hope that tomorrow you will be able to tell me that you have obeyed your Father.

ELIZABETH: I am sorry, Papa — but I shan't drink it.

BARRETT *(Taking a step forward):*   Henrietta — go down to the kitchen and fetch a tankard of porter!

HENRIETTA *(Her voice trembling with anger and agitation.):*   No, I won't!

BARRETT: I beg your pardon?

HENRIETTA *(Desperately):*   It's — it's sheer cruelty. You know how Ba hates the stuff. The Doctor has let her off. You're just torturing her because you — like torturing!

BARRETT: I have told you to fetch a tankard of porter from the kitchen!

HENRIETTA: I won't do it!

BARRETT: Must I ask you a third time! *(Suddenly shouting.)* Obey me this instant!

ELIZABETH *(Sharply):*   Papa! Go and fetch it, Henrietta! Go at once! I can't stand this!

HENRIETTA: No. I —

ELIZABETH: Please — please —? *(After a moment's indecision, HEN-RIETTA turns, exits, leaving door open.)*

BARRETT *(After a pause, quietly.):*   You had all better say good night to your sister.

ARABEL *(Goes to below sofa, whispers.):*   Good night, dearest. *(She kisses ELIZABETH on the cheek. ELIZABETH receives it impassively.)*

ELIZABETH *(In a toneless voice.):*   Good night. *(ARABEL exits. Each of the boys in turn goes to ELIZABETH and kisses her cheek.)*

HENRY: Good night, Ba.

ELIZABETH: Good night. *(HENRY exits.)*

OCTAVIUS: Good night, Ba.

ELIZABETH: Good night. *(OCTAVIUS exits.)*

CHARLES: Good night, Ba.

ELIZABETH: Good night. *(CHARLES exits.)*

SEPTIMUS: Good night, Ba.

ELIZABETH: Good night. *(SEPTIMUS exits.)*

GEORGE: Good night, Ba.

ELIZABETH: Good night. *(GEORGE exits.)*

ALFRED: Good night, Ba.

ELIZABETH: Good night. *(ALFRED exits. BARRETT and ELIZABETH stare before them with expressionless faces. Pause, then HENRIETTA enters* *with a tankard of porter. She stands at threshold glaring at BARRETT and breathing quickly.)* Give it to me, please. *(HENRIETTA starts toward her, when BARRETT suddenly but quietly intervenes.)*

BARRETT: No. *(Takes tankard, speaking to HENRIETTA.)* You may go. *(HENRIETTA makes move to approach ELIZABETH, but BARRETT stops her.)* You may go!

ELIZABETH: Good night. *(HENRIETTA, after a defiant look at BARRETT, exits, closing door.)*

BARRETT *(Places porter on mantel, then goes to sofa and stands looking down at ELIZABETH. She looks up at him with wide fearful eyes. He turns and speaks in gentle voice.):* Elizabeth.

ELIZABETH *(In a whisper):* Yes?

BARRETT: Why do you look at me like that, child? *(Placing hand on her head and bending it slightly back.)* Are you frightened?

ELIZABETH *(As before):* No.

BARRETT: You're trembling, why?

ELIZABETH: I — I don't know.

BARRETT: You're not frightened of me? *(ELIZABETH is about to speak, he continues quickly.)* No — no — you mustn't say it. I couldn't bear to think that. You're everything in the world to me — you know that. Without you I should be quite alone — you know that, too. And you — if you love me, you can't be afraid of me. For love casts out fear. You love me, my darling? You love your Father?

ELIZABETH *(In a whisper):* Yes.

BARRETT *(Eagerly):* And you'll prove your love by doing as I wish?

ELIZABETH: I don't understand. I was going to drink —

BARRETT *(Quickly):* Yes, out of fear, not love. Listen, dear. I told you just now that if you disobeyed me, you would incur my displeasure. I take that back. I shall never in any way reproach you. You shall never know by word, or deed, or hint of mine, how much you have grieved and wounded your Father by refusing to do the little thing he asked.

ELIZABETH: Oh, please, please, don't say any more. It's all so petty and sordid. Please give me the tankard.

BARRETT: You are acting of your own free will —?

ELIZABETH: Oh, Papa, let us get this over and forget it. I can't forgive myself for having made the whole house miserable over a tankard of porter. *(Crossing, he gets tankard from mantel, gives it to her. She drinks it straight off. He places tankard back on mantel and returns to above top end of sofa, looking down at her yearningly.)*

BARRETT: You're not feeling worse tonight, my darling?

ELIZABETH *(Listlessly.):* No, Papa.

BARRETT: Just tired?

ELIZABETH: Yes — just tired.

BARRETT: I'd better leave you now. Shall I say a little prayer with you before I go?

ELIZABETH: Please, Papa. *(He kneels beside sofa, clasps hands, lifts face, shuts his eyes. ELIZABETH clasps her hands but keeps her eyes open.)*

BARRETT *(Kneeling at foot of sofa.):* Almighty and merciful God, hear me, I beseech Thee, and grant my humble prayer. In Thy inscrutable wisdom, Thou hast seen good to lay on thy daughter Elizabeth grievous and heavy affliction. For years she hath languished in sickness, and for years, unless in Thy mercy Thou take her to Thyself, she may languish on. Give her to realize the blessed word that Thou chastisest those whom Thou lovest. Give her to bear her sufferings in patience. Take her into Thy loving care tonight. Purge her mind of all selfish, and bitter, and unkind thoughts, guard her and comfort her. These things I beseech Thee, for the sake of Thy dear son, Jesus Christ. Amen.

ELIZABETH: Amen.

BARRETT *(Rising, goes behind sofa, kisses her forehead.):* Good night, my child.

ELIZABETH *(Receiving kiss impassively, not returning it.):* Good night, Papa. *(He crosses between chair and sofa and exits, meeting WILSON in hall as she is about to enter with FLUSH in her arms. ELIZABETH lies motionless a moment or two staring straight before her, as WILSON enters with FLUSH, closing door after her.)*

WILSON: Are you ready for your bed now, Miss Ba?

ELIZABETH: Oh, Wilson, I'm so tired, tired, tired of it all. Will it never end?

WILSON: End, Miss?

ELIZABETH: This long, long, gray death in life.

WILSON: Oh, Miss Ba, you shouldn't say such things.

ELIZABETH: No, I suppose I shouldn't. Did Flush enjoy his run?

WILSON *(Giving FLUSH to her):* Oh, yes, Miss.

ELIZABETH: Is it a fine night, Wilson?

WILSON: Yes, Miss, and quite warm, and there's such a lovely moon.

ELIZABETH *(Eagerly):* A moon! Oh, do you think I can see it from here?

WILSON: I don't know, I'm sure.

ELIZABETH: Draw back the curtain and raise the blind. *(WILSON does so, and the moonlight, tempered by the lamplight, streams on ELIZABETH's face.)*

WILSON: There you are, Miss. The moon's right above the chimneys, you can see it lovely.

ELIZABETH *(Dreamily.):* Yes — yes. Please put out the lamp and leave me for a little —

WILSON: Very well, Miss Ba.

The Barretts of Wimpole Street

ELIZABETH *(Finishing):* I don't want to go to bed quite yet. *(WILSON extinguishes lamp behind couch, takes lamp from table desk, exits. ELIZABETH is left bathed in strong moonlight. She stares for a while fixedly at the moon. Then her quickened breathing becomes audible, and one sees her whole body shaken with sobs. The only sound is her strangled weeping as curtain falls.)*

CURTAIN

———————— • ————————

SCENE 2

Same as in Scene 1, with the following few changes. The curtains are all open and blinds up. The unlighted lamps are back in their places. The lamp and stand back of sofa have been moved back. Sofa now points somewhat up, and the casters have been removed from it. Table is back of sofa, with bowl of tulips on it. Tea table is before sofa, on it a dinner tray with an untouched sweet. The leather portfolio is on sofa, coverlet from which has been removed to desk chair. The yellow shawl has been taken away, and pewter tankard removed from mantel.

TIME: Mid-afternoon.

AT RISE: The sunshine pours into the room. There are discovered FLUSH, in his basket and ELIZABETH on sofa, a cover over feet, reading with intense absorption, now and again running her fingers through her ringlets, or tossing them back from her face.

ELIZABETH *(To herself with puzzled emphasis as she reads.):*
"With flowers in completeness
All petals, no prickles,
Delicious as trickles
Of wine poured at mass-time" —
  (A knock at door, ELIZABETH, absorbed, takes no notice. She repeats, clutching her forehead.)
"All petals, no prickles,
Delicious as trickles —"
  (Knock is repeated. Continuing.)
"Of wine —"
(Calling.) Come in. *(WILSON enters, crossing to sofa.)* Oh, yes, Wilson, I'm quite ready for lunch.

WILSON *(Stolidly):* You've 'ad your lunch, Miss Ba.

ELIZABETH: Oh, yes, of course. And I enjoyed it very much.

WILSON: You only picked at the fish, Miss Ba. An' I took away the best part of that nice chop, an' I see you 'aven't touched the pudding — cornflower blammonge, too, with raspberry jam.

ELIZABETH *(Wonderingly regarding tray.):* Oh — anyhow it's too late now. *(WILSON takes table and tray away and then crosses to right and leaves table; puts tray on desk, then crosses to dressing table, measures out some medicine into a glass. ELIZABETH, absorbed in her reading, does not notice.)*

WILSON *(Holding glass of medicine to her.):* Your physic, Miss Ba.

ELIZABETH *(Taking glass, eyes still fixed on book.):* Thank you. *(Glass in her hand, she continues reading.)*

WILSON *(Noticing sunlight, crosses up to window.):* I think p'raps I'd better pull down the blind a bit. Too much sun isn't good for you, Miss. *(Half draws blind, returns to sofa.)*

ELIZABETH *(Still holding untouched glass, eyes still on book.):* Thank you.

WILSON: But you 'aven't drunk it yet, Miss.

ELIZABETH: Oh — *(Swallows medicine, and with a little grimace hands glass to WILSON, who takes it across to tray, which she takes up and carries out to hall.)* Please open the door, Wilson. I am expecting visitors this afternoon and I want the room to be quite fresh for them. How I wish we could open the window, Wilson!

WILSON *(Shocked, returning and crossing toward ELIZABETH.):* Open the window, Miss Ba!

ELIZABETH *(Sighing):* Yes — I know it's strictly forbidden. Well, open the door *wide.*

WILSON: I'd best cover you well up, first of all. *(Fetches shawl, covers her.)* Visitors, Miss Ba?

ELIZABETH: Yes. My cousin, Miss Bella Hedley. I haven't seen her since she was a child — such a lovely slip of a child. And now she's just become engaged.

WILSON *(Crossing to open door wider.):* Indeed, Miss! And is she bringing her young gentleman with her?

ELIZABETH: Yes. And Mr. Robert Browning is calling later.

WILSON *(Crossing to foot of sofa):* Indeed, Miss? The gentleman who's always sending you such lovely boukeys?

ELIZABETH: Yes. *(Starts reading again.)*

WILSON: Sure you don't feel a draught, Miss Ba?

ELIZABETH: Quite, thanks.

WILSON *(Arranging scarf on her shoulders.):* Hadn't you better keep your neck covered? These spring days the air is that treacherous!

ELIZABETH *(To herself, with despairing emphasis):* No — it's quite beyond me — I give it up.

WILSON *(Standing above sofa):* Beg pardon?

ELIZABETH *(Intensely):* Wilson?

WILSON: Yes, Miss?

ELIZABETH: Have you noticed anything — *strange* in me, today?

WILSON: Strange, Miss?

ELIZABETH: Yes, strange. I mean, dull-witted — thick-headed — stupid — idiotic?

WILSON: Lor' — no. P'raps a bit absent-minded like, but that isn't anything for *you* to worry about, Miss.

ELIZABETH: Then you don't think I'm going mad?

WILSON: Mercy on us — mad?

ELIZABETH: Very well. But now listen carefully, and tell me what you make of this. *(She reads.)*
"And after, for pastime,
If June be refulgent
With flowers in completeness
All petals, no prickles
Delicious as trickles
Of wine poured at mass-time —
And choose one indulgent
To redness and sweetness;
Or if, with experience of man and of spider,
June used my June-lighting the strong insect-ridder
To stop the fresh film work — why June will consider."
(Questioningly.) Well?

WILSON *(Enthusiastically):* I call that just lovely, Miss Ba.

ELIZABETH: But do you know what it means?

WILSON: Oh, no, Miss.

ELIZABETH: Does it convey *anything* to your mind?

WILSON: Oh, no, Miss.

ELIZABETH *(With a sigh of relief.):* Thank Heaven for that.

WILSON: But then po'try never does, Miss. Leastways, not real po'try, like what you make.

ELIZABETH: But *I* didn't write that. It's by Mr. Browning.

WILSON: He must be a clever gentleman.

ELIZABETH *(With a laugh):* Oh, yes, he's all that.

WILSON *(Taking FLUSH from basket):* And now, Miss Ba, if you're all nice and comfortable, I'll take Flush out for his airing.

ELIZABETH *(Holding out her arms for the dog, which WILSON gives to her.):* Well, Flush dear, are you going to behave nicely today? I shall ask Wilson for a full report, when she gets home. *(To WILSON.)* Where are you taking him?

WILSON: Well, Miss, being so fine, I thought of a little walk in the Park.

ELIZABETH: Oh, Flush, I'd give almost anything to be going with you instead of Wilson. *(Gives FLUSH back to WILSON. OCTAVIUS is seen walking through the hall. She continues as she sees him at door.)* Occy, dear. *(OCTAVIUS enters.)* What on earth are you doing at home at this time of day? *(WILSON exits, carrying FLUSH.)*

OCTAVIUS: Papa's b-bright idea. Suggested I should take a half-holiday, and help you f-feed and entertain the l-love-birds.

ELIZABETH *(Laughing.):*   But why? Henrietta and Arabel are socially quite competent. So am I.

OCTAVIUS *(Sits on end of sofa.):*   But you labor under the d-disadvantage of being all of the same sex. Papa seems to think that at least one male B-Barrett ought to show up.

ELIZABETH: I see. Occy, there's one thing you don't know, and I want you to be diplomatic. Captain Surtees Cook is calling at the same time as Bella and Mr. Bevan. He's coming to see Henrietta.

OCTAVIUS: Is he, by Jove! And won't the gallant feller rejoice when he finds himself chaperoned f-four times over!

ELIZABETH: I've arranged for Arabel to bring Bella and Mr. Bevan up here to see me. You must come with them.

OCTAVIUS: And why?

ELIZABETH: So that Henrietta may have Captain Cook to herself for a little while.

OCTAVIUS: But does it occur to you, my dear Ba, that we may be doing Henrietta an uncommonly b-bad turn by encouraging this b-budding romance?

ELIZABETH: Yes — but I think we ought to chance that. *(OCTAVIUS looks at her questioningly.)* Occy, when you six boys said good night to me yesterday, a queer thought came into my mind — you weren't alive at all — just automata.

OCTAVIUS: By Jove!

ELIZABETH: Like automata you get up at half-past seven every morning. Like automata you eat your breakfast. Like automata you go to your work. Like automata you return home. You dine like automata. You go to bed like automata.

OCTAVIUS: But, I say —

ELIZABETH: You all seem to me to have cut out of life everything that makes life worth living — excitement — adventure — change — conflict — frivolity — love —

OCTAVIUS: We haven't cut 'em out, my dear. That operation was performed by dear P-Papa.

ELIZABETH: I know, but —

OCTAVIUS: Oh, I admit we're a pretty spineless lot. But what would you? We're none of *us* particularly gifted, and we're all of us wholly dependent on Papa, and must obey and be broken. You're not c-counselling sedition?

ELIZABETH: No — but not resignation. Keep your souls alive. What frightens me is that you may become content with a life which isn't life at all. You're going that way, all of you, except Henrietta.

OCTAVIUS: And what does she get by t-trying to be herself? More kicks than ha'pence.

ELIZABETH: Yes — but being kicked keeps one alive. So don't let us do anything just for the sake of peace and quiet, to hinder her little romance.

OCTAVIUS: All very f-fine, my dear Ba — but what about you?

ELIZABETH: Me?

OCTAVIUS: Yes, you. I don't notice that you make much of a struggle against it. Where did that p-porter finally g-get to, last night?

ELIZABETH *(With a dreary little laugh.):* I am quite out of it. You have your lives before you. My life is over. *(HENRIETTA enters.)*

OCTAVIUS: Rubbish!

HENRIETTA *(As she enters):* Why, Occy, what are you doing here?

OCTAVIUS *(Rising, steps to meet her.):* Papa's notion. He somehow got wind that Surtees Cook was p-prowling round this afternoon, and sent me home to read the f-feller off.

ELIZABETH: Occy!

HENRIETTA *(In breathless consternation):* How did he hear? He couldn't have heard unless you — or Arabel —

ELIZABETH: No, dear. Occy — you idiot!

OCTAVIUS *(Sits in chair. To HENRIETTA.):* Sorry — my little joke, you know!

HENRIETTA *(Hotly):* I hate you!

OCTAVIUS: Quite right, too. I repeat, I'm sorry. You may s-slap me if you like.

HENRIETTA *(Half-mollified):* I've a good mind to.

OCTAVIUS *(Pulls her onto his lap. ELIZABETH resumes reading.):* No, my che-ild, it's like this. His Majesty sent me home to represent His Majesty, at the reception. I don't intend to leave Bella's side, not even when she and her beloved come up here to em-embrace Ba. Meanwhile, you'll amuse Cook j-just as you're amusing me now. *(Kisses her.)* In fact, we may take this as a little rehearsal.

HENRIETTA *(Jumping up.):* Occy! How can you be so vulgar? What's that? *(Runs to window.)* Oh, Ba, they've arrived. And in state. The Bevan family — barouche — powdered footmen and all. *(OCTAVIUS joins her.)* Look at Bella. What a gown — what a bonnet! Lovely! Oh, and Mr. Bevan's whiskers! *(Gestures round her chin.)* Aren't you green with envy, Occy?

OCTAVIUS: Positively verdant.

HENRIETTA *(Pushing OCTAVIUS to door.):* Go and help Arabel receive them. Off with you — quick. I'll wait here till Captain Cook arrives. *(She pushes him off; he exits, leaving door open. HENRIETTA goes back up to window, looks eagerly into street.)* What's the time?

ELIZABETH *(Smiling):* Five minutes past three.

HENRIETTA: *Past* three?

ELIZABETH: Past three!

HENRIETTA: I don't understand — he said three — Ba — today is Thursday, isn't it?

ELIZABETH: Yes, dear.

HENRIETTA *(With relief, turning to window.):* Oh — I wish he were able to come in his uniform. That would take the curl out of Mr. Bevan's whiskers. *(ELIZABETH laughs.)* Oh, there he comes. *(She runs out of room, leaving door open.)*

ELIZABETH: Please shut the door. *(HENRIETTA has gone. ELIZABETH smiles, shrugs, takes up book and starts reading again. After a moment, OCTAVIUS re-enters.)*

OCTAVIUS: Are you ready to receive them? *(Turns, starts to go. Voices of BELLA, ARABEL and BEVAN are heard.)*

ELIZABETH: Yes, quite. *(Calling, as he turns to go.)* Occy! What are they like?

OCTAVIUS *(Turning around.):* Oh, she's a dream of l-loveliness — and he isn't. *(He exits. Short pause, as voices grow nearer; then BELLA HEDLEY flutters in, followed by ARABEL, then HENRY BEVAN, lastly OCTAVIUS.)*

BELLA *(Ecstatically, crossing above chair to ELIZABETH above sofa.):* Cousin Elizabeth!

ELIZABETH *(Extending hand.):* Bella, dear. *(ARABEL follows BELLA. BEVAN crosses to foot of sofa. OCTAVIUS crosses to desk.)*

BELLA: Ba. *(Embraces ELIZABETH.)* Dearest Ba. After all these years! But, oh, my poor, poor Ba, how sadly you've changed! So pale! so fwagile, so etheweal.

ELIZABETH: And you, dear Bella, are even lovelier than you promised to be as a child.

BELLA: Flatterer. *(Kisses ELIZABETH's hand, and still holding it, rises.)* You hear that, Ha'wy? This is my dear, dear Ha'wy. Mr. Bevan, Miss Elizabeth Ba'wett.

BEVAN *(Bowing):* Delighted, Miss Barrett, charmed.

BELLA *(Stretching her free hand to him, he takes it.):* No, no, Ha'wy, you must take her hand. *(Tenderly to ELIZABETH.)* Such a lovely hand. So fwail. So spiwitual.

BEVAN *(Takes ELIZABETH's hand, bows over it.):* And the hand that penned so much that is noble and eloquent. I am honored, Miss Barrett.

ELIZABETH: Thank you. And may I congratulate you — both of you? I hope you will be very happy.

BEVAN: Thank you, Miss Barrett. I am indeed a fortunate man.

BELLA: Dear Ha'wy! Dear Ba!

ELIZABETH: But won't you sit down. *(BELLA sits on couch, ARABEL and BEVAN sit on chairs. OCTAVIUS stands.)*

BELLA: I adore your poems, Ba — especially when dear Ha'wy weads them. He wead me "Lady Gewaldine's Courtship" the day after we became engaged. He weads so beautifully. And he too adores your poems, which ought to please you as he is so dweadfully cwitical.

BEVAN *(Stroking his beard.):* Oh, come, come, my pet.

BELLA: Oh, but, Ha'wy, you are. He doesn't quite approve of even Mr. Alfred Tennyson's poems.

ELIZABETH: Really, Mr. Bevan?

BEVAN: I have nothing against them as poetry. No, indeed. Mr. Tennyson always writes like a gentleman. What grieves me, Miss Barrett, is that his attitude towards sacred matters is all to often an attitude tinged with doubt.

ARABEL: How sad —

BEVAN: Sad indeed, Miss Arabel, and, I grieve to say, a very prevalent attitude among the younger men of today. *(BELLA exchanges glances with OCTAVIUS.)* Of course I am not alluding to Mr. Tennyson when I say this. His work is always reverent, even when expressing doubt. Now, your poems, my dear Miss Barrett, show no touch anywhere of these modern tendencies. There's not a line in one of them that I would disapprove of even dear Bella reading.

ELIZABETH: That's very satisfactory.

BELLA: Dear Ha'wy is so fwightfully earnest.

BEVAN: Oh, come, come, my pet.

OCTAVIUS: I say, Mr. Bevan, you've not yet met my Father, have you?

BEVAN: No, that pleasure is yet to come.

OCTAVIUS: I think you and he would g-get on famously together.

BEVAN: Indeed!

BELLA: Oh, yes. For dear Uncle Edward is fwightfully earnest as well. Mama has often told me so.

ELIZABETH: But now tell me, dear, when is the wedding to be? Or am I being indiscreet?

BEVAN: Not at all, dear Miss Barrett, not at all, we —

BELLA *(To ELIZABETH):* Oh, that weminds me. Where's dear Henwietta? The wedding? Early in August. *(Looks about.)* Where's Henwietta?

OCTAVIUS: At the moment she's downstairs entertaining a friend.

BELLA: Oh, I wanted to ask her — a fwiend? Not that tall gentleman we passed in the hall?

ELIZABETH: Yes, Captain Surtees Cook.

BELLA: Oh, in the Army? How thwilling! I thought his ca'wiage was military. So he's a fwiend of dear Henwietta?

ELIZABETH: Yes. You wanted to ask Henrietta something?

BELLA: Oh, yes. Oh, Ba, I do so want her to be one of my bwidesmaids. *(HENRIETTA enters, is visibly distrait. BELLA rises to meet her, and kisses her, taking both her hands. BEVAN rises, steps back.)* Henwietta darling, I was just saying — oh, you must be one of by bwidesmaids, you simply must.

HENRIETTA: Bridesmaids? Oh, yes — at your wedding. I should love to, Bella. It's sweet of you to ask me. And of course I will, if Papa — but I'm sure he won't mind.

BELLA: Mind? Uncle Edward? Why should he mind? Isn't she funny, Ba? You're only asked to be a bwidesmaid, darling — not a bwide.

HENRIETTA: Yes, I know, but of — it's so hard to explain.

BEVAN *(To ELIZABETH):* Perhaps Mr. Barrett looks on bridesmaids as frivolous irrelevancies at so solemn a sacrament as marriage?

HENRIETTA: No, no, Mr. Bevan, It's not that. It's — it's simply that nothing — nothing at all in this house, must happen without Papa's sanction. *(To BEVAN.)* You know he once owned slaves in Jamaica, and as slavery has been abolished there, he carries it on in England.

BEVAN: Oh, come, now!

HENRIETTA: I'm quite serious — we're all his slaves here.

ARABEL: Henrietta! *(BEVAN and BELLA look embarrassed.)*

HENRIETTA: Well, aren't we? We haven't a soul of our own, not one of us. I tell you, Bella, it's more than likely that he'll refuse to let me be your bridesmaid, for no rhyme or reason — except that he's out of temper.

OCTAVIUS *(Breaking in):* I say, what about t-tea?

ARABEL *(Rising quickly.):* Oh, yes, yes.

HENRIETTA *(Going to window.):* Tea is quite ready. I'm sorry — I — I forgot to tell you.

OCTAVIUS: Good Heavens, let's hurry, or Captain Cook will have swallowed it all.

HENRIETTA: He's gone. *(Standing up at window, her face half averted.)*

BELLA: A wivederci, dearest Ba. *(Kisses her.)* It's been so lovely seeing you. May I come again, soon? And next time I shall want you all to myself — without Ha'wy, I mean.

ELIZABETH: Come whenever you like, dear.

BEVAN: But why must I be excluded?

BELLA *(To BEVAN):* Because I've heaps and heaps to tell dear Ba about a certain big, big man, who might easily gwow conceited if he heard me.

BEVAN: Oh, come, come, my pet. *(BELLA crosses to ARABEL, and they start out. BEVAN bows over ELIZABETH's hand.)* Good-day, dear Miss Barrett.

ELIZABETH: Good-bye. It was nice of you to come and see me.

BEVAN: Not at all. I have long been looking forward to the honor of meeting you. Good-day.

BELLA *(Kisses her hand to ELIZABETH):* Au wevoir, darling.

ELIZABETH: Auf wiedersehen. *(BELLA and ARABEL exit, BEVAN follows.)*

BEVAN *(Turns and bows at door):* Good-day.

ELIZABETH: Good-bye. *(BEVAN exits. OCTAVIUS follows, turns and bows at door in imitation of BEVAN, then exits, closing door. ELIZABETH smiles, glances at HENRIETTA, who stands with averted face at window, then takes her book, starts reading.)*

HENRIETTA *(After pause, vehemently):* Well, why don't you say something?

ELIZABETH *(Coldly.):* What do you want me to say?

HENRIETTA: Nothing. Ba, don't scold me. *(Crosses to her at couch and kneels.)* I know I deserve it — I have been dreadful. But I couldn't help it. I'm so miserable.

ELIZABETH *(Quickly):* Miserable, dear?

HENRIETTA: Yes — and so — so — wildly happy. Surtees has just asked me to marry him.

ELIZABETH: Oh, Henrietta!

HENRIETTA: And of course I accepted him — and said that I couldn't. And I had to tell him that we must never see each other again. When he calls here tomorrow we shall have to —

ELIZABETH: You're not talking sense, child. What really has happened?

HENRIETTA: I don't know — except that we both love each other terribly. Oh, Ba, what *are* we to do? Surtees has only just enough money to keep himself decently. And I haven't a penny of my own. If only I had your four hundred a year, I might defy Papa and leave the house, and marry Surtees tomorrow.

ELIZABETH: And what earthly good is that money to me? I'd give it to you, and how gladly —

HENRIETTA: I know you would, darling. But that's utterly impossible. Think what your life would be like when Papa knew that you had made it possible for me to marry. *(With sudden urgency.)* But dear, is there anything, anything at all to be said for Papa's attitude towards marriage? Can it possibly be wrong to want a man's love desperately, and to long for babies of my own?

ELIZABETH: No. But who am I to answer a question like that? Love and babies are so utterly remote from my life —

HENRIETTA: Yes, I know, dear. You're a woman apart. But it's natural to an ordinary girl like me, and what's natural can't be wrong.

ELIZABETH: No — and yet the holiest men and women renounced these things —

HENRIETTA: I daresay. But I'm not holy — and come to that, neither is Papa — not by any means. *(A knock at door. HENRIETTA rises.)*

ELIZABETH: Come in. *(WILSON enters.)*

WILSON: Mr. Robert Browning has called, Miss.

ELIZABETH *(Breathlessly):* Mr. Browning —

WILSON: Yes, Miss.

HENRIETTA: Then I'd better be off. *(Starts to leave.)*

ELIZABETH: N-no, stay here. I can't see him. I — I don't feel up to it — I —

HENRIETTA: But, Ba, what on earth is the matter? You told me yesterday —

ELIZABETH: I know — I know. But I really don't feel that I can see him now. *(To WILSON.)* Please tell Mr. Browning I am very sorry, but I am not well enough to receive him.

HENRIETTA: But that's not true. You can't send him away like that. *(To WILSON.)* Where is Mr. Browning?

WILSON: I showed him into the library, Miss.

ELIZABETH: But I'd much — much rather not see him —

HENRIETTA: Oh, fudge! You're not a silly schoolgirl. I'll bring him up myself. *(Starts out.)* Mr. Kenyon says he's wonderfully romantic-looking, and quite the dandy. *(Runs out.)*

ELIZABETH: Is my hair tidy?

WILSON: Yes, Miss Ba.

ELIZABETH: Oh, please arrange the couvre-pied. *(WILSON does so.)* Thank you. And, Wilson — no — thank you, that will do.

WILSON: Yes, Miss. *(She goes out, closing door. A pause while ELIZABETH, in strained excitement, awaits the coming of BROWNING. Then HENRIETTA enters.)*

HENRIETTA *(As she enters, inside door):* Mr. Robert Browning. *(BROWNING enters, pausing a few steps inside room. HENRIETTA exits again.)*

BROWNING *(As he steps inside room.):* Miss Barrett?

ELIZABETH *(Stretching out her hand.):* How do you do, Mr. Browning?

BROWNING *(Crossing to sofa, takes her hand in his.):* Dear Miss Barrett — at last! *(Raising her hand to his lips.)* At last.

ELIZABETH *(Still all nerves, and overcome by the ardor and unconventionality of his manner.):* I — I've had to put off the pleasure of meeting you much longer than I wished.

BROWNING *(Still holding her hand.):* Would you ever have received me if I hadn't been so tiresomely insistent?

ELIZABETH: As you know from my letters, I've not been at all well during this winter, and I — *(Realizing her hand is still in his.)* But won't you take off your cape?

BROWNING *(Takes off cape, leaves it on chair, leaving hat and cane on desk.):* Thank you.

ELIZABETH: I — I hope you won't find this room very close, Mr. Browning?

BROWNING: No — no —

ELIZABETH: My Doctor obliges me to live in what I am afraid must be to you a hot-house temperature.

BROWNING *(Facing windows, looking around.):* Wonderful. You may think, Miss Barrett, that this is the first time I've been here. You're quite wrong, you know.

ELIZABETH: But I —

BROWNING: I have seen this room more times than I can remember. It's as familiar to me as my own little study at home. Before I came in, I knew how your books were arranged, just how that tendril of ivy slants across the window-panes — and that bust of Homer is quite an old friend, and has looked down on me before.

ELIZABETH: But, really —

BROWNING: But I could never make out who the other fellow is, on the top of the wardrobe, and —

ELIZABETH *(Smiling, now at her ease.):* Oh, come, Mr. Browning. I know that dear Mr. Kenyon is never tired of talking about his friends, but I can't believe that he described my poor little room to you in detail.

BROWNING *(Moving chair to corner of sofa, and sitting.):* I dragged all the details I possibly could out of him, and my imagination supplied the rest. Directly I had read your brave and lovely verses, I was greedy for anything and everything I could get about you.

ELIZABETH *(Smiling):* You frighten me, Mr. Browning.

BROWNING: Why?

ELIZABETH: Well, you know how Mr. Kenyon's enthusiasm runs away with his tongue. He and I are the dearest of friends. What he told you about me I quite blush to imagine.

BROWNING: You mean, Miss Barrett, about you — you yourself?

ELIZABETH: I feel it would be hopeless for me to try to live up to his description.

BROWNING: He never told me anything about you personally that had the slightest interest for me.

ELIZABETH *(Puzzled):* Oh?

BROWNING: Everything he could give me about your surroundings and the circumstances of your life I snatched at with avidity, but all he said about *you* was quite beside the point, because I knew it already — and better than Mr. Kenyon, old friend of yours though he is.

ELIZABETH: But, Mr. Browning — do my poor writings give me so hopelessly away?

BROWNING: Hopelessly — utterly — entirely — to me. I can't speak for the rest of the world.

ELIZABETH: You frighten me again.

BROWNING: No?

ELIZABETH: But you do. For I'm afraid it would be quite useless my ever trying to play-act with you.

BROWNING: Quite useless.

ELIZABETH *(Smiling.):* I shall always have to be just myself.

BROWNING: Always.

ELIZABETH: And you, too, Mr. Browning.

BROWNING: Always — just myself. But really you know, Miss Barrett, I shan't be able to take much credit for that. Being myself comes to me as easily as breathing. It's play-acting I can't manage — and the hot water I've got into in consequence. If life's to run smoothly we should all be mummers. Well, I can't mum.

ELIZABETH: I can well believe that, now I've met you. But isn't it extraordinary? What you are *writing*, you never do anything else but play-act.

BROWNING: I know —

ELIZABETH: You have never been yourself in any one of your poems. It's always somebody else speaking through you.

BROWNING: Yes, and shall I tell you why? I am a very modest man. *(Quickly.)* I am, really.

ELIZABETH: I didn't question it, Mr. Browning.

BROWNING: So modest I fully realize that if I wrote about myself — my hopes and fears, hates and loves, and the rest of it — my poems would be unutterably dull.

ELIZABETH: Well, Mr. Browning, since we are pledged to nothing but the truth, I shan't contradict that until I know you better.

BROWNING *(Laughing.):* Bravo!

ELIZABETH: Oh, but those poems of yours, with their glad and great-hearted acceptance of life, you can't imagine what they mean to me. Here am I, shut in by four walls — the view of Wimpole Street my only glimpse of the world. And they troop into the room and round my sofa, those wonderful people of yours, out of every age and country, and all so tingling with life. No, you'll never begin to realize how much I owe you.

BROWNING *(With emotion):* You — you really mean that?

ELIZABETH: Why, why, Mr. Browning —

BROWNING: But, of course you do, or you wouldn't say it. And you'll believe me when I tell you that what you have just said makes up to me — oh, a thousand times over for all the cold-shouldering I've had from the public.

ELIZABETH: Oh, it infuriates me. Why can we never know an eagle for an eagle until it has spread its wings and flown away from us for good?

BROWNING *(Lightly.):* Mind you, Miss Barrett, I've an uneasy feeling that my style is largely to blame for my unpopularity.

The Barretts of Wimpole Street

ELIZABETH *(A little too eagerly.):*   Oh, surely not.

BROWNING: Didn't we agree not to play-act with each other?

ELIZABETH *(With a laugh):*   Touché! Well, perhaps there are passages in your work a little invol — well, a little too — too profound for the general reader.

BROWNING: Oh, no, it's not what I say, but how I say it. And yet to me, it's all as simple as the rule of three. And to you?

ELIZABETH: Not quite always. Sometimes there *are* passages — *(She picks up a book.)* I have marked one or two in your "Sordello" which rather puzzled me —

BROWNING: Oh, "Sordello."

ELIZABETH *(Opening book and handing it to him):*   Here, for instance.

BROWNING *(Taking book.):*   Somebody once called it a horror of great darkness. I've done my best to forget it. However — *(He reads passage to himself, smiling. Then the smile fades, he passes his hand over his brow, reads it again. She watches him, covertly smiling. He mutters.)* Extraordinary — but a passage torn from its context — *(Rises, goes to window for more light on the subject, reads passage a third time. ELIZABETH has difficulty in suppressing her amusement. He turns to her with an expression of humorous chagrin.)*

ELIZABETH: Well?

BROWNING: Well, Miss Barrett, when that passage was written only God and Robert Browning understood it. Now, only God understands it. *(She laughs, he joins heartily, crossing to sofa.)* What do you say, shall we lighten this great darkness by pitching it on the fire?

ELIZABETH *(Indignantly.):*   No, indeed. We shall do nothing of the kind. Please give me back the book. *(He does so.)* Such passages are only spots on the sun. I love "Sordello."

BROWNING *(Eagerly):*   You would. Of course you would. And shall I tell you why? Because — because it's such a colossal failure.

ELIZABETH: If by a failure you mean an attempt — yes, you're right. That's just why "Sordello" appeals to my very heart. For I too am always making colossal attempts — and always failing.

BROWNING: Isn't one such failure worth a hundred small successes?

ELIZABETH: Oh, a thousand and more.

BROWNING *(Ardently.):*   You think so, too? But of course I knew that. Miss Barrett, you smiled when I told you that Mr. Kenyon had no need to describe you, because I knew you through and through already. And what you have just said about success and failure proves to me finally how right I was. All Kenyon did was to fill in the background. I had painted the portrait with the true soul of you, ardent and lovely, looking out of it.

ELIZABETH: Ardent and lovely. And you think you know me! *(A bitter smile.)* Oh, Mr. Browning, too often impatient and rebellious!

BROWNING: Well, what of it? I've no love for perfect patience under affliction. My portrait is the portrait of a woman, not of a saint. Who has more right to be impatient and rebellious than you?

ELIZABETH: Did Mr. Kenyon paint my background with a very gloomy brush?

BROWNING: Old Rembrandt would have envied him.

ELIZABETH *(Smilingly. BROWNING sits beside her.):* Poor dear Mr. Kenyon. I assure you, my afflictions worry him a great deal more than they worry me. I suppose he told you that I am a dying woman?

BROWNING: We are all of us — dying.

ELIZABETH: And that my family life was one of unrelieved gloom?

BROWNING: Yes, he hinted at something of the sort.

ELIZABETH: He really shouldn't say such things. Frankly, Mr. Browning, do you find me such a pitiable object?

BROWNING: I find you, as I expected to find you, full of courage and gaiety. And yet, in spite of what you say, I'm not at all sure that Kenyon's colors were too sombre.

ELIZABETH: But —

BROWNING: No — no — listen to me. Those colors are not yet dry. They must be scraped off. The whole background must be repainted. And if only you'll allow it, I must have a hand in that splendid task.

ELIZABETH: But, Mr. Browning —

BROWNING: No, listen, I'll dip my brush into the sunrise, and the sunset, and the rainbow. You say my verses have helped you — they're nothing. It's I — I who am going to help you now. We've come together at last, and I don't intend to let you go again.

ELIZABETH: But —

BROWNING: No, listen to me. Give me your hands. *(Bends forward, takes them.)* I've more life in me than is good for one man. It seethes and races in me. Up to now I've spent a little of that surplus energy in creating imaginary men and women. But I've still so much that I've no use for, but to give. Mayn't I give it to you? Don't you feel new life tingling and prickling up your fingers and arms right into your heart and brain?

ELIZABETH *(Rather frightened):* Oh, please — Mr. Browning, please let go my hands! *(He opens his hands, but she still leaves hers in his open palms for a moment, then withdraws them, and clasping her cheeks, looks at him with wide disturbing eyes.)*

BROWNING *(Softly):* Well?

ELIZABETH *(A little shakily, with forced lightness):* Well — you are really rather an overwhelming person, and in sober truth, I'm —

BROWNING: No, — don't tell me again that you are afraid of me. You're not. It's life you're afraid of — and that shouldn't be.

ELIZABETH: Life?

BROWNING: Yes.

ELIZABETH: Well, when life becomes a series of electric shocks —

BROWNING *(Smiling.):* Was it as bad as all that?

ELIZABETH: Indeed, yes. Do you affect other people in the same way?

BROWNING: They've often told me so.

ELIZABETH *(Lightly):* No wonder I hesitated about meeting you, much as I wanted to. You'll laugh at me, Mr. Browning, but when my maid told me you had arrived, I was so panic-stricken that I all but sent down word that I was too unwell to receive you.

BROWNING: I think I must have been about as nervous as you, at that moment.

ELIZABETH: You, Mr. Browning?

BROWNING: Yes, yes, and I'm anything but a nervous man as a rule. But that moment was the climax of my life — up to now. Miss Barrett, do you remember the first letter I wrote to you?

ELIZABETH: Yes, indeed, it was a wonderful letter.

BROWNING: You may have thought I dashed it off in a fit of white-hot enthusiasm over your poems. I didn't. I weighed every word of every sentence — and of one sentence in particular — this sentence: "I love your books with all my heart, and I love you, too." You remember?

ELIZABETH: Yes — and I thought it charmingly impulsive of you.

BROWNING *(Almost with irritation):* But I tell you there was nothing impulsive about it. That sentence was as deeply felt and as anxiously thought-over as any sentence I've ever written.

ELIZABETH: I hope I may have many readers like you! It's wonderful to think I may have good friends all the world over, whom I have never seen nor heard of.

BROWNING: I am not speaking of friendship — but of love. *(ELIZABETH is about to make a smiling rejoinder.)* No, it's quite useless your trying to put aside the word with a smile and a jest. I said love — and I mean love.

ELIZABETH: But, really, Mr. Browning, I must ask you —

BROWNING: I'm neither mad nor morbidly impressionable — I'm as sane and level-headed as any man alive. Yet all these months since first I read your poems, I've been haunted by you — and today you are the center of my life.

ELIZABETH *(Very gravely):* If I were to take you seriously, Mr. Browning, it would, of course, mean the quick finish of a friendship which promises to be very pleasant to both of us.

BROWNING: Why?

ELIZABETH: You know very well that love, in the sense you apparently use the word, has no place, and can have no place, in my life.

BROWNING: Why?

ELIZABETH: For many reasons — but let this suffice. As I told you before, I am a dying woman.

BROWNING *(Passionately):* I refuse to believe it. For if that were so, God would be callous and I know that He's compassionate — and life would be dark and evil, and I know that it's good. You must never say such a thing again. I forbid you to.

ELIZABETH: Forbid, Mr. Browning?

BROWNING: Yes — forbid. If you forbid me to speak of you as I feel, and I accept your orders, as I must — isn't it only fair that I should be allowed a little forbidding, as well?

ELIZABETH: Yes, but —

BROWNING *(With sudden gaiety):* Dear Miss Barrett, what a splendid beginning to our friendship. We have known each other a bare half hour, and we've talked intimately of art, and life, and death, and love. And we've ordered each other about, and we've almost quarrelled. Could anything be happier and more promising? Well, with your permission, I'm going now. *(Rsing.)* Mr. Kenyon impressed upon me to make my first visit as short as possible, as strangers tire you. Not that I'm a stranger — still I can see that you are tired. When may I call again? *(Puts on cape, crosses to sofa.)*

ELIZABETH *(A little dazed):* I don't quite know —

BROWNING: Will next Wednesday suit you?

ELIZABETH: Yes, I — I think so. But perhaps it would be better —

BROWNING: Next Wednesday, then.

ELIZABETH: But —

BROWNING: At half-past three, again?

ELIZABETH: Yes — but I —

BROWNING *(Bowing over her hand.):* Au revoir, then. *(Kisses hand.)*

ELIZABETH: Good-bye.

BROWNING: Au revoir.

ELIZABETH: Au revoir.

BROWNING: Thank you. *(Turns and exits, closing door. The moment door closes, ELIZABETH sits up and clasps her face with both hands. Then slips off sofa, and unsteadily gets to her feet. With the help of a chair she manages to cross the room to window. Grasping curtains to support herself, she stands looking down into the street after the departing BROWNING. Her face is as alive with excitement and joy as though she were a young girl, as curtain falls.)*

CURTAIN

———————— • ————————

SCENE: The scene is the same, with the following changes. The sofa points down, and everything on it has been made untidy, with books, papers, etc., strewn about. The medicine, glass, spoon, and pitcher have been struck from dressing-table. Flowers placed on desk and on table.

TIME: The time is mid-afternoon.

AT RISE: The room is lighted by the bright light of day. There is discovered the dog, FLUSH, lying on sofa. ELIZABETH, walking with firm tread to window, and back downstage again. DR. CHAMBERS stands by fireplace and DR. FORD-WATERLOW sits by sofa. Both Doctors are intently watching ELIZABETH as she walks.

---•---

WATERLOW *(Standing up as ELIZABETH comes down.):* Once again, if you please. *(ELIZABETH walks downstage and back again with greater assurance than before. He meets her as she comes back.)* My dear Miss Barrett, I congratulate you. Now sit down. *(Indicates sofa. She sits. To CHAMBERS.)* When exactly was it you last called me in for consultation, Chambers? *(Taking her wrist to take pulse.)*

CHAMBERS *(Standing back to fire.):* Three months ago — almost to a day.

WATERLOW: Yes, yes, of course — and your patient was in a very low condition at that time. Well, you've done wonders, Chambers.

CHAMBERS: Oh, mine was just the ordinary spade-work. Honesty compels me to give most of the credit to another.

WATERLOW *(Dropping her wrist):* Eh?

CHAMBERS: The real healer is no one but Miss Barrett herself.

ELIZABETH: But, Doctor —

CHAMBERS: I mean it, my dear — I mean it. Three months ago you seemed more than a little inclined to let life and the world slip through your pretty fingers. Then slowly the change began. Oh, believe me, I was watching you like a lynx. Life and the world became more and more worth grasping. The wish to live is better than a dozen physicians, as I think even my distinguished friend will admit.

WATERLOW: The wish to live — h'm — yes. And you are able to get about and take the air occasionally nowadays?

ELIZABETH: Oh, yes, Doctor. I have visited some of my friends and been for several delightful drives around the Park. The only bother is getting up and down stairs. I'm inclined to lose my head going down, and I'm not yet able to undertake the upward journey.

WATERLOW: Quite so — quite so. Well, now, about the future, Miss Barrett. I fully agree with Dr. Chambers that another winter in London must, if possible, be avoided. If you continue picking up strength, as you are doing, I see no reason against your traveling South by October, say.

ELIZABETH *(With barely controlled eagerness):*   Traveling? South?

WATERLOW: To the Riviera — or better still, to Italy.

ELIZABETH: Italy! Oh, Doctor — do you really mean it?

WATERLOW: Why not? You could travel there by easy stages. I have been given to understand that you have set your heart on Italy, and there are no — er — practical difficulties in the way of your going there?

ELIZABETH: If by practical, you mean financial — none at all. I have my own little income, and —

WATERLOW: Quite so — quite so.

CHAMBERS: I've taken the liberty to tell Dr. Ford-Waterlow of the only real difficulty in the way of your wintering abroad, and he is quite prepared to deal with — him.

WATERLOW: Quite — and drastically!

ELIZABETH: Oh, I am sure that won't be necessary. Papa may not raise any kind of objection. It depends on how he is feeling at the time, and —

WATERLOW: Fiddlesticks, my dear young lady! Mr. Barrett's feelings are neither here nor there. All that matters is his daughter's health and happiness, as I intend to make clear to him. Quite clear!

ELIZABETH: Oh, you mustn't think that Papa isn't kindness and generosity itself. But gentlemen have their moods. Italy! Oh, it's hard to take in even the bare possibility of going there. My promised land, Doctor, which I never thought to see otherwise than in dreams.

WATERLOW: Well, well, let us hope realization won't bring disillusion along with it. A grossly overrated country, to my mind. Nothing but heaps of rubbish, dust, flies, stenches, and beggars. Good-bye, my dear Miss Barrett. *(Takes her hand as she starts to rise.)* No, please don't get up. I'm delighted with your improvements. Delighted. And now for a little talk with your Father. Good-bye.

ELIZABETH: Good-bye, Doctor. *(WATERLOW exits.)*

CHAMBERS *(Who has moved to sofa, patting her shoulder and taking her hand.):*   Good-bye, my dear Miss Elizabeth.

ELIZABETH: Good-bye. *(CHAMBERS exits after WATERLOW, closing door after him. ELIZABETH clasps both her cheeks and whispers.)* Italy — Italy — Italy! *(She picks up FLUSH and talks to him.)* And you're coming with us, too, Flushy. We'll see Rome together — Florence — Venice — Vesuvius — (ARABEL enters, closing door. ELIZABETH puts FLUSH down, jumps to her feet and embraces ARABEL.)* Arabel! It's all but settled, my dear. I'm to go to Italy. He says that I shall be quite fit to travel by October. Rome! Florence! Venice! Vesuvius!! Raphael! Dante! Sordello! Oh, I don't know what I'm saying — I'm quite off my head with excitement.

ARABEL: How wonderful for you! I'm so glad. And you think Papa will consent?

ELIZABETH: But of course he will! The Doctors are putting it before him as strongly as they can. Oh, surely he'll never have the heart to refuse when he realizes all this Italian trip means to me.

ARABEL *(Without conviction.):*   No, dear, no —

ELIZABETH: Have you seen him this afternoon?

ARABEL: Yes.

ELIZABETH *(Quickly, taking ARABEL's hand.):*   What was he like?

ARABEL *(Eagerly):*   Oh, quite sunny! He called me "Puss," and he never does that when he's in one of his moods. And afterwards, when Bella came in, he was really merry.

ELIZABETH: Thank Heaven for that.

ARABEL: Which reminds me, dear — Bella has brought the gown Henrietta is to wear as bridesmaid. They want you to see it. They're trying it on now.

ELIZABETH: Oh, I should love to. *(Pulls bell-rope.)* I need badly some distraction to help me over the suspense of waiting for Papa's decision.

ARABEL *(Standing still):*   Somehow I felt, Ba, that it wasn't altogether wise of you to keep this Italian plan secret from Papa, and then spring it suddenly on him. *(A knock at door.)*

ELIZABETH: Come in. *(WILSON enters.)* Wilson, please tell Miss Hedley and Miss Henrietta I shall be delighted to see them now.

WILSON: Yes, Miss.

ELIZABETH *(Going to pick up FLUSH from sofa.):*   Oh, and, Wilson, take Flush with you. He gets so excited when there are several people in the room. *(Hands FLUSH to WILSON, who exits, closing door. ELIZABETH sits on sofa, ARABEL turns to her.)* It was Dr. Chambers himself who advised me to say nothing to Papa until both Doctors were satisfied that I was absolutely fit to travel. I quite agreed with him at the time — but now — Oh, Arabel — *(ARABEL walks toward her, she takes ARABEL's hands.)* I'm not so sure now! I'm so afraid Papa may think — *(The voices of BELLA and HENRIETTA are heard off.)* Don't say anything about this to them. *(ARABEL nods, sits on sofa beside her.)*

BELLA *(Off):*   May we come in?

ELIZABETH *(Rising. ARABEL also rises.):*   Come in, dear. *(BELLA flutters in, followed by HENRIETTA in bridesmaid's gown.)* Bella, dear! *(ELIZABETH goes to meet BELLA. ARABEL moves behind chair. HENRIETTA comes to desk.)*

BELLA *(Embracing ELIZABETH):*   Darling, darling! Oh, but you weally shouldn't get up to weceive little me.

ARABEL *(Contemplating HENRIETTA):*   How perfectly lovely!

ELIZABETH *(Steps towards HENRIETTA):*   Delicious.

BELLA *(As HENRIETTA turns about to show off gown.):*   Yes, isn't it? Isn't she? I should say. Dear Henrietta will be quite the pwettiest of my bwidesmaids. Indeed I'm afwaid she'll dwaw all eyes from the little bwide. At any wate all the gentlemen's. *(Going to ELIZABETH and taking both her hands.)* But, darling Ba, you weally mustn't stand about like this! *(Leads her to sofa.)*

ELIZABETH: But I'm as well able to stand as anyone nowadays.

BELLA *(As ELIZABETH submits to being led to sofa, where she sits.):*   No, no. One has only to see your dear face, so twanspawent and spiwitual, to know how near you are to Heaven. You always have a look in your eyes, darling, as though you alweady saw the angels.

HENRIETTA: She's looking at me, Bella, and I'm no angel.

BELLA: No, I'm afwaid you're not — but you've vewy, vewy beautiful. And, fancy, Ba, if I hadn't spoken to Uncle Edward myself, I should never have had her for my bwidesmaid.

ELIZABETH: Yes, my dear, you certainly have a way with you.

HENRIETTA: Spoken to Papa. I like that. Why, you sat on his knee and stroked his whiskers.

ARABEL: Henrietta, dear! *(ELIZABETH laughs.)*

BELLA: And why not? Isn't he my Uncle? Besides that, I think he's most fwightfully thwilling. I adore that stern and gloomy type of gentleman. It's so exciting to coax and manage them. And so easy — if you know how! And I weally think I do. What I can't understand is his extwaordinawy attitude towards love and mawwiage, and all that. And didn't he mawwy himself — and what's more, have eleven children? *(Uncomfortable silence, as sisters bow their heads.)* Oh, have I said anything vewy dweadful?

ARABEL: No, dear, but perhaps not quite nice. When God sends us children, it's not for us to inquire how and why.

BELLA: I'm so sorry. I didn't mean to be iwevewent. But I do find dear Uncle Edward's attitude extwaordinawy — and so useless. For in spite of it, and wight under his nose, and all unknown to him, his whole house is litewally seething with womance.

ARABEL: Bella!

HENRIETTA *(Sharply):*   What on earth do you mean?

BELLA: *You* ought to know, darling.

HENRIETTA: I?

BELLA *(Enthusiastically):*   I think Captain Surtees Cook is quite fwightfully thwilling. The way he looks at you, dear — and looks, and looks, and looks. If he ever looked at me like that my knees would twemble, and I'd get the liveliest shivers down my back.

ARABEL *(Rising):*   Really, Bella!

BELLA: And then there's George. *You* may not believe it, but I'm absolutely certain he has a thwilling understanding with your little cousin Lizzie. As for poor Occy — I don't mind telling you in confidence that my dear, dear Ha'wy is fwightfully jealous of him.

ARABEL: Mr. Bevan jealous of Occy! But why?

BELLA: Why indeed? Aren't gentlemen silly?

ELIZABETH *(Laughing):*   What an extraordinary girl you are, Bella.

BELLA: Oh, I'm a fwightfully observant little thing. F'w instance, though you hardly ever mention his name, I know that Mr. Wobert Bwowning comes here to see you at least once evewy week. But at other times he sends you flowers, and he often bwings little cakes for dear Flush. Flush! Oh, wouldn't it be fwightfully intewesting if only dear Flush could speak!

ARABEL: Good gracious — why?

BELLA: You see, dear Flush is the only witness to all that goes on at Ba's weekly tete-a-tete with the handsomest poet in England. He — Flush I mean — ought to know a wonderful lot about poetwy by this time! For when two poets are gathered together, they talk about whymes and whythms all the time. *(To ELIZABETH.)* Or don't they? I'm fwightfully ignowant.

ELIZABETH: Oh, no, my dear. On the contrary, you're "fwightfully" knowing.

BELLA: Me?

HENRIETTA: I hope to goodness you won't chatter any of this outrageous nonsense in front of Papa.

BELLA: But of course I won't bweathe a word of it to Uncle Edward. I'm all on the side of womance, and the path of twue love, and all that.

ARABEL: Bella — I regret to say it, but I think you are one of the few girls I know who would have benefited entirely under Papa's system of upbringing. *(ELIZABETH and HENRIETTA laugh.)*

BELLA: Ooh — what a thwilling thought! He was always fwightfully stwict, wasn't he? Did he whip you when you were naughty? How fwightfully exciting it would be to be whipped by Uncle Edward. *(BARRETT opens door, and enters. The sisters are on the alert.)*

ELIZABETH *(As BARRETT enters, closing door after him.):*   Papa!

BELLA: Oh, Uncle Edward — Uncle dear, if I had been your little girl instead of Papa's, would you have been tewibly severe with me? You wouldn't, would you? Or would you?

BARRETT: Would — wouldn't — wouldn't — would? Are you trying to pose me with some silly riddle?

BELLA: No, no, no! Sit down. *(She pushes him into chair in front of desk.)* It's like this — but why that gloomy fwown, Uncle Edward? *(Passes fingers lightly over his forehead.)* There — there, all gone. *(Sits on his knee.)* Arabel says it would have done me all the good in the world to have been brought up by you. She thinks I'm a spoilt, fwivolous little baggage, and —

ARABEL *(Rising):*   Bella — I never said anything of the sort!

BELLA: I know you didn't, but you *do*. *(To others.)* And *you* do — and *you* do. But *you* don't, Uncle, do you?

ARABEL: Really, Bella —

BARRETT *(Speaking to BELLA, but at the others):*   If my children were as bright and affectionate and open as you are, I should be a much happier man.

BELLA: Oh, you mustn't say such things, or they'll hate me.

BARRETT *(The two are quite withdrawn from and oblivious to the others.):* And you're a distractingly lovely little creature.

BELLA: Anything wrong in that?

BARRETT *(Thickly):* I didn't say so.

BELLA: Then why do you look at me so fiercely — do you want to eat me up?

BARRETT: What's that scent you have on?

BELLA: Scent? Me? *(Coyly.)* Don't you like it?

BARRETT: I abominate scent as a rule — but yours is different.

BELLA: Nice?

BARRETT: It's very delicate and subtle — still, I should prefer you not to use it.

BELLA: Why?

BARRETT: Never mind.

BELLA *(Triumphantly):* I never use scent. I haven't a dwop on me! Oh, Uncle, you're a darling! You've called me bwight and open and affectionate, distwactingly lovely, and fwagwent, all within a few minutes. You may kiss me. *(He kisses her roughly on the mouth twice. Suddenly he pushes her abruptly from his knees, and rises. She looks a trifle scared.)*

BARRETT *(Brusquely):* There, there, child, run away now, I want to speak to Ba. *(To others.)* You can go, too. *(Crosses to window and stands looking out, his back to the room. HENRIETTA moves first, and exits. ARABEL goes out. BELLA exchanges looks with ELIZABETH.)*

BELLA *(In a rather injured voice.):* Good-bye, Uncle.

BARRETT *(Without turning):* Good-bye.

BELLA: Good-bye, Ba. *(With a toss of the head she exits, closing door.)*

ELIZABETH *(As she goes.):* Good-bye, Bella. *(Pause as ELIZABETH looks with nervous expectancy at BARRETT: who still stands at window, his back to the room.)*

BARRETT *(Without turning):* When is the wedding?

ELIZABETH: The wedding? Oh, Bella's. On the twenty-seventh.

BARRETT *(Turning, speaking half to himself):* Good. We are not likely to see much of her 'til then — and afterwards — well, she'll be living in the country most of the year.

ELIZABETH: But I thought you were so fond of her, Papa?

BARRETT *(Sharply):* Fond of her? Why not? Isn't she my niece? — She's a disturbing influence in the house. To see your brothers following her about with their eyes — Faugh! The room is still full of her! I shall be glad when she's gone. But I don't want to talk about Bella. Your Doctors have just left me.

ELIZABETH *(Expectantly):* Yes, Papa —?

BARRETT *(With forced heartiness):*   Their report is excellent. Astonishing. I'm more than gratified — I'm delighted. *(Not looking at her.)* Of course, my poor child, it's unlikely that you will ever be a normal woman. Even Chambers — optimistic fool that he is — was forced to admit that. *(Looking at her.)* By the way, who is this Dr. Ford-Waterlow?

ELIZABETH: I've been told he is one of the cleverest physicians in London.

BARRETT: Really? Well, he needs some amazing qualities to counterbalance his execrable manners. But even this medical phenomenon was unable to account for the sudden improvement in your health. He put it down to Chambers' ministrations — which is, of course, arrant nonsense.

ELIZABETH: Perhaps the wonderful weather we've been having has more to do with it. I always thrive in warmth and sunshine.

BARRETT: Rubbish! Last summer was sweltering, and you have never been worse than then. No — to my mind there is only One whom we have to thank — though this Doctor what's-his-name was pleased to sneer when I mentioned HIM.

ELIZABETH: HIM?

BARRETT: I mean Almighty God. It amazes me, Elizabeth, that you on whom this miracle of recovery has been worked should ascribe it to mere earthly agencies. Haven't I knelt here night after night and implored our all-loving Father to have compassion on His child? It amazes me. It grieves me unspeakably. This is all I have to say for the present. *(He crosses to door.)*

ELIZABETH: Papa. *(BARRETT stops.)*

BARRETT *(Turning):*   Well?

ELIZABETH: Didn't Dr. Ford-Waterlow speak to you about — about next winter?

BARRETT: Dr. Ford-Waterlow talked, if I may say so, a great deal of nonsense. *(He turns to go.)*

ELIZABETH *(Stops him at door.):*   But, Papa —

BARRETT *(Testily, turning.):*   What is it?

ELIZABETH: Didn't he tell you that I should avoid spending next winter in England?

BARRETT: Well?

ELIZABETH: And that he thinks I shall be fit to travel to Italy in October, if you —

BARRETT: So! It's out at last. And how long has this precious plot been hatching, may I ask?

ELIZABETH: It's now several weeks since Dr. Chambers first mentioned Italy as a real possibility.

BARRETT: And do your brothers and sisters know anything of this delightful project?

ELIZABETH: I believe I mentioned it to them.

BARRETT: You believe you mentioned it to them! And Mr. Kenyon, and Mr. Horne, and the Hedleys, and that charlatan Browning — all your friends and relations, in short — you've discussed all your plans with a lot of them, I suppose?

ELIZABETH: Oh, Papa, what does it matter? My only reason —

BARRETT: Matter? Not in the least! It's nothing at all that I alone should be shut out of my favorite daughter's confidence, treated like a cipher, ignored, insulted —

ELIZABETH: Insulted?

BARRETT: Grossly insulted. When that fellow Ford-Waterlow sprung your carefully-prepared mine on me, and I naturally expressed my astonishment and displeasure he became extremely offensive.

ELIZABETH: Believe me, Papa, my one reason for not worrying you with this Italian idea before, was —

BARRETT: The fear that I should nip it in the bud at once. Exactly, I quite understand.

ELIZABETH: But —

BARRETT: No. I beg you to spare me explanations and excuses. The whole miserable business is abundantly clear. I am cut to the heart that *you* — the only one of my children whom I trusted implicitly — should be capable of such underhand conduct.

ELIZABETH: No — no!

BARRETT: If returning health must bring with it such a sad change of character, I shall be driven to wish that you were once more lying helpless on that sofa. There is nothing more to be said. *(He once more turns to door.)*

ELIZABETH *(With dignified and restrained passion, rises and walks toward him. He stops.):* But there is something more to be said, and I must beg you to listen to me, Papa. How many years have I lain here? *(He slowly turns to face her.)* Five? Six? It's hard to remember, as each year has been like ten. And all that time I've had nothing to look forward to, or hope for, but death.

BARRETT *(Completing turn, and crossing to her.):* Death —?

ELIZABETH: Yes, death! I was born with a large capacity for happiness — you remember me as a young girl? And when life brought me little happiness and much pain, I was often impatient for the end.

BARRETT: You shock me! Elizabeth! *(Steps towards her.)*

ELIZABETH: And now this miracle has happened. Day by day I am better able to take and enjoy such good things as everyone has a right to — able to meet my friends — to breathe the open air, and feel the sun, and see grass and flowers growing under the sky. When Dr. Chambers first spoke to me of Italy, I put the idea away from me — it seemed too impossibly wonderful! But as I grew stronger it came over me like a blinding revelation, that Italy wasn't an impossibility at all, that nothing really stood in the way of my going, that I had every right to go.

BARRETT: Right!

ELIZABETH: Yes! Every right! If only I could get your consent. So I set about consulting my friends, meeting all obstacles, settling every detail, so as to have a perfectly arranged plan to put before you, after the Doctors had given you their opinion. In my eagerness I may have acted stupidly, mistakenly, tactlessly. But to call my conduct underhand and deceitful is more than unkind — it's unjust, it's cruel!

BARRETT *(More in sorrow than in anger.):* Self! Self! Self! No thought, no consideration for anyone but yourself, or for anything but *your* pleasure.

ELIZABETH: But, Papa —

BARRETT: Didn't it even once occur to you that all through those long dark, dark months you proposed to enjoy yourself in Italy, your father would be left here utterly alone.

ELIZABETH: Alone?

BARRETT: Utterly alone. Your brothers and sisters might as well be shadows for all the companionship they afford me. And you — oh, my child, don't think that I haven't noticed that even you, now that you are stronger and no longer dependent on me, are slowly drawing away from your father.

ELIZABETH: It's not true.

BARRETT: It is true, and in your heart you know it's true.

ELIZABETH: No!

BARRETT: New life, new interests, new pleasures, new friends — and little by little, I am being pushed into the background. I, who used to be your whole world — I who love you — who love you.

ELIZABETH: But Papa —

BARRETT: No. There is nothing more to be said. You want my consent for this Italian jaunt. I shall neither give it nor withhold it. To give it would be against my conscience, as encouraging selfishness and self-indulgence. To withhold it would be a futile gesture. You are at liberty to do as you wish. And if you go, I hope you will sometimes spare a thought for your father. Think of him at night stealing into this room which once held all he loved. Think of him kneeling alone beside the empty sofa, and imploring the Good Shepherd to — *(A knock at door.)* Eh —?

ELIZABETH *(With a start, her hand to her heart.):* Oh —

BARRETT *(Testily):* Who's that? Come in. *(WILSON enters.)*

WILSON *(A little flustered.):* If you please, Miss, Mr. Browning has called.

BARRETT *(Under his breath.):* That fellow again!

WILSON: I showed Mr. Browning into the drawing-room, Miss, seeing as you were engaged.

ELIZABETH: Wouldn't you like to meet Mr. Browning, Papa?

BARRETT: Certainly not. I should have thought you knew by this time, I never inflict myself on any of my children's friends. *(To WILSON.)* You may show Mr. Browning up.

WILSON: Very good, sir. *(She exits, closing door.)*

BARRETT: Mr. Browning appears to consider this his second home.

ELIZABETH: I have not seen him since last Wednesday.

BARRETT: Indeed. *(He exits, closing door. ELIZABETH rises to await BROWNING's entrance.)*

WILSON *(Opens door and steps inside, announcing.):*   Mr. Browning. *(BROWNING enters and WILSON exits, closing door.)*

BROWNING *(Crossing to her, taking her hands.):*   Oh, but how splendid. This is the fourth time you've received me standing.

ELIZABETH *(Her whole manner has changed, she is now all sparkle and life.):* If ever I receive you from my sofa again, you may put it down to my bad manners and nothing else.

BROWNING: I will, with all my heart, I will. Tell me quickly, I've been dithering with suspense all day? You've seen them? What did they say?

ELIZABETH: Dr. Ford-Waterlow was quite taken out of his grumpy self with astonished delight at my improvement.

BROWNING *(Delightedly.):*   Say that again.

ELIZABETH: Must I? The whole sentence?

BROWNING *(Walking about in enthusiasm. ELIZABETH sits on sofa.):*   I should like to see it in letters of fire burning at me from each of these four walls. This is the best moment I've had since I got your note giving me permission to call on you! How many years ago was that?

ELIZABETH: Three months.

BROWNING: Absurd! We've always been friends. I've known you a lifetime and over! So, he was quite taken out of his grumpy self with astonished delight, was he? *(Sits.)* Splendid! Of course, I never once doubted that you would turn the corner some day. But even I little dreamt recovery would be so rapid. And Italy? Are both Doctors agreed about your wintering there?

ELIZABETH *(With a note of reserve in her voice.):*   Yes.

BROWNING: And when do they think you'll be fit for traveling?

ELIZABETH: The middle of October — unless there's a relapse.

BROWNING: Relapse? There isn't such a word! October! Extraordinary! For you know, October suits my own plans to perfection.

ELIZABETH: *Your* plans?

BROWNING: Don't you remember my telling you that I had thought of wintering in Italy myself? Well, now I have quite decided. You see, I have practically made up my mind to remodel "Sordello." I should never be able to grapple with the task satisfactorily in England. Impossible to get the Italian atmosphere in a land of drizzle and fog. May I call on you often in Italy? Where do you intend to stay? *(ELIZABETH laughs.)* Why are you laughing?

ELIZABETH: In Italy I'm afraid you'll need seven-league boots when you call on me.

BROWNING: What do you mean?

ELIZABETH: I shall be at 50 Wimpole Street next winter.

BROWNING: Here?

ELIZABETH: Yes.

BROWNING: But didn't you tell me that both Doctors were agreed —?

ELIZABETH: Doctors may propose, but the decision rests — elsewhere.

BROWNING: Your Father?

ELIZABETH: Yes.

BROWNING: He has vetoed the plan?

ELIZABETH: No — not exactly. But I am quite sure that he — that it will be impossible for me to go.

BROWNING: But didn't the Doctors make it clear to him that this move of yours may mean all the difference between life and death?

ELIZABETH: I believe Dr. Ford-Waterlow spoke very forcibly.

BROWNING: Then, in Heaven's name —!

ELIZABETH: Oh, it's hard to explain to someone who doesn't know all the circumstances. You see, Papa is very devoted to me, and —

BROWNING: Devoted?

ELIZABETH: He's very devoted to me and depends a great deal on my companionship. He hasn't many points of contact with my brothers and sisters. If I were away for six months, he —

BROWNING *(Visibly restraining himself, rising and going toward her.):* Miss Barrett, may I speak plainly?

ELIZABETH: Oh, do you think you'd better? I know — more or less — how you feel about this. But you see, you don't quite understand all the situation. How should you?

BROWNING: Oh, very well — then I'll say nothing. *(His control suddenly gives way, and his words pour out.)* You tell me I don't understand. You are quite right. I don't. You tell me he is devoted to you. I don't understand a devotion that demands favors as if they were rights, demands duty and respect, and obedience and love, demands all and takes all, and gives nothing in return. I don't understand a devotion that spends itself in petty tyrannies and gross bullying. I don't understand a devotion that grudges you any ray of light and glimpses of happiness, and doesn't even stop at risking your life to gratify its colossal selfishness. Devotion! Give me good, sound, honest hatred, rather than devotion like that!

ELIZABETH: Mr. Browning, I must ask you —

BROWNING: Forgive me, but I won't be silent any longer. Even before I met you, I was aware that sickness wasn't the only shadow in your life. And all these months, even though you never once breathed a syllable of complaint, I felt that other shadow deepening, and I've stood by and looked on, and said nothing. I might find you tired and sick after hateful scenes I could picture only too vividly — and I must pretend to know nothing, see nothing, feel nothing? Well — I've done with pretense from today on. I refuse any longer to let myself be gagged and handcuffed. It's not just your comfort and happiness which are at stake now. It's your very life — and I forbid you to play with your life! And I have the right to forbid you!

ELIZABETH *(Desperately.):*   No — no — no — oh, please don't say any more.

BROWNING *(With compelling ardor.):*   The right — and you won't deny it — you're too utterly candid and true. At our first meeting you forbade me to speak of love — there was nothing more than friendship between us. I obeyed you, but I knew very well — we both knew — that I was to be much more than just your friend. Even before I passed that door, and our eyes first met across the room, I loved you, and I've gone on loving you — and I love you more now than words can tell — and I shall love you to the end and beyond. You know that? You've always known?

ELIZABETH *(Brokenly.):*   Yes — I've always known. And now, for pity's sake — for pity's sake — leave me. *(Rising.)*

BROWNING *(With a firm grasp of both her hands, rises, comes to end of sofa.):* No!

ELIZABETH: Oh, please — please — let me go! Leave me. We must never see each other again.

BROWNING *(Maintaining his grasp.):*   I shall never let you go — I shall never leave you! *(Draws her into his arms.)* Elizabeth — Elizabeth!

ELIZABETH *(Struggling feebly.):*   No — no — Oh, Robert, have mercy on me —

BROWNING: Elizabeth, my darling — *(He kisses her, and at the touch of his lips her arms go round his neck.)*

ELIZABETH: Oh, Robert — I love you — I love you — I love you. *(They kiss again, then she sinks onto sofa. He sits, holding her hands.)*

BROWNING: And yet you ask me to take my marching orders, and go out of your life.

ELIZABETH: Yes, Robert, for what have I to give you? I have so little of all that love asks for. I have no beauty, and no health — and I'm no longer young —

BROWNING: I love you.

ELIZABETH *(With restrained spiritual ecstasy.):*   I should have refused to see you after our first meeting. For I loved you then, though I denied it even to myself. Oh, Robert, I think Eve must have felt as I did when her first dawn broke over Paradise — the terror — the wonder — the glory of it. I had no strength to put up any kind of resistance, except the pitiful pretense of mere friendship. I was paralyzed with happiness that I had never dreamt it was possible to feel. That's my only excuse — and God knows I need one — for not having sent you away from me at once.

BROWNING: I love you.

ELIZABETH: My life had reached its lowest ebb. I was worn out, and hope was dead. Then you came. Robert, do you know what you have done for me? I could have laughed when Dr. Chambers said that I had cured myself by wanting to live. He was right — oh, he was right. I wanted to live — eagerly, desperately, passionately — and all because life meant you — you — *(He leans down to kiss her hands.)* — and the sight of your face, and the sound of your voice, and the touch of your hand. Oh, and so much more than that! Because of you the air once more was sweet to breathe, and all the world was good and green again.

BROWNING *(Rising from kissing her hands.):*   And with those words singing in my ears, I'm to turn my back on you and go?

ELIZABETH: But, Robert, can't you see how impossible —?

BROWNING: I've never yet turned my back on a friend or an enemy. Am I likely to turn it on you?

ELIZABETH: But how is it all to end? What have we to look forward to? And how —?

BROWNING: I love you, and I want you for my wife.

ELIZABETH: Robert, I can't marry you. How can I, when —?

BROWNING: Not today or tomorrow. Not this year, perhaps, or next year. Perhaps not for years to come —

ELIZABETH: I may never be able to marry you.

BROWNING: What then? If you remain to the last beyond my reach I shall die proud and happy in having spent a lifetime fighting to gain the richest prize a man was ever offered.

ELIZABETH: Oh, Robert, put aside your dream of me and look on me as I am. I love you too well to let you waste your manhood pursuing the pale ghost of a woman.

BROWNING: Do you think I'm a boy to be swept off my feet by an impulse, or a sentimental dreamer blind to reality? There's no man alive who sees things clearer than I do, or has his feet more firmly planted on the earth. And I tell you in all soberness that my need of you is as urgent as your need for me. If your weakness asks my strength for support, my abundant strength cries out for your weakness to complete my life and myself.

ELIZABETH *(After pause.):*   Robert, have you thought what your position here would be like if you went on seeing me after today?

BROWNING: Yes.

ELIZABETH: We should have to keep our love secret from everyone lest a whisper of it get to my Father's ears.

BROWNING: I know.

ELIZABETH: If he had the least suspicion that you were more than a friend, the door would be slammed in your face, my letters supervised, and my life made unbearable.

BROWNING: I know.

ELIZABETH: And you, my dear, you're as frank and open as the day. How would you enjoy coming here under false pretenses, and all the subterfuges and intrigues we'd be forced to use?

BROWNING *(Smiling.):* I shall detest it — I shall hate it with all my heart and soul — and I thank God for that.

ELIZABETH: But Robert —

BROWNING: For it's splendid and right that I should suffer some discomfort at least for such a reward as you. The immortal garland was never won without dust and heat.

ELIZABETH *(Bitterly.):* Immortal! Oh, Robert, fading, if not already faded. *(He is about to protest.)* No, don't speak! Don't speak! *(She rises.)* Robert, if we were to say good-bye today, we should have nothing but beautiful memories of each other to last to the end of our lives. We should be unhappy, but there are many kinds of unhappiness. Ours would be the unhappiness of those who have put love away from them for the sake of love. There would be no disillusion in it, or bitterness, or remorse.

BROWNING *(Turning to her, in low tense voice.):* Is it *you* who are speaking?

ELIZABETH: What do you mean?

BROWNING: I don't know you. I thought yours was the courage that dared the uttermost, careless of defeat. Here's life — *life* — offering us the best that life can give, and you dare not grasp at it for fear it will turn to dust in your hands. We're to dream away the rest of our lives in tepid sadness, rather than risk utter disaster for utter happiness. I don't know you — I never thought you were a coward.

ELIZABETH *(Proudly and indignantly.):* A coward? I? *(With a sudden change of voice.)* Yes, I am a coward, Robert, a coward through and through — but it's not for myself that I'm afraid.

BROWNING *(Going swiftly to her and taking her in his arms.):* I know that, my darling.

ELIZABETH: What's another disaster, great or small, to me who have known little but disaster all my life? But you're a fighter, and you were born for victory and triumph. If disaster came to you through me —

BROWNING: Yes, a fighter. But I'm sick of fighting alone. I need a comrade-at-arms to fight beside me.

ELIZABETH: Not one already wounded in the battle?

BROWNING: Wounded, but undefeated, undaunted, unbroken!

ELIZABETH: Yes, but —

BROWNING: Then what finer comrade could a man ask for?

ELIZABETH: But, Robert — *(He bends down and kisses the protests from her lips.)*

BROWNING: No.

ELIZABETH: But, Robert —

BROWNING: No. *(Continues kissing away her protests as curtain falls.)*

CURTAIN

SCENE 1

The scene is the same. The room is the same as in Act 2, with the following few changes. The sofa is now straight. A book has been placed on mantel. The desk has been tidied up. All the flowers have been removed. There are five letters recently received for ELIZABETH on desk.

TIME: The time is late afternoon.

AT RISE: The room is lighted by the light of the late afternoon sun. The stage is empty at rise. When curtain is well up ARABEL, in outdoor clothes and carrying FLUSH, opens door and enters.

ARABEL *(Speaking as she enters.):*   You had really better let Wilson help you up the last few stairs, Ba.

ELIZABETH: No! No, Wilson! I'm quite all right!

ARABEL: But, my dear — *(ELIZABETH, also in outdoor attire, enters, breathless but triumphant. WILSON follows at her heels.)*

ELIZABETH: There! All the way up and without one pause or help of any kind! And I feel splendid — just a little out of breath, that's all. *(Sways a little, and WILSON stretches out her hand to support her.)* No, don't touch me — I'm quite all right. Now, wasn't that a glorious triumph? *(Sits on sofa.)* And you know, Wilson, I got out of the carriage and walked quite two miles in the Park!

WILSON: Lor', Miss! *(ELIZABETH gives bonnet to WILSON: who crosses to put them in wardrobe.)*

ARABEL: Ba, *dear* —!

ELIZABETH: Well, one mile then. Anyhow, that's what I'm going to tell Dr. Chambers.

ARABEL: Really, Ba —

ELIZABETH: Oh, my dear, Flush has muddied your gown disgracefully. *(To FLUSH.)* What a filthy state you're in, Flushy! Wilson, you had better take him and get Jenny to bathe him. He's not been properly washed for ages.

WILSON *(Taking FLUSH from ARABEL.):*   Very good, Miss. *(WILSON exits, carrying FLUSH.)*

ELIZABETH *(Pointing to letters on desk.):*   Oh, the post has come. Please give me those letters, dear?

ARABEL *(Crosses to desk and returns, handing her letters.):* Why, that's Mr. Browning's handwriting! I'm sorry, I couldn't help seeing it. But aren't you expecting him this afternoon?

ELIZABETH: Yes — *(Opens letter and reads it with a smile, throws envelope in fire, and stops at corner of sofa.)* Yes, dear, he should be here very soon now. This was just to wish me good night.

ARABEL: To wish you good night?

ELIZABETH: Yes, you see it was written yesterday evening.

ARABEL: Oh!

ELIZABETH *(Running through other letters.):* Mr. Hayden — Miss Martineau — Mr. Horne — *(With a sharp change in her voice.)* Oh! This is from Papa —

ARABEL *(Anxiously):* From Papa? But he's returning today.

ELIZABETH *(Opening letter.):* Perhaps he's been detained.

ARABEL *(Hopefully.):* Oh, do you think so?

ELIZABETH *(Quickly scanning letter, then in consternation.):* Oh! Oh — Arabel —!

ARABEL: What is it, my dear?

ELIZABETH: We're leaving.

ARABEL: Leaving?

ELIZABETH: Yes — leaving this house. Leaving London. Listen — *(A knock at door, and HENRIETTA's voice is heard.)*

HENRIETTA: May I come in, Ba?

ELIZABETH: Come in, dear. *(In a hurried whisper to ARABEL.)* Don't speak of this yet. *(HENRIETTA enters, leaving door open.)*

HENRIETTA *(In great excitement.):* Oh, Ba, you must see him at once! You positively must!

ELIZABETH: See *him?*

HENRIETTA: He's in his full regimentals! He's just been to St. James to receive — or whatever you call it — his adjutancy or something from Queen Victoria herself. He's wonderful! He's gorgeous! May I bring him up here for you to look at?

ELIZABETH: But —

HENRIETTA: Papa need never know. *(ELIZABETH sits on sofa.)* Oh, Ba, do let me! You've never seen him yet — it's high time you met — and you couldn't see him to better advantage than now. I'm talking of Captain Cook, you know.

ELIZABETH: Yes, so I gathered. But I can't see him now, dear, as I'm expecting Mr. Browning any minute.

HENRIETTA *(Crestfallen but resigned.):* Oh — then of course it's impossible. But I tell you what, Ba! I'll try to keep him until Mr. Browning goes. I don't think he'll mind. He likes sitting and staring at me. We can both stare at each other. He's well worth staring at today. You can keep your poet here as long as you like. *(Exits, closing door.)*

ELIZABETH *(With a short laugh ending in a sigh, staring after her.):*   Yes, she had best make the most of her soldier while she can, poor darling. *(She takes up BARRETT's letter.)*

ARABEL: Oh, Ba — tell me quickly —

ELIZABETH *(Taking up letter, reading.):*   He writes from Dorking: "This is to let you know that we shall be leaving London on Monday the twenty-second of this month. I have taken a furnished house at Bookham, in Surrey, some twenty miles from London, and six miles from Leatherhead, the nearest railway station. Whether we shall eventually make it our permanent home, I have not yet decided. At any rate we shall spend the winter there. You will benefit by the country air, and the complete seclusion of your new surroundings. I have felt for some time now that your present feverish restless mode of life in London will, if continued, affect you harmfully, both physically and morally. I am writing this letter so that you may inform your brothers and sisters of my decision, and tell them that I decline absolutely to discuss it when I return home tomorrow." That's today. — "The matter is finally settled, and you and they will make such preparations as are needful for the move."

ARABEL: Oh, Ba —

ELIZABETH *(Bitterly.):*   That's not quite all. He finishes up with a characteristic touch of humor.

ARABEL: Humor?

ELIZABETH: Yes. He signs himself, "Your loving Papa."

ARABEL: The twenty-second. That gives us barely a fortnight longer here.

ELIZABETH *(Walking to fireplace, where she crumples and throws letter into grate.):*   My "feverishly restless mode of life"! A few drives — a few calls on my friends — a few visitors! I wonder he doesn't describe me as a recklessly dissipated woman! He made my going to Italy impossible and now I am to be cut off from any little pleasures I have begun to find here. *(Drops into chair.)*

ARABEL: I know, dear, I understand and I'm dreadfully sorry for you. The change won't hit me so hard. My only ties in London are my Mission work and district visiting. But you and Henrietta —

ELIZABETH: Well?

ARABEL *(With sudden earnestness.):*   Oh, Ba, don't be angry with me. We all pretend to be ignorant of each others' affairs in this house — except poor Henrietta's. It's safer so. And yet we know — we all know — that you and Mr. Browning —

ELIZABETH: Well —?

ARABEL: Oh, Ba, one has only to look at your face when you're expecting him — and again after he has left you —

ELIZABETH *(Proudly.):*   I love him and he loves me. What of it? Haven't I as much right to love and be loved as any other woman?

ARABEL: Oh, yes dear — but how is it all to end? As long as Papa's alive none of us will ever be able to marry with his consent — and to marry without it is unthinkable. And in your case it isn't only a question of Papa's consent. Of course it's — it's wonderful how much stronger and better you are. You walked upstairs splendidly just now — but — but —

ELIZABETH: But even if I can manage to walk up a few steps, it doesn't mean that I shall ever be fit to marry — is that what you're trying to say?

ARABEL: Oh, Ba, darling, it's because I love you so dearly, and don't want you to suffer, that I'm forcing myself to speak. I know very little about gentlemen — except that they all want to marry the ladies they fall in love with. I don't know Mr. Browning at all — but even great poets want to settle down in time, and have a home — of their own — and a wife — and little ones. It would be so dreadful, if —

ELIZABETH *(Springing up, crosses to window.):* Oh, be quiet! Be quiet! Do you suppose I haven't thought of all that a thousand times already? *(She turns to window and looks out.)*

ARABEL: I am sorry — I — I didn't mean to interfere. *(Rising.)* All I want is to save you any — *(Notices that ELIZABETH, her face transformed with joy, is no longer listening, but is waving her hand to someone in the street.)* Oh —! *(She crosses and exits quietly, closing door softly, unnoticed by ELIZABETH.)*

ELIZABETH *(Turning.):* Mr. Browning has just — *(She realizes the empty room.)* Oh —! *(Her eyes fall on crumpled letter in grate, she picks it out, smooths it, and puts it on mantelpiece, her face emptied of joy. Knock at door. She crosses.)* Come in. *(BROWNING enters. They look at each other in silence for a second.)*

BROWNING *(Crosses to her, takes her in his arms.):* My love!

ELIZABETH: Oh, Robert! *(They kiss.)*

BROWNING *(Holding her at arms' length.):* You look tired, sweetheart. What have you been doing today?

ELIZABETH *(With forced lightness.):* I went for a drive and a walk in the Park. And then I ran all the way upstairs without help, and without one stop —

BROWNING: Oh, but you know! Of course, dearest, it's a splendid feat and I'm proud of you! Come and sit down. *(Points to chair, she sits, he stands, facing her.)* Now, don't you think you're being a trifle too ambitious?

ELIZABETH *(Looking aside.):* I don't think so — I'm feeling wonderfully well.

BROWNING: Look at me. *(She does so.)* What's the matter, Ba?

ELIZABETH *(Looking away.):* Nothing —

BROWNING: Has your Father returned?

ELIZABETH: No — we expect him today.

BROWNING: Those talking eyes of yours give you hopelessly away. Something has gone wrong. What is it? You must tell me.

ELIZABETH: Read that letter on the mantelpiece, Robert.

BROWNING *(Crossing to mantelpiece, taking BARRETT's letter.):*   From your Father?

ELIZABETH: Yes. *(He reads letter to himself, then looks at her, a peculiar smile on his face.)* Well?

BROWNING *(Still smiling.):*   I think, by the look of it, you crumpled up this letter furiously in your hand — and I'm quite sure you pitched it into the grate.

ELIZABETH: Yes, I did.

BROWNING *(Replacing letter on mantel, crossing to her.):*   Why?

ELIZABETH: Oh, Robert, don't you see what this means to us?

BROWNING: Yes — and perhaps a great deal better than you do.

ELIZABETH: Better than I? Oh, you mustn't deceive yourself. You don't know Papa as I do. He's grown jealous of my life here, my pleasures and my friends, and I'm slowly and surely to be parted from them. Oh, Robert, it will soon be made impossible for me to see you at all.

BROWNING: This precious letter may mean all that. But it means a great deal more than you haven't as yet been able to grasp.

ELIZABETH: A great deal more —?

BROWNING: It means that you will be in Italy before the month is out.

ELIZABETH *(In a whisper.):*   Italy?

BROWNING: Yes, and with me. It means that we must be married at once.

ELIZABETH: Do you know what you are saying?

BROWNING: Yes, I know what I'm saying — and I repeat it. We must be married at once! My darling, listen to me — *(He is about to take her hands.)*

ELIZABETH: No! Don't touch me! What you say is madness. I can't marry you. I can never marry you.

BROWNING: You can and you shall! You'll marry me if I have to carry you out of this house and up to the altar. Do you seriously imagine I'm going to allow myself to be elbowed out of your life, now? And just to satisfy the selfish jealousy of a man whom I no longer believe to be sane? You ought to know me better by this time.

ELIZABETH *(Quickly breaking in.):*   Oh, Robert, it's not only Papa who stands between us. It's I — it's I —

BROWNING: We've been into that a hundred times already, and —

ELIZABETH: Yes — and now we shall go into it once again, and frankly, and for the last time. Robert, it's no use deceiving ourselves. However much stronger I become, I shall always remain an invalid. You tell me that you want me, sick or well. And it's wonderful of you to say this. But I — Robert, I'm not generous enough — I'm too proud, if you like. As your wife I should be haunted by the thoughts of all the glories you would have enjoyed but for me — freedom — adventure — and passionate love I could never really satisfy.

BROWNING: Oh, no, listen —

ELIZABETH: Oh, Robert, I should be haunted by the ghosts of your unborn children. When I read that letter my world seemed to fall to pieces. But now I thank God that it came while we're still free, and have the strength to say good-bye.

BROWNING *(Matter-of-fact.):*   On the whole I think this will be our best plan of campaign. The family leave here on the twenty-second. So we have barely a fortnight to get everything done in. You told me last week that Mr. Hedley had invited your sisters to picnic in Richmond Park next Saturday. So the house will be conveniently empty. We'll meet at Mary-le-Bone Church, and be married quietly some time in the morning. I'll see about the license and interview the Vicar at once.

ELIZABETH *(Who has been staring at him in bewilderment.):*   Robert —

BROWNING: It would be madness to leave England on the same day. You'll want all the rest and quiet you can get before the journey. So after the ceremony I think you had better come back here and take things easily for a week or two. You'll have six days if we leave here on Saturday week. Now — *(Takes paper from pocket.)*

ELIZABETH: Oh, stop! I can't listen to you!

BROWNING *(Consulting paper.):*   For some time now I've kept careful note of the sailings from Southampton in case of just such an emergency as this. The Packet leaves the Royal Pier on Saturday at nine o'clock. We must catch the five o'clock express at Vauxhall. *(Rises.)* It arrives at Southampton at eight.

ELIZABETH *(Laughs wildly, changing to sobs.):*   Oh —! And I always thought that Papa was the most overbearing man in the world —

BROWNING *(Kneeling and smiling.):*   And yet you've known me for some time now.

ELIZABETH: But I mustn't give way, Robert, I daren't.

BROWNING: There's one other thing, my darling, of the utmost importance, that we must settle at once. You can't possibly travel without a maid. You tell me Wilson is entirely devoted to you. Do you think she will be willing to come abroad with us?

ELIZABETH *(After a pause, in a low voice.):*   Robert — have you ever thought that my strength may break down on the journey?

BROWNING: Yes.

ELIZABETH: Suppose I were to die on your hands?

BROWNING *(Quietly.):*   Are you afraid, Ba?

ELIZABETH *(Proudly, indignantly.):*   Afraid? I? You know that I am not afraid. You know that I would sooner die with you beside me, than live a hundred lives without you. But how would *you* feel if I were to die like that? And what would the world say of you?

BROWNING *(Quietly.):*   I should be branded as little less than a murderer, and what I should feel I leave you to imagine —

ELIZABETH: And yet you ask me to come with you?

BROWNING: Yes. I am prepared to risk your life and much more than mine, to get you out of this dreadful house into the sunshine, and to have you for my wife.

ELIZABETH: You love me like that?

BROWNING: I love you like that. *(A long pause. ELIZABETH sits motionless staring in front of her.)*

ELIZABETH: Robert — give me a little time?

BROWNING: Time is short, my dear.

ELIZABETH *(Rising.):*   Yes, I know. But I must have a little time. I can't decide now. I daren't. *(BROWNING rises.)* Give me a few hours. Before I sleep tonight, I'll write and tell you my decision. Please, Robert?

BROWNING *(Following after ELIZABETH.):*   You promise me that?

ELIZABETH: I promise.

BROWNING: Very well.

ELIZABETH: Thank you.

BROWNING: Shall I go now?

ELIZABETH: Please — *(He kisses her hand, goes straight out, closing door. ELIZABETH stands motionless, staring at door. A slight pause, then a knock at door, another pause then a louder knock. ELIZABETH starts from her reverie.)* Come in. *(HENRIETTA enters.)*

HENRIETTA: I saw Mr. Browning going down the stairs. May I bring him in?

ELIZABETH: Him?

HENRIETTA: He's standing on the landing outside. Wake up, Ba! I'm talking of Surtees.

ELIZABETH: Won't some other time do as well?

HENRIETTA: No — no! I told you he was in uniform. You promised to see him, Ba.

ELIZABETH *(With a sigh.):*   Very well, dear —

HENRIETTA *(Runs to door, speaking off into passage.):*   Come in, Surtees. *(CAPT. SURTEES COOK, arrayed in regimentals, and with his headgear under his arm, enters.)* Captain Surtees Cook, Ba — my sister, Elizabeth.

COOK *(Bowing stiffly.):*   Your servant, Miss Barrett.

ELIZABETH: How do you do. *(She sits on sofa.)*

COOK *(Crossing to her, taking her hand and bowing over it.):*   Greatly honored, upon my word I am, Miss Barrett. Understand not everyone received here.

HENRIETTA: No, indeed, Surtees! With the exception of the family very few gentlemen have ever been allowed in Ba's room.

COOK: Twice honored in one day, ye know. First by Her Majesty, now by you, Miss Barrett. Can't think what I've done to deserve it.

ELIZABETH: Oh, I had forgotten! You've just come from the Palace! I have never seen the Queen. What is she like?

COOK: Very little lady, Ma'am, but royal, every inch of her.

HENRIETTA: Surtees, you haven't got your sword on!

COOK: Not etiquette, as I told you, to wear it indoors.

HENRIETTA: Oh, bother etiquette! I wanted Ba to see you in full war paint. Where did you leave it?

COOK: In the hall.

HENRIETTA: I'll fetch it. *(Runs to door.)*

COOK *(Following.):* No, but really — Miss Barrett doesn't want —

ELIZABETH: But indeed I do, Captain Cook. I don't think I've ever seen an officer in — full war paint before.

COOK *(After short pause, steps to her.):* Indeed? Er — Miss Barrett —

ELIZABETH *(Encouragingly.):* Yes, Captain Cook?

COOK: I say, Miss Barrett —

ELIZABETH: You want to tell me something about Henrietta?

COOK *(Eagerly.):* Just so, Miss Barrett, just so. Exactly. You know, Miss Barrett, you know — *(He is unable to go on.)*

ELIZABETH *(Very kindly.):* Yes, Captain Cook, I know. And though I'm powerless to help, believe me you have my heartfelt sympathy. *(She gives him her hand.)*

COOK *(As he takes her hand.):* Thank you. Thank you. More than I deserve. Than you, Miss Barrett. Never was such a girl, y'know — Henrietta, I mean. Dunno what I've done to deserve it.

HENRIETTA *(Re-enters with sword, closing door.):* Oh, yes, I thought he'd seize the opportunity to tell you something while I was out of the room. Did he really manage to get it out?

ELIZABETH *(Smiling.):* Well, not quite. Did you, Captain Cook?

COOK: Well — ah — y'know — still, like most ladies — quick in the uptake.

ELIZABETH: Yes, I understand. My dear, how I wish I could do something for you both!

HENRIETTA: Well, you can't — nobody can. Surtees wants to ask Papa — for my hand and all that — quite like the conventional suitor. I can't get it into his poor old head that such things simply are not possible at 50 Wimpole Street. *(COOK sits.)*

ELIZABETH *(Earnestly.):* Oh, believe me, Captain Cook, it would be more than useless.

COOK: Quite aware that I'm not much of a match, Miss Barrett. Poor man, y'know. Still, decent family and all that. Should be more than willing, if necessary to throw soldiering and take to some money-making business, but —

HENRIETTA: And a fine mess you'd make of it, my poor dear!

COOK: Well, I'm not so sure about that. Admit, of course, that soldiering's my special job. Haven't the brain for much else, I'm afraid. Still, you never know what a fellah can't do with a prize like Henrietta to reward his efforts.

HENRIETTA: Well, anyhow, you're not to speak to papa, and I forbid you to give up soldiering. Now that I've seen you in your glory, do you suppose I should ever take you without your uniform? *(Rises and crosses to him.)* Get up. I want to buckle on your sword. *(She kneels.)*

COOK: Aw, I say — *(Rises, smiling rather sheepishly.)*

HENRIETTA *(Starting to fasten on sword.):* Ba thinks poets are the flower of manhood — a certain poet, at any rate. I mean to show her that she's mistaken —

COOK: I say, you've got it wrong. Sword hangs from the left hip, y'know.

HENRIETTA: Why?

COOK: Well — *(Door opens and BARRETT enters, taking in scene with a look of amazement, his face hardening. HENRIETTA rises; both girls stare in consternation. COOK stands rigid.)*

ELIZABETH: Papa — you're — you're home earlier than I expected, Papa.

BARRETT *(Slowly and deliberately closing door.):* I don't think I have the privilege of this gentleman's acquaintance.

HENRIETTA: Captain Cook, may I introduce my Father? Papa — Captain Surtees Cook.

COOK: Your servant, Sir. *(Both men bow stiffly.)*

HENRIETTA: Captain Cook is a great friend of George and Occy's.

BARRETT: Indeed? *(To COOK.)* My sons are very rarely at home at this time of day.

COOK: Fact is — just passing the house — thought I'd look in on the off chance, y'know, sir — finding one of them in, and all that —

BARRETT: I see.

ELIZABETH *(Breaking a pause.):* Captain Cook has just come from Buckingham Palace and Henrietta thought I should like to see him in all the splendor of his regimentals.

BARRETT: Indeed. *(Takes out his watch.)*

COOK: Nothing much to look at, of course — but ladies like a bit of color, and — er — m-m — By Jove, must be getting late.

BARRETT: It's nineteen and a half minutes past five.

COOK: By Jove! High time I were moving — Good-bye, Miss Barrett.

ELIZABETH *(Giving him her hand.):* Good-bye, Captain Cook. *(BARRETT crosses to door and holds it open.)*

COOK: Good-bye, Miss Henrietta.

HENRIETTA: I'll see you out. *(COOK moves to door, followed by HENRIETTA.)*

COOK *(To BARRETT.):* Your servant, sir. *(BARRETT returns his bow in silence. COOK exits and HENRIETTA is about to follow. BARRETT stays her with a gesture.)*

HENRIETTA: I am seeing Captain Cook to the door.

BARRETT: The servant will attend to that. *(He closes door in silence, crosses to fireplace, stands with his back to it, speaking straight before him.)* Your list of gentlemen visitors appears to be lengthening, Elizabeth.

ELIZABETH: This is the first time I have had the pleasure of meeting Captain Cook.

BARRETT *(Turning.):* Indeed. But I infer from what I saw as I came into the room, that Henrietta's acquaintance is of somewhat longer standing? Or am I *mistaken?*

HENRIETTA: I have known Captain Cook for some time now.

BARRETT: Ah! And since when it has been your custom to buckle on his accoutrements?

HENRIETTA: I have never seen him in uniform before.

BARRETT: And I think it improbable that you will see him in uniform, or in mufti, very frequently in the future.

HENRIETTA *(In a strained voice.):* Why?

BARRETT *(To ELIZABETH.):* You received my letter?

ELIZABETH: Yes, Papa.

BARRETT: What has just happened fully confirms me in the wisdom of my decision. This house is fast becoming a rendezvous for half London. I have neither time nor inclination to find out whether all the persons visiting here are desirable acquaintances for my children. Fortunately our new home is so far from town that your London friends are not likely to trouble us — at least during the winter.

HENRIETTA *(Blankly.):* Our new home?

BARRETT *(To ELIZABETH.):* You have not told your sisters?

ELIZABETH: Arabel knows.

HENRIETTA: *I* don't understand. Are we — are we leaving Wimpole Street?

BARRETT *(Without looking at HENRIETTA.):* I have taken a house at Bookham, in Surrey, and we move in on the twenty-second.

HENRIETTA: Why?

BARRETT: I am not in the habit of accounting for my actions to anyone — least of all to my children.

HENRIETTA: But one thing I have a right to ask you, Papa. If Captain Cook is to be forbidden to visit us, is it because you found him here in Ba's room, and saw me fastening on his sword?

BARRETT: I understood you to say that Captain Cook was George's friend, and Occy's?

HENRIETTA: Yes, and my friend, too.

BARRETT: Ah!!

HENRIETTA: Yes, and since it was I who suggested his seeing Ba, and I who asked him to show me how to buckle on his sword, it's unjust to penalize him for —

ELIZABETH *(Sharply.):* Henrietta —

BARRETT *(In a sharp low voice, advancing slowly toward HENRIETTA.):* Come here.

HENRIETTA *(Takes a few steps towards him, and says somewhat breathlessly.):* Yes, Papa?

BARRETT *(Regards her steadily, and points to the floor at his feet.):* Come here. *(She goes right up to him, breathing quickly and fearfully. He keeps his eyes on her face, then in a low ominous voice.)* What is this fellow to you?

HENRIETTA: I — I've told you — he's a friend of ours.

BARRETT: What is he to *you*?

HENRIETTA: A — a friend.

BARRETT: Is that all?

HENRIETTA *(In a whisper.):* Yes.

BARRETT *(Suddenly grasping her wrist, his voice like the crack of a whip.):* You liar!

ELIZABETH *(Sharply.):* Papa!

HENRIETTA *(Gaspingly.):* Let me go!

BARRETT *(Tightening his grip.):* What's this man to you? Answer me! *(She tries to free herself and cries out.)* Answer me!

HENRIETTA *(Wildly.):* Oh, Papa, — please —

BARRETT: Answer me!

HENRIETTA *(Trying to resist.):* Oh, don't — don't —

BARRETT: Answer me!

HENRIETTA *(In a strangled voice.):* He's — he's — Oh, Papa, I love him.

BARRETT *(Between his teeth, seizing her other wrist, forcing her to her knees.):* And you — you — you — *(She gives a cry of pain.)*

ELIZABETH *(Rising from sofa, crosses to BARRETT, seizing his arm.):* Let her go, Papa! I won't have it! Let her go, at once! *(He flings HENRIETTA off, and she collapses in a heap on floor, her face buried in her hands, sobbing.)*

BARRETT *(Turning to ELIZABETH.):* And you — you knew of this filthiness?

ELIZABETH: I've known for some time that Henrietta loved Captain Cook, and I've given her all my sympathy.

BARRETT: You dare to tell me —

ELIZABETH: Yes — and I would have given her all my help as well, if I had had it to give.

BARRETT: I'll deal with you later. *(To HENRIETTA.)* Get up.

HENRIETTA *(Suddenly clasping his knees, in a voice of passionate entreaty):* Oh, Papa, please listen to me — please! I — I'm not a bad girl — I swear to you I'm not. I know I've deceived you — and I'm sorry. I'm sorry — but I couldn't help it. I — I love him — and if you'd known, you'd have turned him from the house. Oh, can't you understand — won't you try to understand? He's a good man — and it can't be wrong to love him. Other women love — why must I be forbidden? I want love. Remember — remember how you loved Mama, and how she loved you — and — you'll understand and pity me —

BARRETT *(Inexorably.):* Get up!

HENRIETTA *(Drops to floor again from his knees. ELIZABETH sits on sofa.):* Have pity on me, Papa.

BARRETT: Get up. *(She brokenly rises.)* Sit there. *(He points to chair. She sits, he crosses to her.)* How long has this been going on? *(No answer.)* Do you hear me? How long have you been carrying on with this fellow?

HENRIETTA: I — I've known him a little over a year.

BARRETT: And you've been with him often?

HENRIETTA: Yes.

BARRETT: Alone?

HENRIETTA: Yes.

BARRETT: Where?

HENRIETTA: We — I — I've met him in the Park, and — and —

BARRETT: And — here?

HENRIETTA: Yes.

BARRETT: Here! And alone? *(HENRIETTA is silent.)* Have you met him in this house alone?

HENRIETTA: Yes.

BARRETT: So! Furtive unchastity under my roof. *(Turning to ELIZABETH.)* And abetted by one whom I believed to be wholly chaste and good —

HENRIETTA: No — no.

ELIZABETH *(Fiercely.):*   How dare you, Papa!

BARRETT: Silence! *(To HENRIETTA.)* Now attend to me. Something like this happened a year or two ago, and I thought I had crushed the devil in you, then. I was wrong. It needed sterner measures than I had the courage to use. But now, unless I have your solemn word that you will neither see nor have any communication with this man again, you leave this house at once, as you are, with nothing but the clothes you have on. In which case you will be your own mistress and can go to perdition any way you please. But of this you may be certain. Once outside my doors you will never again be admitted under any pretext whatever, so long as I live. I think by this time you have learnt that it's not my habit to make idle threats, and that I never go back on my word. Very well. You have your choice. Take it.

HENRIETTA *(After an agonized mental struggle.):*   Is it nothing to you that I — that I shall hate you for this to the end of my life?

BARRETT: Less than nothing.

HENRIETTA: But — but I must let Captain Cook know that —

BARRETT: No. I will deal with Captain Cook.

HENRIETTA *(Desperately, dropping her head in her hands.):*   But, Papa —

BARRETT: Will you give me your word that you will neither see nor have any communication with this man again?

HENRIETTA *(After a pause, in a choked voice.):*   I — I have no choice —

BARRETT: Give me your Bible, Elizabeth.

ELIZABETH: Why?

BARRETT: I am not prepared to accept your sister's bare promise, but I think even she would hesitate to break an oath made with her hand resting on the Word of God. Give me your Bible.

ELIZABETH: No. My Bible belonged to Mama. I can't have it used for such a purpose.

BARRETT: Give me your Bible!

ELIZABETH: No.

BARRETT: You refuse?

ELIZABETH: Yes. *(Without a word, BARRETT crosses and pulls bellrope, then stands tapping his fingers on mantel. A pause. No one speaks or moves, then WILSON enters.)*

BARRETT: I want you to go to my bedroom and fetch my Bible. *(WILSON starts to go, he stops her.)* Are your hands clean?

WILSON *(Bewildered, looks at her hands.):*   My hands, sir?

BARRETT: Are they clean?

WILSON *(With a touch of asperity.):*   Yes, sir. I've just been helping to bathe Flush.

BARRETT: You will find the Bible on the table beside my bed.

WILSON: Very good, sir. *(She turns; exits. All are silent and motionless till she returns. After a moment she re-enters with Bible.)*

BARRETT *(Pointing to desk.):*   Place it on the table. *(WILSON does so, turns and exits. BARRETT crosses to desk. To HENRIETTA.)* Stand up! *(HENRIETTA rises and goes to desk.)* Place your hand upon the book. *(She does so.)* Repeat after me: "I give my solemn word that I will neither see, nor have any communication with Captain Cook again."

HENRIETTA *(In a toneless voice.):*   "I give you my solemn word that I will neither see, nor have any communication with Captain Cook again."

BARRETT: You will now go to your room and remain there until you have my permission to leave it. *(Without a word, but with head held high, HENRIETTA goes out. BARRETT continues after a pause.)* Have you anything to say to me, Elizabeth?

ELIZABETH: *(In a dead voice.):*   No.

BARRETT: Then I must leave you under my extreme displeasure. I shall not see you again. I can have nothing to do with you, until God has softened your heart, and you repent of your wickedness and ask His forgiveness — and mine. *(He picks up Bible and goes out. The moment he has closed door, ELIZABETH gets up with an air of decision, crosses and pulls bell-rope. A pause, then WILSON enters.)*

ELIZABETH: Shut the door, please. *(Impulsively, as WILSON does so.)* Wilson, are you my friend?

WILSON *(Bewildered.):*   Your — friend, Miss?

ELIZABETH: Yes, my friend. I am in dire need of friendship and help at the moment.

WILSON: I — I don't quite understand, Miss Ba — but I'm that fond of you, I'd do anything to help you.

ELIZABETH: You would? And I know I can trust you?

WILSON: Yes, indeed, Miss.

ELIZABETH: Wilson, next Saturday I am going to marry Mr. Browning.

WILSON *(With a gasp.):*   Marry —

ELIZABETH: Hush! We're to be married secretly at Mary-le-Bone Church. Will you come with me?

WILSON: Me, Miss — yes, Miss — and gladly —

ELIZABETH: Directly afterwards I shall return here for a few days, and —

WILSON *(In boundless amazement.):*   Here! With Mr. Browning!

ELIZABETH *(With a hysterical laugh.):*   No — no — no! Just alone with you. Then on the following Saturday I shall join Mr. Browning and we're going abroad. We're going to Italy. Will you come with us?

WILSON *(In a whisper.):*   To Italy —?

ELIZABETH: Yes — will you come with me?

WILSON: Well, Miss, I can't see as how I can help myself. Not that I 'old with foreign parts — I don't. But 'usband or no 'usband, you'd never get to Italy alive without me.

ELIZABETH: Then you'll come? Then you'll come! Oh, I am so glad! I'll tell Mr. Browning — *(Crosses to desk, takes out writing materials.)* I'm writing to him now. And I shall want you to take the letter to the post at once. Go and put on your things — I'll have finished by the time you're ready.

WILSON: Yes, Miss. *(WILSON goes out. ELIZABETH is writing as curtain falls.)*

CURTAIN

————— • —————

SCENE 2

The scene is the same, with the following few changes. Chair has been moved up to window. Lamp on desk has been taken away. Most of the books have been removed from small bookcase. ELIZABETH's coat and hat are in wardrobe. Nine letters written by ELIZABETH to members of her family are on desk.

TIME: The time is early evening.

AT RISE: ELIZABETH is discovered kneeling beside FLUSH's basket, fastening a lead to his collar. She pats his head abstractedly, rises, picks up little pile of letters from desk, runs through them, crosses and places them on mantel. Then with a shuddering sigh, she walks to window, clasping and unclasping her hands in agitation. After a moment she sighs again, crosses to mantel, picks up letters and crossing, places them one by one on desk again. After a moment WILSON enters, hurries in with two traveling rugs on her arm. ELIZABETH at desk walks to upper armchair, crosses back to desk chair.

WILSON: Ah, Miss Ba, I'm that sorry! In my flurry to get the luggage off to the railway station yesterday, I clean forgot to pack these rugs, and there was 'eaps of room in the carpet-bag.

ELIZABETH: Never mind.

WILSON *(Putting rugs over back of chair.):* I do hope we haven't forgotten nothing else.

ELIZABETH: And if we have it won't matter much. Mr. Browning insisted that we should travel as lightly as possible. We shall be able to get all we need in Paris.

WILSON: Lor,' Miss, it don't seem possible we'll be in Paris tomorrow!

ELIZABETH: No — *(Consulting watch.)* Oh, how the time crawls. We've still an hour and a half of this dreadful waiting. You're sure, Wilson, they quite understood at the livery stables, exactly when, and where, the cab was to meet us?

WILSON *(Taking ELIZABETH's things from wardrobe.):* Oh, yes, Miss, I was most particular to see that the young man took it all down — the cab to be at the corner of Wimpole Street at ha' past three, punctual. It won't take us more than ten minutes to get to Hodgson's Library, and then Mr. Browning will 'ave us in his charge. *(Drops voice to a warm conversational tone.)* Your 'usband, Miss Ba, dear —

ELIZABETH *(Coming to her.):* Oh, hush! Hush! Don't breathe that word here —

WILSON: But, Miss Ba —

ELIZABETH: I'm foolishly nervous, but I can't help it. The very walls seem to be listening.

WILSON: There is no one in the house except Miss Henrietta. She was putting on her bonnet as I came along the passage, so she should have gone out by now. *(WILSON gets bag and hat from wardrobe.)*

ELIZABETH: Oh, Wilson, it's impossible to believe that in a little more than an hour I shall have left this room, never in all likelihood to see it again.

WILSON: And glad you'll be to see the last of it, I'm sure, Miss Ba.

ELIZABETH: Yes — and no. I've been very miserable here, and very happy. Oh, I wish it were time to go! This waiting is killing me.

WILSON: 'ave you finished writing your letters, Miss?

ELIZABETH *(Almost hysterically.):* Yes. Yes. I've written to them all. I've just been reading over my letter to Mr. Barrett to see if there was something I could add — something — anything. But I can't think — I can't think —

WILSON: Least said, soonest mended, Miss. *(With chuckling laugh.)* Oh, Miss Ba, I know I shouldn't say such things — but there's a lot I'd give to be here tonight when the Master reads your letter.

ELIZABETH: The very thought terrifies me. I can see his face — I can hear his voice. Thank God, we shall be miles and miles away. *(Looks at watch.)* An hour and twenty minutes still — Will time never pass?

WILSON: Why don't you write some poetry, Miss?

ELIZABETH *(Turns dumbfounded.):* Poetry —?

WILSON: Yes, Miss. That'll make the time pass nicely, I know.
(ELIZABETH bursts into laughter, as HENRIETTA in bonnet and shawl enters with letter in hand. ELIZABETH looks at her frightened.)

ELIZABETH *(Turning her letters on their faces.):* I — I thought you had gone out.

HENRIETTA: Wilson, I want to speak to Miss Ba.

WILSON: Yes, Miss. *(Crosses, exits, closing door.)*

HENRIETTA: I was just going out when I ran into a messenger at the door. He brought this letter — it's for you.

ELIZABETH *(Anxiously, reaching for letter.):* For me?

HENRIETTA *(Retaining letter.):* Yes, but it's in — in *his* handwriting.

ELIZABETH: Captain Cook's?

HENRIETTA: Yes.

ELIZABETH: Open it, dear.

HENRIETTA *(Tears open letter and reads.):* "Dear Miss Barrett, I know I am doing very wrong in drawing you once again into my and Henrietta's affairs. But the matter is so urgent I am sure you will forgive me. My regiment has been ordered to Somerset at short notice, and I must positively see Henrietta before I go. If I wrote to her directly, my letter would certainly be read by Mr. Barrett. I understand he opens all her correspondence. Hence my trespass on your kindness. Will you please give Henrietta the enclosed letter, and believe me your grateful and obedient servant, Surtees Cook." *(She lets letter drop to floor, while she opens enclosure, which she reads eagerly. ELIZABETH picks up letter from floor, tears it into bits, and throws them into fireplace.)* You remember Papa threatened to turn me out of the house unless I swore on the Bible not to write to or see Surtees?

ELIZABETH *(Turning to face her.):* Yes.

HENRIETTA: Well — I am going to break that "Bible oath" today!

ELIZABETH *(Quietly.):* Are you, dear?

HENRIETTA: Yes — and I shall glory in breaking it! And if Papa asks where I have been, I shall go out of my way to lie to him as often and as grossly as I can.

ELIZABETH *(Quietly.):* I see. But why do you tell me this?

HENRIETTA *(Fiercely.):* Because I want you to say that I'm a wicked, deceitful, perjured, *loose* woman, so that I can fling the words back in your face. *(ELIZABETH crosses to her, and HENRIETTA suddenly flings her arms round ELIZABETH.)* Oh, Ba, darling, forgive me! I'm not myself these days. I am all love and hate — and I don't know which is the worst torture.

ELIZABETH *(With passionate tenderness, arms about HENRIETTA.):* My dear, you think I don't understand! I do — I do. And I feel for you and pity you with all my heart. I can do nothing to help you — I daren't even advise you. But never lose hope — never lose courage — never — *(WILSON enters quickly, in great agitation.)*

WILSON: Oh, Miss Ba — Miss Ba —! The Master! *(They stare at WILSON, HENRIETTA in amazement, ELIZABETH in terror.)*

ELIZABETH: Shut the door!

WILSON *(As she does so, then crosses to ELIZABETH.):* He's just come in — just this minute. He must 'ave heard — someone must 'ave told him —

ELIZABETH: Be quiet. *(WILSON steps back up a little.)*

HENRIETTA *(In amazement.):* But, Ba, what on earth is the matter?

ELIZABETH: Nothing — nothing! It's — it's only that Papa hasn't been to see me for ten days now — ever since — you remember? And — and scenes of forgiveness are always trying. *(To WILSON.)* Put away my hat and cloak quick. *(WILSON does so, in wardrobe.)*

HENRIETTA *(Crossing to ELIZABETH.):* I don't believe that's all. You're as white as a sheet. What did Wilson mean? Ba, is there anything I can —?

ELIZABETH *(Softly, intensely.):* No — no — no! Don't speak — don't ask me anything. You know nothing — you understand? Nothing — nothing!

HENRIETTA: But —

ELIZABETH *(To WILSON.):* These rugs —! *(WILSON picks up rugs from chair. A knock at door. WILSON gasps. ELIZABETH answers in a whisper, turning towards fireplace.)* Come in. *(Clears her throat, then louder.)* Come in. *(Turning from fireplace. They are standing in tense attitudes when BARRETT enters. HENRIETTA is watching ELIZABETH, who commands her voice.)* You're home early, Papa. *(BARRETT, without replying, looks at each of the three in turn, then crosses to front of fireplace. WILSON, obviously terror-stricken, exits with rugs over her arm.)*

BARRETT *(To ELIZABETH.):* What's the matter with that girl?

ELIZABETH: Wilson?

BARRETT: Yes.

ELIZABETH: Nothing, Papa —

BARRETT *(After staring broodingly at her for a moment, crosses to HENRIET-TA.):* Where have you been?

HENRIETTA: Nowhere.

BARRETT: Where are you going?

HENRIETTA: To tea with Aunt Hedley.

BARRETT: Is that the truth?

HENRIETTA: Yes.

BARRETT: You remember your oath?

HENRIETTA: Yes.

BARRETT: Have you kept it?

HENRIETTA: Yes.

BARRETT: Are you going to keep it?

HENRIETTA: Yes.

BARRETT: I wish to speak to your sister — you can go. *(Without a glance at either of them HENRIETTA crosses, exits, closing door. ELIZABETH stands at fireplace. BARRETT walks to armchair and turns.)* Do you know why I am back so early?

ELIZABETH *(In a whisper.):* No, Papa.

BARRETT *(In a low intense voice.):* Because I could bear it no longer. It's ten days since last I saw you.

ELIZABETH: Am I to blame for that, Papa?

BARRETT: You dare to ask me such a question? Weren't you a party to your sister's shameless conduct? Haven't you encouraged her? And did you expect to go scot-free of my displeasure? *(Stopping himself with a violent gesture.)* I've not come to speak about that — but to put it behind me — to forget it! I wonder, my child — have you been half so miserable these last ten days as your Father?

ELIZABETH: Miserable, Papa?

BARRETT: Do you think I can be happy when I'm bitterly estranged from all I love in the world? Do you know that night after night I had to call up all my will-power to hold me from coming here to forgive you?

ELIZABETH: Papa —

BARRETT: All my will-power, I tell you — all my sense of duty, and right, and justice. But today I could bear it no longer. The want of your face and your voice became a torment. I had to come. I am not so strong as they think me — I had to come — and I despise myself for coming, despise myself, hate myself —

ELIZABETH (*Crossing to him on sofa, puts hands on his shoulders*): Oh, Papa, can't you see, won't you ever see, that strength may be weakness, and your sense of justice and right and duty may be mistaken and wrong?

BARRETT (*In a tense voice, putting her hands off his shoulders.*): Mistaken and wrong? What do you mean? (*Quickly stopping her.*) No, be silent. Don't answer me. Mistaken and wrong? You don't know what you're saying.

ELIZABETH: If you'll only listen to me, Papa, I —

BARRETT: No.

ELIZABETH: But, Papa —

BARRETT: No! (*Crosses to fireplace, stands half turned away. A pause, his voice calm as he continues.*) If there were even a vestige of truth in what you say, my whole life would be a hideous mockery. For always, through all misfortunes and miseries, I've been upheld for knowing beyond a doubt what was right, and doing it unflinchingly, however bitter the consequences. And bitter they've been — how bitter only God knows. It's been my heavy cross that those whom I was given to guide and rule have always fought against the right that I knew to be the right, and was in duty bound to impose upon them. Even you. Even your Mother.

ELIZABETH (*In a whisper, turning to him.*): My Mother?

BARRETT (*His back to fireplace.*): Yes, your Mother. But not at first. You — you, my eldest child, were born of love, and only love. But the others — long before they came, the rift began to open between your Mother and me. Not that she ever opposed me — never once. Or put into words what she felt. She was silent, and dutiful, and obedient. But love died out, and fear took its place —

ELIZABETH (*A whisper.*): Oh, dear God, what she must have suffered!

BARRETT: She? She? And what of me?

ELIZABETH: You? Oh, Papa, then you loved her after her love for you had died?

BARRETT (*Embarrassed, looking aside.*): Love? What's love? She was my wife. You — you don't understand —

ELIZABETH (*In same horrified whisper.*): And all those children — born in fear! Oh, it's horrible — it's horrible —! (*Covers face with her hands.*)

BARRETT (*Embarrassed, taking a couple of steps toward her.*): Ba, my dear — don't — don't. I shouldn't have spoken — I shouldn't have told you all that. Forget it, my child. (*Crosses to her.*) Take your hands from your face. (*Gently* *takes her wrists, she starts away from him with frightened eyes.)* Don't look at me like that. *(In a low thick voice, averting his eyes.)* You don't understand. How should you? You know nothing of the brutal tyranny of passion, and how the strongest and best are driven by it to hell. You would have abetted your sister in her —

ELIZABETH: Henrietta's love — how dare you speak of it in the same breath as —

BARRETT: Her love? You ignorant little fool! What do *you* know of love? Love! The lust of the eye — the lowest urge of the body!

ELIZABETH *(Starting to rise.):* I won't listen to you. ´

BARRETT *(Taking her hands and putting her down again.):* You must — you shall! Do you suppose I should have guarded this house like a dragon from this so-called love, if I hadn't known from my own life all it entails of cruelty and loathing, and degradation and remorse? With the help of God, and through years of tormenting abstinence, I strangled it in myself. And so long as there's breath in my body, I'll keep it away from those I was given to protect and care for. You understand me?

ELIZABETH *(A low voice, looking him in the face.):* Yes — I understand you.

BARRETT *(Turns away from her. She sits quite still looking straight before her.):* This has been a hateful necessity. I had to speak plainly, but we must turn over this ugly page and forget what was on it.

ELIZABETH *(Drawing her hand from his.):* I shall never forget what you said!

BARRETT: Never — perhaps that's as well. *(With sudden urgency.)* But for God's sake, my darling, don't let this raise any further barrier between us! Your love is all I have left to me in the world.

ELIZABETH: You had Mamma's love once — you might have had the love of all your children.

BARRETT: Yes, if I'd played the coward's part, taken the easier way, shirked my duty. I'd rather be hated by the whole world than gain love like that.

ELIZABETH: Oh, Papa, you don't know how I pity you!

BARRETT: Pity? I don't want your pity, but if I should ever lose you, or if I should ever lose your love — *(He seizes her unwilling hands.)* Ba, my darling, next week we shall have left this house. I've grown to loathe it — even this room has become hateful to me. In our new home we shall draw close to each other again. There will be little to distract you in the country — nothing and no one to come between us. *(He draws her stiffening form into his arms.)* My child, my darling, you must look up to me and depend on me, lean on me. You must share your thoughts with me, your hopes, your fears, your prayers. I want all your heart and all your soul. *(He draws her passionately close to him. She leans away from him, her face drawn from fear and pain.)*

ELIZABETH *(Sobbingly.):* I can't bear it — I can't bear any more. Let me go, Papa — please let me go! *(He releases her, she stands aside, her arm covering her face.)*

BARRETT: Forgive me, dear — I was carried away. I'll leave you now.

ELIZABETH *(In a whisper.):* Please —

BARRETT *(Rising.):* Shall I see you again tonight?

ELIZABETH *(As before.):* Not tonight.

BARRETT: I shall pray for you.

ELIZABETH *(Half to herself.):* Pray for me? Tonight? Yes, pray for me tonight — if you will. *(He touches her forehead gently, goes out. ELIZABETH sits a moment staring before her, then with frightened eyes around the room, she whispers.)* I must go at once — I must go — I must go — *(Rises quickly, gets cloak and bonnet from wardrobe. WILSON enters stealthily and hurriedly, rugs on her arm.)*

WILSON: He's gone to the study.

ELIZABETH *(Putting on her bonnet.):* We must go — now — at once!!

WILSON: But, Miss Ba —

ELIZABETH: At once! Help me on with my cloak.

WILSON *(Doing so.):* But the cab won't be there yet — not for an hour. Besides —

ELIZABETH: Then we must walk the streets. I can't stay here any longer. I'm frightened — I'm frightened. Fetch your cloak and bonnet. Quick!

WILSON: Walk about the streets, Miss? You can't — you can't! Besides, the Master's at home — he may see us leaving —

ELIZABETH *(Crossing to desk, arranging letters.):* He can't stop me. I don't belong to him any more — I belong to my husband. Papa can kill me, but he can't stop me!

WILSON: I daren't, Miss — I daren't!

ELIZABETH: Then I must go alone!

WILSON: You can't do that!

ELIZABETH *(With compelling earnestness, turning to face WILSON.):* Wilson — things have passed between my father and me which force me to leave this house at once. Until today I've never really known him. He's not like other men — he's dreadfully different. I — I can't say any more. If you draw back, you need never reproach yourself. But I must go now.

WILSON: I'll fetch my hat and cloak, at once, Miss. *(ELIZABETH puts her arm about her neck and kisses her.)* Oh, Miss Ba — *(Crosses, and exits quickly. ELIZABETH turns, spreads out letters on desk, then from a ribbon on which it is hung she draws her wedding ring from her bosom, and slips it onto her fingers. She looks at it a moment, then slowly draws on her gloves. WILSON re-enters quickly and softly in cloak and bonnet.)*

ELIZABETH: I am quite ready. You take the rugs Wilson — I had better carry Flush.

WILSON *(Breathlessly.):* Yes, Miss. *(Gets FLUSH from basket and gives him to ELIZABETH.)*

ELIZABETH: And now just slip downstairs and see whether the study door is shut.

WILSON: Very well, Miss. *(She exits quickly, leaving door open. ELIZABETH, with an indescribable expression on her face, stands with FLUSH under her arm, and looks about room. WILSON re-enters speaking in a breathless whisper.)* Yes, Miss — the door is shut, and all is quiet.

ELIZABETH: Very well. *(Speaking to FLUSH as she goes.)* If you bark now, Flush, we're lost! *(She passes out, exits, WILSON follows, closing door softly after her. The room stands empty for a moment, then lights slowly dim down and out to darkness.)*
  (A period of darkness for thirty seconds to indicate the passage of an hour or more of time, then lights slowly come back. After lights are up, a moment's pause, then ARABEL enters.)

ARABEL: Ba dear, I want — *(Realizes the room's emptiness, and looks bewilderedly about, exits and immediately returns with lamp which she places on desk, where she sees letters ELIZABETH has left. Picks one up in agitation, and whispers.)* For me — what can it mean? *(Sits in chair by desk, tears letter open, reads it with little gasping exclamations.)* Oh — No! No! Married! — No! Oh — Oh! Married! Gone — *(She looks up from letter, her face transformed in excitement, crosses to sofa and sits, then suddenly goes off into shrieks and peals of laughter. After a moment the voices and hurriedly approaching footsteps of GEORGE, CHARLES, OCTAVIUS, are heard outside, and they hurriedly enter.)*

GEORGE: Arabel! For Heaven's sake!

CHARLES: What is it?

GEORGE: Arabel! What on earth?

OCTAVIUS: High-strikes! B-by Jove! *(ARABEL continues laughing.)*

GEORGE *(Slapping one of her hands.):* Stop that, Arabel! Stop it at once!

ARABEL *(Half gasping, half shrieking.):* Married — gone! Married — gone! *(Another wild peal of laughter.)*

GEORGE: Be quiet! *(Slaps her hand again.)* Fetch some water, someone! *(Rises, starts up.)*

OCTAVIUS: Eau-de-cologne — *(Crosses up to dressing-table. ALFRED, HENRY, SEPTIMUS, two dressed, other without coat and collar, enter quickly.)*

ALFRED: What's the matter?

HENRY: Is Ba ill? Arabel!

ARABEL *(Gaspingly.):* She's married — she's gone — married — gone — *(HENRIETTA enters in cloak and bonnet. Stands a moment taking in scene, as ARABEL continues.)* Married and gone — married and gone — *(She moans and sobs. Realization begins to dawn on others.)*

CHARLES: What does she mean? Where's Ba?

ARABEL: Married and gone!

SEPTIMUS: Married and gone — she's mad!

GEORGE *(Taking ARABEL's shoulders.):* Arabel — what do you mean?

OCTAVIUS: Married!

HENRIETTA *(Suddenly pushing them aside, seizes ARABEL by shoulders, shaking her vigorously.)* Arabel — Arabel! Pull yourself together at once! Where's Ba? Answer me! Where's Ba?

ARABEL: She — she's m-m-married Mr. Robert Browning —

HENRIETTA *(In a whisper.):* Married — *(Consternation among others and amazed exclamations: "Married!" "Married!" "It can't be true!" — "Robert Browning." "Good God!" etc. HENRIETTA continues to ARABEL, who is still sobbing.)* Where is she?

ARABEL *(Indicating letters on desk.):* She — she's gone! Those letters — she's written to — to — all of us! She — she's gone — *(OCTAVIUS crosses to desk, followed by ALFRED, HENRY, and SEPTIMUS. ALFRED takes his letter. HENRIETTA gets her letter.)*

GEORGE: Yes — she was married last Saturday.

OCTAVIUS *(From desk, holding up a letter.):* And this one is for P-papa. *(There is a frightened silence, only HENRIETTA looks before her with a frightened smile on her face.)*

ARABEL *(In a shuddering whisper.):* P-p-papa!

SEPTIMUS: Is he in?

GEORGE: He's dressing for dinner.

OCTAVIUS: What's to be d-done?

HENRY: Someone must give him Ba's letter.

HENRIETTA: Let me — I should love to.

ARABEL *(In a whisper.):* Oh, hush — hush —! *(She tremblingly indicates door, and all stand breathless. Footsteps are heard approaching. BARRETT, in evening dress, appears on threshold as he enters.)*

BARRETT *(Looks at assembled family in stern amazement, no one stirs.):* What is the meaning of this? *(No one stirs or replies.)* Who was making that hideous noise just now? *(Still no one stirs or replies, he continues sharply.)* Where is Elizabeth? *(A silence, he crosses to HENRIETTA. ARABEL rises, clings to HENRIETTA's arm.)* Do you hear me? *(To HENRIETTA.)* Where is your sister?

HENRIETTA *(Freeing herself from ARABEL, hands BARRETT his letter.):* She left you this letter.

BARRETT *(Without touching it, in a low voice, his face a dreadful mask.):* Left me? What do you mean?

HENRIETTA: She left letters for all of us — this is yours. *(ARABEL sits on sofa. BARRETT, his eyes fixed on HENRIETTA's face, takes letter and is about to open it, when she suddenly springs forward and seizes his arm, continuing passionately and entreatingly.)* You must forgive her, Papa — you must forgive her — not for her sake — but for yours. I thought I hated you — but I don't. I pity you — I pity you! And if you've any pity on yourself — forgive her. *(He looks at her steadily for a moment, then pushes her aside. He opens and reads letter. No one stirs. Nothing but the fury of his quickened breathing shows his emotion. He starts as if to collapse, HENRIETTA and OCTAVIUS go to him; he pushes them aside. He turns and walks up to window, quite steadily, but his gait gives the impression that he is blind. He stands in front of window, his back to room, his hands tightly clasped behind him, grasping letter. The movement of his shoulders shows that he is breathing quickly and heavily. No one stirs.)*

BARRETT *(Half to himself, turning from window.):* Yes — yes — her dog. *(An ugly smile flickers across his face.)* Yes — I'll have her dog — Octavius!

OCTAVIUS: Sir?

BARRETT: Her dog must be destroyed! At once! *(Slightly raising his voice.)* You will take it to the vet — tonight! You understand me? Tonight! *(A pause.)* You understand me!

OCTAVIUS *(Desperately.):* I really d-don't see what the poor little beast has d-done to —

BARRETT *(Ominously.):* You understand me?

HENRIETTA *(Vainly trying to control the triumph in her voice.)* In her letter to me, Ba writes that she has taken Flush with her! *(BARRETT's face once more becomes a still white mask. He stands perfectly still, staring straight before him, mechanically tearing letter into little pieces which drop to his feet, as curtain falls.)*

CURTAIN

——————————— • ———————————

Consider the Play

1. The first scene of a play must give the audience background information on action which has already taken place and the action which is presently taking place. How does Besier give the audience information about this antecedent action?

2. What does the father's note to Henrietta tell us about his character and personality?

3. What do Arabel's comments to Elizabeth tell us about Arabel's character? Explain.

4. Define Edward Barrett's idea of love. Do you agree with this conception of love? Why?

5. Compare and contrast the speaking styles of Elizabeth, Octavius, Bella, and Bevan.

6. Select one subplot of the play. Describe it briefly, and discuss its importance to the overall drama.

7. When Robert Browning's poem *Sordello* was published, it was such a huge failure that it took him years to overcome the bad impression left in the public mind. It also became a joke among his friends. Alfred, Lord Tennyson, for example, quipped that it had only two lines which he understood, the first and the last, and that both were lies. Jane Carlyle claimed that she had read the entire poem without being able to make out whether Sordello was a man, a city, or a book. In the play, Elizabeth is honest with Robert in her appraisal of his poem. What is her opinion? Explain and discuss.

8. In what way is the beginning of Act 3 similar to the beginning of Act 1? How have things changed?

9. Bella refers to her father as a misogynist (a person who hates women). Do you agree with Henrietta's view that her father is "the king of misogynists"? Why? In what other way could his character be described? Discuss.

10. Discuss the effectiveness of the scene between Robert and Elizabeth in Act 3. Do you find this scene moving? Do you think that this scene is effective for today's audiences? Why?

11. Act 4 could be considered a pivotal act. How? Suggest reasons and explain.

12. Act 5 reveals a great deal about Besier's view of the character of Elizabeth's father. What is revealed? Do you agree? Explain and discuss.

13. Why do you think Besier broke the last act into two scenes? Do you feel that the last scene is an effective curtain? Explain.

14. How does Besier prepare the audience for the outcome of the play? Discuss.

15. In your opinion, what concept of masculinity is presented in the play? Give specific examples to support your view. Do you agree with this idea of masculinity? Why?

16. Discuss the importance of the setting to this play. Show the ways in which the setting is designed to carry out the playwright's intentions for the plot and characters. Also, discuss what might happen if the setting were changed.

17. Research and write a brief background reported on Victorian customs and beliefs. Then discuss how Victorian views were dramatized in Besier's play, and compare and contrast those views with the views generally held by society today.

18. Have you ever been unexpectedly saved from misfortune? Do you know of someone who has? Describe such an incident. Was the outcome good or bad? Why?

19. Friends can teach us a great deal and help us grow as human beings. Describe a friendship which you have had or now have which helps you in this way, or describe what you think is the ideal friendship. Discuss.

20. Children can be affected by the disappointments of their parents. Discuss the ways in which this can happen. In your opinion, will this always be harmful? Can it be helpful as well? Discuss.

———————— • ————————

The Life of Galileo

by Bertolt Brecht

The Playwright

Bertolt Brecht was born in 1898 in Augsburg, Germany, where he attended elementary and high school. In 1917 he enrolled in medicine at the University of Munich, but his interest in writing was already taking hold. He began work on his first play in 1918 when he was doing military service as a medical orderly in Augsburg. His second play, written in 1919, won him the Kleist Prize.

In 1920, Brecht moved to Munich where he earned his living as a freelance writer. He liked working-class districts and the exciting pleasures big cities offered. He adopted a style of dress and an appearance which suited him and his surroundings. It was the style of workers of the time. His hair was cut short and brushed forward, and he wore a flat leather cap, a leather jacket, and wire spectacles.

Brecht wrote many plays in the years that followed, despite the difficulties he faced in life. He married, divorced, and remarried. He was forced to leave Germany in 1932 because of his intellectual commitment to Marxism, which made him a target of the Nazis who had gained control of the government. He wandered to Czechoslovakia, Austria, Switzerland, Denmark, France, Sweden, Finland, and the United States. In 1941 he settled in Santa Monica, California, and began a new phase of his career, writing movie scripts for the flourishing industry in nearby Hollywood.

Brecht's troubles continued, however. In 1947 he was called to appear before the Committee on Un-American Activities, led by Joseph McCarthy. The Committee was formed to root out Communists and Communist sympathizers in the United States. Brecht was accused of being a Communist sympathizer. When asked the question, "Have you ever made application to join the Communist Party?", Brecht replied, "No, no, no, no, no, never." The day after he appeared, he left North America.

From then until his death in 1956, Brecht lived in Europe. He continued to write furiously and he earned many honours, including the East German National Prize in 1951 and the Stalin Peace Prize in 1954. He was described by many as one of the most remarkable and stimulating dramatists in the world.

The Play

Bertolt Brecht is one of the most talked-about and mysterious dramatists of the twentieth century. He was described by Max Frisch, a Swiss playwright and novelist, as "reserved, yet observant, a refugee who has left innumerable stations, too shy for a man of the world, too experienced for a scholar, too knowing not to be anxious, a stateless person . . . a scientist, a poet without incense." Brecht's plays contribute to the mystery of the man. They deal with the disintegration of human values and the impossibility of human communication.

The Life of Galileo was first produced a year after Brecht's death. It is the story of the struggle of reason against superstition and against the forces which cling to superstition in order to hold on to social power. It is the story of Galileo Galilei, the Italian astronomer and physicist who challenged the authorities of the Roman Catholic Church in the seventeenth century by suggesting that the earth revolved around the sun rather than the other way around. He was arrested, threatened with torture, forced to recant his views, and released. But he continued to state his views and, as a result, he spent much of his life under house arrest. Brecht's play, although based on the astronomer's life, explores the paradoxes within it.

Brecht wrote three versions of *The Life of Galileo*. The first was in 1938 and 1939. In 1945 and 1946, Brecht wrote a second version, and in 1954, Brecht began work on his third version, making changes while the second version was being rehearsed on the stage of the Berliner Ensemble.

This third version reflects Brecht's recognition of facts which he could not ignore — the development and first use of the atomic bomb at the end of World War II. Brecht was looking at the past of 300 years ago in the light of the times in which he lived and its terrible problems. In *The Life of Galileo,* Brecht expressed a contemporary view of the events of the atomic age and the problems of conscience. When Galileo, fearing torture, recants his theories, his most devoted pupil cries out, "Unhappy the land that has no heroes!" Brecht's point of view is clear when he has Galileo reply, "No. Unhappy the land that is in need of heroes." It is possible to see, in Galileo's failure, the seeds of an increasing alienation of science from humanitarian goals.

Bertolt Brecht

This translation by Desmond I. Vesey of *The Life of Galileo* by Bertolt Brecht is reprinted by permission of Methuen London Ltd.

The Life of Galileo

Bertolt Brecht

Translation by Desmond I. Vesey

The Characters (In Order of Appearance)

Galileo Galilei
Andrea Sarti (Boy and Man)
Signora Sarti, Galileo's housekeeper
Ludovico Marsili, Virginia's fiancé
Priuli, the Curator
Sagredo, Galileo's friend
Virginia, Galileo's daughter
Federzoni, a scholar
The Doge
Senators
His Highness, the Grand Duke of Tuscany, Cosimo de' Medici
The Chamberlain
Older Court Lady
Younger Court Lady
The Theologian
The Philosopher
The Mathematician
Grand-ducal Lackey
Two Nuns
Baker
Woman
Two Soldiers
Old Woman
Man
Two Men
Fat Prelate
First Scholar
First Monk
Second Scholar
Second Monk
First Astronomer
Second Astronomer
Monk

Very Thin Monk
Very Old Cardinal
Christopher Clavius
Fulganzio, the Little Monk
The Cardinal Inquisitor
Lackey
First Clerk
Second Clerk
Masked Ladies and Gentlemen
Cardinal Bellarmin
Cardinal Barberini (later Pope Urban VIII)
Two Young Ladies
Filippo Mucius
Signor Gaffone, Rector of the University
Two Strolling Players
Two Children
Marketplace Crowd and Procession
 (Two Men in Rags, The "Grand Duke of
 Florence," Four Masked Men, Dwarf,
 Beggar, Men, Women, and Children)
Following Man
Signor Vanni, the iron-founder
Signor Mincio, an official
High Official
Individual
Voice of the Crier
Monk
Peasant
Coachman
Frontier Guard
First Boy
Second Boy
Third Boy
Clerk

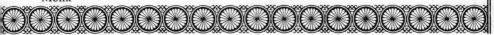

GALILEO GALILEI, TEACHER OF MATHEMATICS AT PADUA,
DETERMINES TO PROVE THE NEW COPERNICAN SYSTEM

In the year sixteen hundred and nine
Science's light began to shine.
At Padua City, in a modest house
Galileo Galilei set out to prove
The sun is still, the earth is on the move.

SCENE 1: GALILEO'S HUMBLE STUDY IN PADUA

It is morning. A boy, ANDREA, the son of the housekeeper, brings in a glass of milk and a roll of bread.

GALILEO *(washing the upper part of his body, puffing, and good-humoured):* Put the milk on the table. But don't shut any of my books.

ANDREA: Mother says we must pay the milkman. If we don't, he'll soon be taking a circle round our house, Signor Galilei.

GALILEO: The expression is: he will be *describing* a circle, Andrea.

ANDREA: All right. If we don't pay, he'll be describing a circle round us, Signor Galilei.

GALILEO: While the bailiff, Signor Cambione, will come straight here by taking what sort of a line between two points?

ANDREA *(grinning):* The shortest.

GALILEO: Good. I've got something for you. Look behind the star-charts.
  (ANDREA fishes out from behind the star-charts a large wooden model of the Ptolemaic system.)

ANDREA: What is it?

GALILEO: That shows how, according to the ancients, the stars move round the earth.

ANDREA: How?

GALILEO: Let's examine it. Begin at the beginning: description.

ANDREA: In the middle is a little stone.

GALILEO: That is the earth.

ANDREA: Then all around, one outside the other, there are globes.

GALILEO: How many?

ANDREA: Eight.

GALILEO: Those are the crystal spheres.

ANDREA: And the globes have little balls fixed on . . .

GALILEO: The stars.

ANDREA: There are strips with words painted on them.

GALILEO: What words?

ANDREA: The names of stars.

GALILEO: Such as?

ANDREA: The lowest ball is the moon, it's written on it. And above it is the sun.

GALILEO: And now make the sun move.

ANDREA *(moves the globes):*   That's beautiful. But we're so shut in.

GALILEO *(drying himself):*   Yes, I felt that too when I saw the thing for the first time. Some people do feel it. *(He throws the towel to ANDREA, for him to dry his back.)* Walls and globes and immobility! For two thousand years men have believed that the sun and all the stars of heaven revolve around them. The pope, the cardinals, the princes, the scholars, captains, merchants, fishwives and schoolboys believed themselves to be sitting motionless in the centre of this crystal globe. But now we are travelling headlong into space, Andrea. For the old age is past, and this is a new age. During the last hundred years it has been as though men were expecting something.

The cities are narrow and so are men's minds. Superstition and plague. But now we say: because it is so, it will not remain so. For everything moves, my boy.

I like to think that it began with ships. Ever since men could remember they crept only along the coasts; then suddenly they left the coasts and sped straight out across the seas.

On our old continent a rumour started: there are new continents! And since our ships have been sailing to them the word has gone round all the laughing continents that the vast, dreaded ocean is just a little pond. And a great desire has arisen to fathom the causes of all things: why a stone falls when you drop it, and how it rises when you throw it in the air. Every day something new is discovered. Even centenarians let the youngsters shout the latest novelty into their ears.

Already much has been discovered, but there is more still to be found out. And so there are always new things for new generations to do.

When a young man in Siena, I saw how a couple of builders, after five minutes argument, replaced a thousand-year-old system for moving granite blocks by a new and more practical arrangement of the tackle. Then and there I knew — the old age is past and a new age is here. Soon mankind will know the truth about their home, about the heavenly body on which they dwell. What is written in the old books no longer satisfies them.

For where belief has prevailed for a thousand years, doubt now prevails. All the world says: yes, that's written in books but now let us see for ourselves. The most solemn truths are being tapped on the shoulder; what was never doubted is now in doubt.

And because of that a great wind has arisen, lifting even the gold-embroidered coat-tails of princes and prelates, so that the fat legs and thin legs underneath are seen; legs like our legs. The heavens, it has turned out, are empty. And there is a gale of laughter over that.

But the waters of the earth are driving our new spindles and in the dockyard, in the rope and sail shops, five hundred hands are moving together in a new way of working.

I predict that in our lifetimes astronomy will be talked about in the market-places. Even the sons of fishwives will go to school. For these city people seeking after novelty will be glad that the new astronomy now lets the earth move freely, too. It has always been said that the stars are affixed to a crystal sphere to prevent them falling down. But now we have plucked up courage and we let them soar through space, unfettered and in full career, like our ships, unfettered and in full career.

And the earth rolls happily round the sun, and the fishwives, merchants, princes and cardinals and even the Pope roll with it.

Overnight the universe has lost its centre, and by morning it has countless ones. So that now each — and none — is regarded as its centre. For suddenly there is plenty of room.

Our ships sail far across the seas, our stars travel far through space; even in chess the castles have lately taken to moving all over the board.

What does the poet say? 'Oh happy morning of beginning . . .'

ANDREA: 'Oh happy morning of beginning!
Oh scent of winds from new and distant shores!'
And you must drink your milk; for people will start coming again soon.

GALILEO: Do you understand what I told you yesterday?

ANDREA: What? All that about Kippernicus and his rotation?

GALILEO: Yes.

ANDREA: No. How do you expect me to understand it? It's very difficult, and I'm only eleven next October.

GALILEO: I particularly want *you* to understand it too. That's why I'm working and buying expensive books instead of paying the milkman — so that people like you can understand it.

ANDREA: But I can *see* that the sun is in a different place in the evening from what it was in the morning. So it can't be standing still. Never, never.

GALILEO: You *see!* What do you see? You see nothing. You only goggle. Goggling is not seeing. *(He sets the iron wash-basin in the middle of the room.)* Well, that's the sun. Sit down. *(ANDREA sits on the one chair. GALILEO stands behind him.)* Where is the sun, right or left?

ANDREA: Left.

GALILEO: And how can it get to your right?

ANDREA: If you carry it to the right, of course.

GALILEO: Is that the only way? *(He picks him up with the chair and rotates him through a semicircle.)* Now where is the sun?

ANDREA: On the right.

GALILEO: And did it move?

ANDREA: No! *It* didn't.

GALILEO: Well, what did move?

ANDREA: I did.

GALILEO *(shouts):* Wrong, you idiot! The chair.

ANDREA: But I went with it!

GALILEO: Of course you did. The chair is the earth. You are sitting on it.

SIGNORA SARTI *(has entered to make the bed. She has been looking on):* Whatever are you doing with my boy, Signor Galilei?

GALILEO: I'm teaching him to see, Sarti.

SIGNORA SARTI: By lugging him round the room?

ANDREA: Stop it, mother. You don't understand this.

SIGNORA SARTI: Don't I? But you understand it, eh? — A young gentleman wishing tuition. Very well dressed and brings a letter of recommendation. *(She hands this over.)* You'll soon have my Andrea saying twice two is five. He already muddles up everything you tell him. Yesterday evening he actually was proving to me that the earth goes round the sun. He is firmly convinced that a gentleman by the name of Kippernicus has worked that out.

ANDREA: Didn't Kippernicus work it out, Signor Galilei? Tell her yourself.

SIGNORA SARTI: What! Are you really teaching him such nonsense? So that he'll chatter about it at school and the reverend gentlemen will come complaining to me because he repeats all this unholy stuff. You ought to be ashamed of yourself, Signor Galilei.

GALILEO *(breakfasting):* As a result of our investigations, Signora Sarti, and after bitter dispute, Andrea and I have made discoveries which we can no longer withhold from the world. A new era has dawned, a great age in which it is a joy to be alive.

SIGNORA SARTI: Well! I hope we shall also be able to pay the milkman in this new age, Signor Galilei. *(Pointing to the letter of recommendation.)* Just do me one favour and don't send *him* away too. I'm thinking of the milk bill.
   (Exit.)

GALILEO *(laughing):* At least let me finish my milk! *(To ANDREA):* So we did understand something yesterday, after all!

ANDREA: I only said it to her to astonish her. But it isn't true. When I was in the chair, you only turned it round — and not like that. *(He makes a vertically circular movement with his arm.)* Because if you had done that I should have fallen off, and that's a fact. Why didn't you turn the chair upside down? Because then it would have proved that I should also fall off the earth if it turned like that. There you are!

GALILEO: But I have proved to you . . .

ANDREA: But last night I discovered that if the earth really turned like that I'd be hanging head downwards at night. And that's a fact.

GALILEO *(taking an apple from the table):* Look, this is the earth.

ANDREA: Don't take examples like that, Signor Galilei. You can prove anything with them.

GALILEO (*putting the apple back*):   All right.

ANDREA: You can do anything with examples if you're clever enough. Only I can't lug my mother about in a chair like you did me. So you see what a bad example that is. And what about it, if the apple *is* the earth? That's nothing.

GALILEO (*laughs*):   You don't want to know.

ANDREA: Pick it up again. Why don't I hang head downwards at night?

GALILEO: Well, here is the earth, and this is you standing on it.
   (*He sticks a splinter from a piece of kindling wood into the apple.*)
And now the earth rotates.

ANDREA: And now I'm hanging head downwards.

GALILEO: How? Look carefully. Where is your head?

ANDREA (*points at the apple*):   There. Down below.

GALILEO: What? (*He turns the apple back.*) Isn't your head in the same place? Aren't your feet still on the ground? Are you like this when I turn it?
   (*He takes the splinter out and turns it upside down.*)

ANDREA: No. Then why don't I feel the earth turning?

GALILEO: Because you're turning with it. You and the air around you and everything that's on the globe.

ANDREA: And why does it look as if the sun's moving?

GALILEO (*once more rotates the apple with the splinter in it*):   Now, below you you see the earth, that stays the same, it's always below you and never moves so far as you are concerned. But now look above you. Now the lamp is over your head. But now, when I've turned the earth, what's over your head now — that is, up above?

ANDREA (*rotates himself too*):   The stove.

GALILEO: And where is the lamp?

ANDREA: Down below.

GALILEO: There you are!

ANDREA: That's fine. That'll amaze her!
   (*LUDOVICO MARSILI, a rich young man, enters.*)

GALILEO: This place is like a cross-roads.

LUDOVICO: Good morning, signor. My name is Ludovico Marsili.

GALILEO (*studying his letter of recommendation*):   You have been in Holland?

LUDOVICO: Where I heard much of you, Signor Galilei.

GALILEO: Your family owns estates in the Campagna?

LUDOVICO: My mother wants me to have a look round. See what's happening in the world, and so on.

GALILEO: And you heard in Holland that I, for example, was happening in Italy?

LUDOVICO: And since my mother wishes me to have a look round in the world of science too . . .

GALILEO: Private tuition, ten scudi a month.

LUDOVICO: Very well, signor.

GALILEO: What are your interests?

LUDOVICO: Horses.

GALILEO: Ah.

LUDOVICO: I have no head for learning, Signor Galilei.

GALILEO: Indeed. In that case it will be fifteen scudi a month.

LUDOVICO: Very well, Signor Galilei.

GALILEO: I shall have to take you early in the morning. That will be your loss, Andrea. For of course you'll have to drop out. You understand; *you* don't pay.

ANDREA: All right, I'm going. Can I have the apple?

GALILEO: Yes.
  (Exit ANDREA.)

LUDOVICO: You will have to have patience with me. Particularly since in science everything is different from what plain commonsense tells one. You take for example that funny tube they're selling in Amsterdam. I examined it closely. Just a casing of green leather and two lenses, one like that — *(he indicates by gesture a concave lens)* — and one like that — *(he indicates a convex lens)*. I hear that one enlarges and the other diminishes. Any sensible person would think that they'd cancel each other out. Wrong. One sees everything five times as large through the thing. That's your science for you.

GALILEO: What does one see five times as large?

LUDOVICO: Church spires, doves; everything that's far away.

GALILEO: Have you yourself seen church spires enlarged like that?

LUDOVICO: Yes, signor.

GALILEO: And the tube had two lenses? *(He makes a sketch on a piece of paper.)* Did it look like that? *(LUDOVICO nods.)* How old is this discovery?

LUDOVICO: I don't think it was more than a few days old when I left Holland; in any case it hadn't been longer on the market.

GALILEO *(almost friendly):* And why must it be physics? Why not horse-breeding?
  (Enter SIGNORA SARTI, unnoticed by GALILEO.)

LUDOVICO: My mother thinks that a little science is necessary. All the world takes a drop of science with their wine nowadays, you know.

GALILEO: You could just as well choose a dead language or theology. That's easier. *(He sees SIGNORA SARTI.)* All right, come on Tuesday morning.
  (Exit LUDOVICO.)

GALILEO: Don't look at me like that. I've accepted him.

SIGNORA SARTI: Because you saw me at the right moment. The Curator of the University is outside.

GALILEO: Bring him in, he's important. It may mean five hundred scudi. Then I won't need any pupils.
   (SIGNORA SARTI brings in the CURATOR. GALILEO has finished dressing and is scribbling figures on a scrap of paper.)
Good morning, lend me half a scudo. *(He gives the coin, which the CURATOR digs out of his purse, to SARTI.)* Sarti, send Andrea down to the spectacles-maker for two lenses; here are the particulars.
   (Exit SARTI with the note.)

THE CURATOR: I have called respecting your application for an increase in salary to a thousand scudi. Unfortunately, I cannot recommend this to the University. You know that at the present time the mathematical faculty is no attraction at a university. Mathematics is a profitless art, so to speak. Not that the Republic does not esteem it most highly. It is not as necessary as philosophy, nor as useful as theology, but it affords its devotees such endless pleasures.

GALILEO *(over his papers):*   My dear man, I cannot manage on five hundred scudi.

THE CURATOR: But Signor Galilei! You lecture twice a week, two hours at a time. Your exceptional reputation must surely bring you as many pupils as you wish, all of whom can pay for private lessons. Have you no private pupils?

GALILEO: Sir, I have too many! I teach and teach, and when have I time to study? God above, I am not as omniscient as the gentlemen of the philosophic faculty. I am stupid. I understand absolutely nothing. So I am compelled to patch up the holes in my knowledge. And when am I to do that? When am I to research? Sir, my science is still hungry for knowledge! For the answers to our greatest problems, we have so far nothing but hypotheses. And *we* demand proofs. But how can I progress when, to keep my household going, I am driven to drum into any blockhead who can pay the fact that parallel lines meet at infinity?

THE CURATOR: You should not altogether forget that, while the Republic may not pay as much as certain Princes do, it guarantees freedom of research. We in Padua admit even Protestants to our lectures! And we grant them doctorates. Not only did we not surrender Signor Cremonini to the Inquisition when it was proved to us — *proved*, Signor Galilei — that he gives vent to irreligious utterances, but we even voted him a higher salary. As far away as Holland it is known that Venice is the republic where the Inquisition has no say. And that is worth something to you who are an astronomer — that is, devoting yourself to a science which has for a considerable time ceased to show a due respect for the teachings of the Church!

GALILEO: Your people here handed Signor Giordano Bruno over to the authorities in Rome. Because he spread the teachings of Copernicus.

THE CURATOR: Not because he spread the teachings of Copernicus, which are moreover false, but because he was not a Venetian and also had no appointment here. So you can leave out of your argument this man who was burnt at the stake. By the way, for all our freedom you would be well advised not to utter so loudly a name on which the Church has laid its anathema. Not even here, Signor Galilei. Not even here.

GALILEO: Your protection of freedom of thought is quite a profitable business, eh? By pointing out that elsewhere the Inquisition rules and burns, you get good teachers cheap. In return for protection from the Inquisition you reimburse yourselves by paying the worst salaries.

THE CURATOR: Unjust! Unjust! What good would it do you to have all the free time in the world for your researches if every ignorant monk of the Inquisition could simply forbid your thoughts? No rose without a thorn, no princes without monks, Signor Galilei.

GALILEO: And what use is freedom of research without free time in which to research? What happens to the results? Perhaps you would care to show the gentlemen of the Signoria these investigations into the Laws of Falling Bodies — *(he points to a bundle of manuscripts)* — and ask them whether that is not worth a few more scudi?

THE CURATOR: It is worth infinitely more, Signor Galilei.

GALILEO: Not infinitely more, but five hundred scudi more, sir.

THE CURATOR: Scudi are worth what scudi will buy. If you want money, you must produce something else. For the knowledge which you sell, you can only demand as much as it profits whoever buys it from you. For example, the philosophy which Signor Colombe is selling in Florence brings the Prince at least ten thousand scudi a year. Your Laws of Falling Bodies have created a stir, admittedly. Men applaud you in Paris and Prague. But the gentlemen who applaud there do not, unfortunately, pay the University of Padua what you cost it. Your misfortune is your subject, Signor Galilei.

GALILEO: I understand. Free trade, free research. Free trading in research, eh?

THE CURATOR: But, Signor Galilei! What a suggestion! Permit me to say that I do not understand your jesting remarks. The flourishing trade of the Republic seems to me to be scarcely a subject for derision. Even less could I, for so many years Curator of the University, bring myself to speak of research in that — may I say — frivolous tone. *(As GALILEO casts longing glances at his worktable.)* Consider the conditions in the world outside: the whips of bondage under which learning groans in certain places — whips which the authorities have cut from their old leather folios. In those places people must not know how a stone falls, only what Aristotle writes on the subject. Eyes are just for reading. What need for new laws of falling bodies, where only the laws of a footfall are important? Set against the endless pleasure with which our Republic accepts your ideas, however daring they may be. Here you can research. Here you can work. No one supervises you, no one oppresses you. Our merchants, who appreciate the importance of better linen in their struggle against Florentine competition, listen with interest to your call for better physics; and how greatly is the science of physics indebted to the call for better looms! Our most eminent citizens interest themselves in your researches, visit you, watch demonstrations of your discoveries, and they are gentlemen whose time is precious. Do not despise trade, Signor Galilei! No one here would tolerate your work being disturbed in the slightest degree or that intruders should make difficulties for you. Admit, Signor Galilei, that you can work here.

GALILEO *(in desperation):* Yes.

The Life of Galileo

THE CURATOR: And as far as the material side is concerned, why don't you invent something else as pretty as your wonderful proportional compasses which — *(he counts off on his fingers)* — enable one without any mathematical knowledge to protract lines, calculate compound interest on capital, reproduce ground plans in varying scales, and determine the weight of cannon-balls.

GALILEO: A toy!

THE CURATOR: Something that has delighted and amazed the highest in the Republic and also brought in cash, you call a toy. I hear that even General Stefano Gritti is able to extract square roots with this instrument.

GALILEO: Indeed a miracle! — Nevertheless, Priuli, you have made me thoughtful. Priuli, perhaps I have something of the sort you mentioned. *(He picks up the paper with the sketch on it.)*

THE CURATOR: Have you? That would be the solution. *(He stands up.)* Signor Galilei, we know that you are a great man. A great but discontented man, if I may say so.

GALILEO: Yes, I am discontented, and *that* is what you would pay me for, if you had the wit! For I am discontented with myself. But instead of that you force me to be discontented with you. I admit that it amuses me to prove my worth to you gentlemen of Venice, in your famous arsenal and your dockyards and your cannon foundries. But you leave me no time to pursue the far-reaching speculations on my own subject which crowd into my mind when I am there. You muzzle the ox which threshes! I am forty-six years old and have done nothing which satisfies me.

THE CURATOR: Then let me disturb you no longer.

GALILEO: Thank you.
(Exit the CURATOR. GALILEO, alone for a few moments, starts to work. Then ANDREA comes running in.)

GALILEO *(working):* Why haven't you eaten the apple?

ANDREA: So that I could show her that it turns.

GALILEO: I must say something to you, Andrea. Don't talk to other people about our ideas.

ANDREA: Why not?

GALILEO: The authorities have forbidden them.

ANDREA: But they're the truth.

GALILEO: But they forbid them. In this case there is something else as well. We physicists still cannot prove what we believe to be correct. Even the teaching of the great Copernicus has not yet been proved. It is only a hypothesis. Give me the lenses.

ANDREA: The half scudo wasn't enough. I had to leave my coat behind. Pledge.

GALILEO: What will you do in winter without a coat?
(A pause. GALILEO arranges the lenses on the sheet of paper bearing the sketch.)

ANDREA: What is a hypothesis?

GALILEO: It is when one accept something as probable, but has no facts. That Signora Felice down the street by the basketmaker's shop, who has a child at the breast, gives the baby milk and doesn't take milk from it, is a hypothesis until one goes and sees it and can prove it to be a fact. But in dealing with the stars we are like worms with clouded eyes who can see only very little. The old teachings, which were believed for a thousand years, are collapsing; there is less wood in those gigantic structures than in the props that are supposed to shore them up — the many laws that explain little. Whereas this new hypothesis has few laws that explain much.

ANDREA: But you have proved everything to me.

GALILEO: Only that it *can* be so. You understand, the hypothesis is a very fine one, and there is nothing against it.

ANDREA: I should like to be a physicist too, Signor Galilei.

GALILEO: I believe it — seeing the infinity of questions to be cleared up in our field. *(He has crossed to the window and looked through the lenses. Mildly interested):* Take a look through this, Andrea.

ANDREA: Holy Mary, everything comes close. The bell on the campanile is quite near. I can even read the copper letters: Gratia Dei.

GALILEO: That will bring us in five hundred scudi.

————————— • —————————

2

GALILEO PRESENTS THE REPUBLIC OF VENICE WITH A NEW DISCOVERY

> No one's virtue is complete:
> Great Galileo likes to eat.
> You will not resent, we hope,
> The truth about his telescope.

SCENE 2: THE GREAT ARSENAL OF VENICE, BY THE HARBOUR

Senators, at their head the DOGE. To one side, GALILEO's friend SAGREDO and fifteen-year-old VIRGINIA GALILEO with a velvet cushion on which lies a telescope which is about two foot long and covered with crimson leather. On a dais, GALILEO. Behind him the stand for the telescope, attended by FEDERZONI, the lens-grinder.

GALILEO: Your Excellency, noble Signoria! As a teacher of mathematics at your University of Padua and director of your great arsenal here in Venice, I have always regarded it as my duty not only to fulfil my high responsibility of teaching, but also to provide especial benefits for the Republic of Venice by means of practical discoveries. With deep pleasure and all due humility I am able to display and present to you here today a completely new instrument, my distance-glass or telescope, produced in your world-famous Great Arsenal according to the highest scientific and Christian principles, the fruit of seventeen years patient research by your obedient servant.

(GALILEO leaves the dais and takes up position beside SAGREDO. Clapping. GALILEO bows.)

GALILEO *(softly to SAGREDO):* Waste of time!

SAGREDO *(softly):* You'll be able to pay your butcher, my friend.

GALILEO: Yes, it will bring them in money. *(He bows again.)*

THE CURATOR *(stepping on to the dais):* Excellency, noble Signoria! Once again a page of fame in the great books of the arts is embellished with Venetian characters. *(Polite applause.)* A scholar of world repute here presents to you, and you alone, a highly saleable cylinder to manufacture and put on the market in any way you please. *(Stronger applause.)* And has it occurred to you that in war-time by means of this instrument we shall be able to distinguish the build and number of an enemy's ships a full two hours earlier than he can descry ours, so that we, knowing his strength, can decide whether to pursue in order to give battle or to fly? *(Very loud applause.)* And now, Your Excellency, noble Signoria, Signor Galilei begs you to receive this instrument of his own inventing, this testimony to his intuition, from the hands of his charming daughter.

(Music. VIRGINIA advances, bows, and presents the telescope to the CURATOR, who passes it on to FEDERZONI. FEDERZONI places it on the stand and adjusts it. The DOGE and senators climb on to the dais and peer through the telescope.)

GALILEO *(softly):* I can't promise you that I shall be able to last out this carnival. These people here think that they're getting a profitable toy; but it's far more. I pointed the tube at the moon last night.

SAGREDO: What did you see?

GALILEO: It has no light of its own.

SAGREDO: What?

SENATOR: I can see the fortifications of Santa Rosita, Signor Galilei! — On that boat over there they're having their midday meal. Grilled fish. It makes my mouth water.

GALILEO: I tell you, astronomy has stood still for a thousand years because they had no telescope.

SENATOR: Signor Galilei!

SAGREDO: They're speaking to you.

SENATOR: One sees too well with that thing. I'll have to tell my womankind that bathing on the roof won't do any more.

GALILEO: Do you know what the Milky Way consists of?

SAGREDO: No.

SENATOR: One could easily ask ten scudi for a thing like that, Signor Galilei.
(GALILEO bows.)

VIRGINIA *(bringing LUDOVICO to her father):* Ludovico wants to congratulate you, father.

LUDOVICO *(embarrassed):* I congratulate you, sir.

GALILEO: I have improved it.

LUDOVICO: Of course, sir. I see you have made the cover red; in Holland it was green.

GALILEO *(turning to SAGREDO):*   I'm just wondering whether with this thing I may not be able to prove a certain theory.

SAGREDO: Take care.

THE CURATOR: Your five hundred scudi are safe and sure, Signor Galilei.

GALILEO *(paying no attention to him):*   Of course I am very wary of drawing any premature conclusion.
(The DOGE, a fat, unassuming man, has come up to GALILEO and is trying with clumsy dignity to speak to him.)

THE CURATOR: Signor Galilei, his Excellency the Doge.
(The DOGE shakes GALILEO's hand.)

GALILEO: Of course! The five hundred! Are you satisfied, your Excellency?

THE DOGE: Unfortunately, in the Republic we always need a pretext to enable our city fathers to agree to grant anything to our scholars.

THE CURATOR: And for that matter, Signor Galilei, where else would your incentive lie?

THE DOGE *(smiling):*   We need the pretext.
(The DOGE and the CURATOR lead GALILEO to the senators, who sur-round him. VIRGINIA and LUDOVICO walk slowly away.)

VIRGINIA: Did I do it all right?

LUDOVICO: I thought it was all right.

VIRGINIA: What's the matter with you then?

LUDOVICO: Oh, nothing. Perhaps a green cover would have been just as good.

VIRGINIA: I think they are all pleased with father.

LUDOVICO: And I think I'm beginning to understand something about science.

———————————— • ————————————

3

10TH JANUARY, 1610: BY MEANS OF THE TELESCOPE GALILEO DISCOVERS PHENOMENA IN THE SKY WHICH PROVE THE COPERNICAN SYSTEM. WARNED BY HIS FRIEND AGAINST THE POSSIBLE CONSEQUENCES OF HIS RESEARCHES, GALILEO PROFESSES HIS BELIEF IN MAN'S REASON.

January ten, sixteen ten:
Galileo Galilei abolishes heaven.

SCENE 3: GALILEO'S WORK-ROOM IN PADUA

Night. GALILEO and SAGREDO, wrapped in thick cloaks, at the telescope.

SAGREDO *(looking through the telescope, half to himself):* The edge of the crescent is quite uneven, jagged and irregular. In the dark half, near the luminous edge, are luminous spots. The appear one after the other. From these spots the light streams over ever-widening areas until it merges into the greater, luminous part.

GALILEO: How do you explain those luminous spots?

SAGREDO: It cannot be.

GALILEO: But it is. They are mountains.

SAGREDO: On a star?

GALILEO: Giant mountains. Whose summits are gilded by the rising sun, whilst all around night still covers their slopes. You see the light descending from the topmost peaks into the valleys.

SAGREDO: But that contradicts all astronomy for the last two thousand years.

GALILEO: Yet that's how it is. What you see has never been seen by any man besides myself. You are the second.

SAGREDO: The moon cannot be an earth with mountains and valleys, any more than the earth can be a star.

GALILEO: The moon *can* be an earth with mountains and valleys, and the earth *can* be a star. An ordinary heavenly body — one among thousands. Look again. Do you see the darkened part of the moon quite dark?

SAGREDO: No. Now when I look closely I can see a pale, ashen light upon it.

GALILEO: What sort of light could that be?

SAGREDO: ?

GALILEO: It's light from the earth.

SAGREDO: That's nonsense. How can the earth shine — a dead body, with its mountains and forests and seas?

GALILEO: In the same way as the moon shines. Both stars are illuminated by the sun — that is why they shine. What the moon is to us, we are to the moon. Sometimes it sees us as a crescent, and sometimes full, and sometimes not at all.

SAGREDO: So there would be no difference between the moon and the earth?

GALILEO: Evidently not.

SAGREDO: Not ten years ago a man was burnt in Rome. His name was Giordano Bruno, and he alleged just that.

GALILEO: He did. And now we can see it. Keep your eye at the telescope, Sagredo. What you see means that there is no difference between Heaven and Earth. Today is the tenth of January, sixteen hundred and ten. Mankind will write in its journal: Heaven abolished.

SAGREDO: That is appalling.

GALILEO: I have discovered yet another fact. Perhaps even more astonishing . . .

SARTI *(enters):* The Curator.
(The CURATOR bursts in.)

THE CURATOR: Forgive the lateness of the hour. I should be obliged if I could speak to you alone.

GALILEO: Signor Sagredo can hear anything that I can hear, Signor Priuli.

THE CURATOR: But you may not find it pleasant for the gentleman to hear what has happened. It is, unfortunately, something absolutely incredible.

GALILEO: Signor Sagredo is accustomed to encountering the incredible with me, you know.

THE CURATOR: I fear, I fear. *(Pointing to the telescope.)* Yes, there it is, that marvellous thing! The thing you might just as well throw away. It's worthless, absolutely worthless.

SAGREDO *(who has been wandering around restlessly):* What do you mean?

THE CURATOR: Do you know that this discovery of yours, which you have described as the fruit of seventeen years research, can be bought on any street corner in Italy for a few scudi? And, what is more, made in Holland! At this moment a Dutch cargo ship in the harbour is unloading five hundred telescopes!

GALILEO: Really?

THE CURATOR: I fail to understand your equanimity, Signor.

SAGREDO: What are you worrying about? Let me tell you that in these last few days Signor Galilei, by means of this instrument, has made revolutionary discoveries concerning the universe.

GALILEO *(laughing):* You can have a look through it, Priuli.

THE CURATOR: Well, let me tell you that it is quite enough for me — as the man who got Signor Galilei's salary doubled for this trash — to have made *this* discovery. And it is pure coincidence that the gentlemen of the Signoria, believing that they were securing for the Republic an instrument which could only be produced here, did not, the first time they looked through it, perceive at the nearest street corner, seven times enlarged, a common pedlar selling this tube for a song.
(GALILEO laughs uproariously.)

SAGREDO: My dear Signor Priuli, I may not be able to assess this instrument's value to commerce, but its value to philosophy is so incalculable that . . .

THE CURATOR: To philosophy! What has Signor Galilei, the mathematician, to do with philosophy? — Signor Galilei, in your day you have invented an excellent water-pump for the city, and your irrigation plant functions satisfactorily. The cloth-weavers, too, praise your machines. However could I have expected such a thing!

GALILEO: Not so fast, Priuli. Sea passages are still long, uncertain and expensive. We still lack any sort of reliable clock in the sky. Some signpost for navigation. Now, I have reason to believe that with this telescope certain stars which follow very regular courses may be observed clearly. New star-charts could save millions of scudi in navigation, Priuli.

THE CURATOR: Enough, enough. I have already listened to too much from you. In reward for my kindness you have made me the laughing-stock of the city. I shall always be remembered as the Curator who was taken in by a worthless spy-glass. You have every reason to laugh. You have your five hundred scudi. But I can tell you — and it is an honest man speaking — this world disgusts me!
   (Exit, slamming the door behind him.)

GALILEO: In his rage he becomes almost likeable. Did you hear that: a world where there are no bargains to be made disgusts him!

SAGREDO: Had you known about these Dutch instruments?

GALILEO: Of course, from hearsay. But I constructed one twice as good for those signorial money-bags. How can I work with a bailiff in the room? And Virginia will certainly be needing a dowry soon. She's not intelligent. And then, I like to buy books — not only about physics — and I like to eat decently. It's when I'm eating that I get most inspiration. A rotten age! They haven't paid me as much as the man who drives their wine-carts. Four cords of kindling wood for two lectures on mathematics. I have now extracted five hundred scudi from them, but I still have debts, some of them twenty years old. Five years respite for research, and I should have proved everything. — Now I will show you something else.

SAGREDO *(hesitates to approach the telescope):*   I have a feeling very like fear, Galileo.

GALILEO: I am now going to show you one of the shining, milk-white clouds of the Galaxy. Tell me what it is composed of.

SAGREDO: Those are stars. Countless stars.

GALILEO: In the constellations of Orion alone there are five hundred fixed stars. Those are the many worlds, the numberless others, the further stars of which Giordano spoke. He did not see them; he predicted them.

SAGREDO: But even if the earth is a star, that's still a long way from the assertions of Copernicus that it revolves round the sun. There is no star in Heaven round which another one revolves. Except that the moon revolves round the earth.

GALILEO: Sagredo, I have been wondering. Since the day before yesterday I have been wondering. There is Jupiter. *(He focuses on it.)* There are four smaller stars close by it, which you can only see through the telescope. I saw them on Monday, but took no particular notice of their position. Yesterday I looked again. I could have sworn that all four had changed their position. I made a note of it. Now their position is different again. What's this? I saw four. *(Excitedly):* Look! Look!

SAGREDO: I see three.

GALILEO: Where is the fourth? Here are the tables. We must calculate what movements they could have made.
   (They set to work excitedly. It grows dark on the stage, but on the circular horizon Jupiter and its satellites are still visible. When it becomes light again, GALILEO and SAGREDO are still sitting there, with their winter cloaks on.)

GALILEO: It is proved. The fourth can only have gone behind Jupiter, where it cannot be seen. There you have a star round which another revolves.

SAGREDO: But the crystal sphere to which Jupiter is attached?

GALILEO: Yes, where is it now? How can Jupiter be attached to anything when other stars circle round it? There is no framework in Heaven, there is no fixity in the universe. There is another sun!

SAGREDO: Calm yourself. You think too quickly.

GALILEO: Quickly! Rouse yourself, man! What you have seen, no one has seen before. — They were right.

SAGREDO: Who? The Copernicans?

GALILEO: And the others! The whole world was against them, and they were right. This is something for Andrea! *(Beside himself with excitement, he runs to the door and shouts:)* Signora Sarti! Signora Sarti!

SAGREDO: Galileo, calm yourself!

GALILEO: Sagredo, excite yourself! Signora Sarti!

SAGREDO *(turns the telescope away):* Will you stop roaring around like a lunatic?

GALILEO: And will you stop standing there like a cod-fish — when the truth has been discovered.

SAGREDO: I am not standing like a cod-fish, but I tremble lest it may in fact be the truth.

GALILEO: What?

SAGREDO: Have you entirely lost your senses? Do you really no longer know what you are involved in, if what you see there is true? And you go shouting about for all the world to hear: that the earth is a star and not the centre of the universe.

GALILEO: Yes! And that the whole, vast universe with all its stars does not revolve round our tiny earth — as must be obvious to everyone.

SAGREDO: So that there are only stars there! — And where then is God?

GALILEO: What do you mean?

SAGREDO: God! Where is God?

GALILEO *(angrily):* Not there! Any more than he could be found on earth, if there were beings up there and they were to seek him here!

SAGREDO: Then where *is* God?

GALILEO: Am I a theologian? I'm a mathematician.

SAGREDO: First and foremost, you are a man. And I ask you, where is God in your universe?

GALILEO: In us or nowhere.

SAGREDO *(shouting):* As the heretic Giordano said?

GALILEO: As the heretic Giordano said.

SAGREDO: That was why he was burnt! Not ten years ago!

The Life of Galileo

GALILEO: Because he could prove nothing. Because he only stated it. — Signora Sarti!

SAGREDO: Galileo, I have always regarded you as a shrewd man. For seventeen years in Padua and for three years in Pisa you patiently instructed hundreds of pupils in the Ptolemaic system which the Church supports and the Scriptures, on which the Church is founded, confirm. You thought it untrue, like Copernicus; but you taught it.

GALILEO: Because I could *prove* nothing.

SAGREDO *(incredulously):* And you believe that makes a difference?

GALILEO: All the difference in the world! Look here, Sagredo. I believe in mankind, and that means I believe in its commonsense. Without that belief I should not have the strength to get up from my bed in the morning.

SAGREDO: Then I will tell you something. I do *not* believe in it. Forty years among men has consistently taught me that they are not amenable to commonsense. Show them the red tail of a comet, fill them with black terror, and they will all come running out of their houses and break their legs. But tell them one sensible proposition, and support it with seven reasons, and they will simply laugh in your face.

GALILEO: That is untrue — and a slander. I cannot understand how you, believing such a thing, can yet love science. Only the dead are no longer moved by reason.

SAGREDO: How can you confuse their miserable cunning with reason?

GALILEO: I am not speaking of their cunning. I know they call a donkey a horse when they want to sell, and a horse a donkey when they want to buy. That is their cunning. The old woman who, on the eve of a journey, gives her mule an extra bundle of hay with her horny hand; the mariner who, when laying in stores, thinks of storms and calms ahead; the child who pulls on his cap when it is proved to him that it may rain — they are my hope — they all listen to reason. Yes, I believe in the gentle power of reason, of commonsense, over men. They cannot resist it in the long run. No man can watch for long and see how I — *(he lets fall a stone from his hand to the floor)* — drop a stone, and then say: 'It does not fall.' No man is capable of that. The temptation offered by such a proof is too great. Most succumb to it, and in the long run — all. Thinking is one of the greatest pleasures of the human race.

SIGNORA SARTI *(enters):* Do you want something, Signor Galilei?

GALILEO *(who is again at his telescope making notes, very amiably):* Yes, I want Andrea.

SIGNORA SARTI: Andrea? He is in bed and asleep.

GALILEO: Can't you wake him?

SIGNORA SARTI: But what do you need him for?

GALILEO: I want to show him something that will please him. I want him to see something that nobody besides ourselves has seen since the world began.

SIGNORA SARTI: Something through your tube again?

GALILEO: Something through my tube, Signora Sarti.

SIGNORA SARTI: And for that you expect me to wake him up in the middle of the night? Are you in your senses? He needs his sleep. I wouldn't think of waking him.

GALILEO: Definitely not?

SIGNORA SARTI: Definitely not.

GALILEO: Signora Sarti, perhaps you can help me then. — Look, a question has arisen about which we cannot agree, probably because we have read too many books. It is a question about the Heavens, a question concerning the stars. It is: would you say the larger revolves round the smaller, or the smaller round the larger?

SIGNORA SARTI (suspiciously): One never knows where one is with you, Signor Galilei. Is that a serious question, or are you trying to make fun of me again?

GALILEO: A serious question.

SIGNORA SARTI: Then you can have a quick answer. Do I set the dinner before you or do you set it before me?

GALILEO: You set it before me. Yesterday it was burnt.

SIGNORA SARTI: And why was it burnt? Because I had to bring you your shoes in the middle of cooking. Didn't I bring you your shoes?

GALILEO: I expect so.

SIGNORA SARTI: You see, you are the one who has studied and can pay.

GALILEO: I see. I see. That's simple. — Thank you, Signora Sarti.
(Exit SIGNORA SARTI, amused.)

GALILEO: And such people cannot understand the truth? They hunger for it!
(A bell for early Mass has begun to ring. Enter VIRGINIA in a cloak carrying a shaded candle.)

VIRGINIA: Good morning, father.

GALILEO: Why are you up already?

VIRGINIA: I am going with Signora Sarti to early Mass. Ludovico is coming too. What was the night like, father?

GALILEO: Clear.

VIRGINIA: May I look through it?

GALILEO: Why? *(VIRGINIA does not know what to answer.)* It's not a toy.

VIRGINIA: No, father.

GALILEO: Besides, the telescope is a disappointment — you'll hear that everywhere. It's being sold for three scudi on the streets and has already been discovered in Holland.

VIRGINIA: Haven't you seen any more new things in the sky with it?

GALILEO: Nothing for you. Only a few small cloudy spots on the left side of a big star; somehow I shall have to draw attention to them. *(Speaking across his*

The Life of Galileo

daughter to SAGREDO): Perhaps I will christen them the 'Medicean Stars' after the Grand Duke of Florence. *(To VIRGINIA again):* You will be interested to hear, Virginia, that we shall probably be moving to Florence. I have written a letter there, asking if the Grand Duke could make use of me as Court Mathematician.

VIRGINIA *(radiant):* At the Court?

SAGREDO: Galileo!

GALILEO: My friend, I need leisure. I need proofs. And I want the flesh-pots. And with that appointment I shouldn't have to drum the Ptolemaic System into the heads of private pupils. I'd have time, time, time, to work out my proofs — for what I have now is not enough. It's nothing, paltry jottings. With them I can't confront the whole world. As yet there is not a single proof that any celestial body revolves round the sun. But I will produce proofs, proofs for everyone from Signora Sarti up to the Pope. My one anxiety is that the Court won't take me.

VIRGINIA: Of course they will take you, father, with those new stars and everything.

GALILEO: Go to your Mass.
 (Exit VIRGINIA.)

GALILEO: I rarely write letters to great personages. *(He hands SAGREDO a letter.)* Do you think I've done it all right?

SAGREDO *(reads out loud the end of the letter which GALILEO has given him):* 'But I desire nothing so much as to be nearer you, the rising sun that will illuminte this epoch in the world's history.' — The Grand Duke of Florence is nine.

GALILEO: That's it. I see you find my letter too servile. I have been wondering whether it is servile enough, not too formal, as if I really lacked the proper humility. A reticent letter can be written by anyone who has had the merit of expounding Aristotle, but not by me. A man such as I can only obtain a moderately dignified situation by coming crawling on his belly. And you know, I despise people whose brains are not capable of filling their bellies.
 (SIGNORA SARTI and VIRGINIA pass through on their way to Mass.)

SAGREDO: Don't go to Florence, Galileo.

GALILEO: Why not?

SAGREDO: Because the monks are in control there.

GALILEO: At the Florentine court there are scholars of repute.

SAGREDO: Lackeys.

GALILEO: I will seize them by their necks and drag them in front of the telescope. Even monks are human, Sagredo. They succumb to the temptation of proof. Copernicus, don't forget, demanded that they believe his figures; but I only demand that they believe their eyes. If the truth is too weak to defend itself, it must go over to the attack. I will take hold of them and force them to look through that telescope.

SAGREDO: Galileo, I see you setting out on a fearful road. It is a night of disaster when a man sees the truth. And an hour of delusion when he believes in the commonsense of the human race. Of whom does one say 'he's going into it with his eyes open'? Of the man on the path to perdition. How could those in power leave at large a man who knows the truth, even though it be about the most distant stars? Do you think the Pope will hearken to your truth when you say he is in error, and yet not hear that he is in error? Do you think that *he* will simply write in his diary: January the tenth, 1610 — Heaven abolished? How can you wish to leave the Republic, with the truth in your pocket, and fall into the snares of monks and princes, telescope in hand? Sceptical as you are in your science, you are as credulous as a child about everything that seems to you to facilitate your tasks. You don't believe in Aristotle, but you believe in the Grand Duke of Florence. A little while ago, when I watched you at your telescope and you saw those new stars, it seemed to me as if I saw you standing amid the blazing faggots, and when you said you believed in proof, I smelt flesh burning. I love science, but I love you more, my friend. Do not go to Florence, Galileo.

GALILEO: If they accept me, I will go.
(In front of the curtain appears the last page of his letter:)
When I bestow on these new stars which I have discovered the illustrious name of the Medici family, I am conscious that elevation into the starry firmament was once sufficient ennoblement for the gods and heroes, but this case is the very reverse, for the illustrious name of the Medicis will guarantee these stars immortal fame. I, however, venture to bring myself to your notice as one among the number of your most humble and devoted servants and as one who counts it his highest honour to have been born your subject.

But I desire nothing so much as to be nearer to you, the rising sun that will illuminate this epoch in the world's history.

Galileo Galilei

————————— • —————————

4

GALILEO HAS EXCHANGED THE REPUBLIC OF VENICE FOR THE FLOREN-
TINE COURT. HIS DISCOVERIES WITH THE TELESCOPE MEET WITH
DISBELIEF AMONG THE SAVANTS THERE.

The Old says: As I am now, I have always been so.
The New says: If you're no good, then go.

SCENE 4: GALILEO'S HOUSE IN FLORENCE

SIGNORA SARTI in GALILEO's study, preparing it for the reception of guests. Her son, ANDREA, is sitting and tidying up star-charts.

SIGNORA SARTI: Ever since we arrived in this blessed Florence, the bowing and scraping and lick-spittling has never stopped. The whole city traipses through to look at that tube, and I have to clean up the floor after them! And it's not a bit of good! If there was anything in these discoveries, the holy fathers would be the first to know. I was four years in service with Monsignor Filippo and was never able to dust all through his library. Leather books right to the ceiling and not so much as a love poem. And the good Monsignor had a mass of bunions on his bottom from all that sitting over his learning, and wouldn't a man like that know what was what? And the great viewing today will be such a fiasco that again tomorrow I shan't be able to look the milkman in the face. I knew what I was

talking about when I advised him first to set a good supper for the gentlemen, a nice piece of lamb, before they look over his tube. But no! *(She mimics GALILEO):* 'I have something else for them.'
(A sound of knocking below.)

SIGNORA SARTI *(looks into the spy-mirror at the window):* Heaven save us, here's the Grand Duke already. And Galileo is still at the University! *(She runs down the stairs and lets in the Grand Duke of Tuscany, COSIMO DE' MEDICI, who is accompanied by his CHAMBERLAIN and two court ladies.)*

COSIMO: I want to see the telescope.

THE CHAMBERLAIN: Perhaps your Highness will wait patiently until Signor Galilei and the other gentlemen have arrived from the University. *(To SIGNORA SARTI):* Signor Galilei wished the astronomers to test his discovery of the new Medicean Stars.

COSIMO: They don't believe in the telescope. They don't at all. And where is it?

SIGNORA SARTI: Upstairs, in his study.
(The boy nods, points up the stairs, and at a nod from SIGNORA SARTI runs up.)

THE CHAMBERLAIN *(a very old man):* Your Highness! *(To SIGNORA SARTI): Must* one go up there? I have only come because the tutor is ill.

SIGNORA SARTI: The young gentleman will come to no harm. My own boy is up there.

COSIMO *(entering upstairs):* Good evening.
(The boys bow ceremoniously to one another. Pause. Then ANDREA turns again to his work.)

ANDREA *(very like his teacher):* It's like a cross-roads here.

COSIMO: Many visitors?

ANDREA: Clumping around, gaping — and not understanding a sausage.

COSIMO: I see. Is that . . . ? *(He points to the telescope.)*

ANDREA: Yes, that's it. But orders are: hands off!

COSIMO: And what's that? *(He points at the wooden model of the Ptolemaic system.)*

ANDREA: That's the Ptolemaic.

COSIMO: That shows how the sun revolves, doesn't it?

ANDREA: Yes, so they say.

COSIMO *(sits down on a chair and takes the model on his lap):* My tutor's got a cold. So I was able to get away early. It's nice here.

ANDREA *(restless, wanders about undecidedly, looking at the strange boy mistrustfully. At last, unable to resist the temptation any longer, he pulls out a second wooden model from behind the charts. It is a representation of the Copernican system):* But it's really like this, of course.

COSIMO: What's like that?

ANDREA *(pointing to COSIMO's model):* That's what they think it's like, and this — *(pointing to his model)* — is what it is. The earth turns round the sun, do you see?

COSIMO: Do you really think so?

ANDREA: Of course. It's proved.

COSIMO: Really? I'd like to know why they don't ever let me see the old man any more. Yesterday he was there at supper.

ANDREA: They don't seem to believe it, eh?

COSIMO: Of course they do.

ANDREA *(suddenly pointing at the model in COSIMO's lap):* Give it here. You don't even understand *that* one.

COSIMO: You don't need two.

ANDREA: Give it here. It's not a toy for little boys.

COSIMO: I don't mind giving it to you, but you must be a little more polite, you know.

ANDREA: You're a silly fool, and be polite yourself! Give it to me or you'll be sorry.

COSIMO: Don't touch me, do you hear!
(They begin to struggle and are soon rolling on the floor.)

ANDREA: I'll teach you how to treat a model. Give up!

COSIMO: Now it's broken. You're twisting my arm.

ANDREA: We'll soon see who's right and who's wrong. Say it revolves or I'll give you a clout on the head.

COSIMO: Never. Ow! You carrots! I'll teach you manners.

ANDREA: Carrots? Me a carrots?
(They fight on in silence.
Down below GALILEO and several professors of the University enter.
Behind them FEDERZONI.)

THE CHAMBERLAIN: Gentlemen, a slight indisposition has prevented His Highness's tutor, Signor Suri, from accompanying His Highness here.

THE THEOLOGIAN: Nothing serious, I trust?

THE CHAMBERLAIN: Not at all. Not at all.

GALILEO *(disappointed):* His Highness is not here?

THE CHAMBERLAIN: His Highness is upstairs. But pray, gentlemen, do not wait. The Court is exceedingly curious to learn the illustrious University's opinion on this extraordinary instrument of Signor Galilei's and to become acquainted with his wonderful new stars.
(They go up.
The boys are lying still, having heard the sounds downstairs.)

COSIMO: They're here. Let me up.
(They get up quickly.)

VARIOUS GENTLEMEN *(as they climb the stairs):* No, no, everything's perfectly all right. — The medical faculty declare it impossible for the sickness in the Old Town to be cases of plague. The miasmas would freeze at the present temperature. — The worst thing in such circumstances is always panic. — Nothing but the epidemic of colds usual at this time of year. — Any suspicion out of the question. — Everything's perfectly all right.
(Greetings upstairs.)

GALILEO: Your Highness, I am happy, in your presence, to be able to acquaint the gentlemen of your University with my latest discoveries.
(COSIMO bows very formally in all directions, even to ANDREA.)

THE THEOLOGIAN *(seeing the broken Ptolemaic model on the floor):* Something seems to have got broken here.
(COSIMO bends down quickly and politely hands the model to ANDREA. Meanwhile GALILEO surreptitiously moves the other model out of sight.)

GALILEO *(at the telescope):* As your Highness doubtless knows, for some time past we astronomers have been in great difficulties with our calculations. For these we use a very old system which appears to coincide with philosophy, but not, alas with facts. According to this old system — the Ptolemaic — the movements of the stars are presumed to be extremely complicated. For instance, the planet Venus is supposed to follow an orbit of this sort. *(On the blackboard he draws the epicyclic orbit of Venus according to the Ptolemaic conception.)* But even accepting such complicated movements, we are still not able to calculate the positions of the stars correctly. We do not find them in the places where they apparently should be. And furthermore there are certain movements of the stars for which the Ptolemaic system has no explanation at all. Movements of this sort seem to me to be described by the little stars round the planet Jupiter, which I have recently discovered. Would the gentlemen care to begin with an observation of the satellites of Jupiter, the Medicean stars?

ANDREA *(pointing to the stool in front of the telescope):* Please sit here.

THE PHILOSOPHER: Thank you, my child. I fear that things are not quite as simple as all that. Signor Galilei, before we apply ourselves to your famous instrument we would like to have the pleasure of a disputation. The theme: Can such planets exist?

THE MATHEMATICIAN: A formal disputation.

GALILEO: I thought you could simply look through the telescope and convince yourselves.

ANDREA: Here, please.

THE MATHEMATICIAN: Of course, of course. — Naturally, you know that according to the ancient stars revolving about a centre other than the earth cannot exist, nor can there be stars which have no support in the Heavens?

GALILEO: Yes.

THE PHILOSOPHER: And quite apart from the possibility of such stars, which the mathematician — *(he bows to the mathematician)* — appears to doubt,

I would, in all modesty, as a philosopher, like to pose the question: are such stars necessary? Aristotelis divini universum . . .

GALILEO: Should we not continue in the vernacular? My colleague, Signor Federzoni, does not understand Latin.

THE PHILOSOPHER: Is it of importance that he should understand us?

GALILEO: Yes.

THE PHILOSOPHER: Excuse me. I thought he was your lens-grinder.

ANDREA: Signor Federzoni is a lens-grinder and a scholar.

THE PHILOSOPHER: Thank you, my child. If Signor Federzoni insists . . .

GALILEO: *I* insist.

THE PHILOSOPHER: The argument will lose in elegance, but it is your house. — The cosmos of the divine Aristotle, with its mystical, music-making spheres and crystal domes and the gyrations of its heavenly bodies and the oblique angle of the sun's orbit and the secrets of the satellite tables and the rich catalogue of constellations in the southern hemisphere and the inspired construction of the celestial globe, is a conception of such symmetry and beauty that we should do well to hesitate before disturbing that harmony.

GALILEO: How would it be if your Highness were now to observe these impossible as well as unnecessary stars through this telescope?

THE MATHEMATICIAN: One might be tempted to reply that your telescope, showing something which cannot exist, may not be a very reliable telescope, eh?

GALILEO: What do you mean?

THE MATHEMATICIAN: It would be much more helpful, Signor Galilei, if you were to tell us the reasons which lead you to the assumption that in the highest spheres of the immutable Heaven stars can move freely through space.

THE PHILOSOPHER: Reasons, Signor Galilei, reasons.

GALILEO: The reasons? — When a glance at the stars themselves and my own observations will demonstrate the phenomenon. Sir, the disputation is becoming absurd.

THE MATHEMATICIAN: If one could be sure that you would not excite yourself further, one might suggest that what is in your telescope and what is in the Heavens may be two different things.

THE PHILOSOPHER: That could not have been more courteously expressed.

FEDERZONI: You think we painted the Medicean stars on the lens!

GALILEO: Are you accusing me of fraud?

THE PHILOSOPHER: But how could we? In the presence of his Highness!

THE MATHEMATICIAN: Your instrument — whether one calls it your child or your pupil — is certainly most cleverly made, no doubt about that!

THE PHILOSOPHER: And we are entirely convinced, Signor Galilei, that neither you nor anyone else would dare to bestow the illustrious name of our ruling house on stars whose existence was not beyond all possible doubt.

(They all bow low to the Grand Duke.)

COSIMO *(looks round to the court ladies):* Is there something not right with my stars?

THE OLDER COURT LADY *(to the Grand Duke):* Everything is all right with the stars, your Highness. The gentlemen are only asking whether they really and truly are there.
  (Pause.)

THE YOUNGER COURT LADY: One is said to be able to see every hair on the Great Bear through that instrument.

FEDERZONI: Yes, and all sorts of things on the Bull.

GALILEO: Well, will you gentlemen now look through it, or not?

THE PHILOSOPHER: Certainly, of course.

THE MATHEMATICIAN: Of course.
  (Pause. Suddenly ANDREA turns and walks stiffly across the whole room. His mother catches hold of him.)

SIGNORA SARTI: What's the matter with you?

ANDREA: They're stupid. *(He tears himself loose and runs off.)*

THE PHILOSOPHER: Deplorable child.

THE CHAMBERLAIN: Your Highness, gentlemen, may I remind you that the Court Ball opens in three-quarters of an hour?

THE MATHEMATICIAN: Why mince matters? Sooner or later Signor Galilei will have to reconcile himself with the facts. His planets of Jupiter would break through the crystal spheres. It is quite simple.

FEDERZONI: You'll be astonished! There are no crystal spheres.

THE PHILOSOPHER: Every school-book will tell you they exist, my good man.

FEDERZONI: Then hurrah for new school-books.

THE PHILOSOPHER: Your Highness, my worthy colleague and I rely on the authority of none less than the divine Aristotle himself.

GALILEO *(almost obsequiously):* Gentlemen, belief in the authority of Aristotle is one thing; facts, tangible facts, are another. You say that according to Aristotle there are crystal spheres up there and therefore certain movements cannot take place because the stars would have to break through those spheres. But what if you can confirm those movements? Perhaps that will persuade you that those crystal spheres simply don't exist. Gentlemen, I beseech you in all humility to trust your eyes.

THE MATHEMATICIAN: My dear Galileo, old-fashioned though it may sound to you, I am accustomed among other things to read Aristotle, and I can assure you that there I do trust my eyes.

GALILEO: I am used to seeing members of all faculties shutting their eyes against every fact and behaving as though nothing has happened. I offer my observations, and they smile. I place my telescope at their disposal so that they can convince themselves, and they quote Aristotle. But the man had no telescope!

THE MATHEMATICIAN: Certainly not. Certainly not.

THE PHILOSOPHER *(sweepingly):* If Aristotle — an authority recognised not only by the entire learning of antiquity but also by the Holy Fathers of the Church — if Aristotle is to be dragged through the mud, then it seems, to me at least, that a continuation of this discussion is superfluous. I avoid pointless discussion. Enough!

GALILEO: Truth is the child of time, not of authority. Our ignorance is infinite, so let us diminish it by a fraction. Why try to be so clever now, when at last we can become a little less stupid? I have had the unbelievable good fortune to lay my hands on a new instrument by means of which one can see any tiny corner of the universe a little clearer. Not much — but a little. Make use of it!

THE PHILOSOPHER: Your Highness, ladies and gentlemen, I am just asking myself where all this may lead.

GALILEO: I would suggest that as scientists it is not for us to ask where the truth may lead us.

THE PHILOSOPHER *(furiously):* Signor Galilei, the truth may lead us to absolutely anything.

GALILEO: Your Highness. On nights such as these, all over Italy telescopes are being turned towards the Heavens. Jupiter's moons will not make milk any cheaper. But they have never been seen before, and they are there. From that the man in the street draws the conclusion that there may be many more things to see if only he opens his eyes. You owe him that confirmation. It is not the movements of a few distant stars that make all Italy prick up its ears, but the news that opinions hitherto held inviolable have now begun to totter — and everyone knows there are too many of those. Gentlemen, let us not defend dying teachings.

FEDERZONI: You, as teachers, should hasten their end.

THE PHILOSOPHER: I should prefer your man not to proffer advice in a scientific disputation.

GALILEO: Your Highness. My work in the Great Arsenal of Venice brought me into daily contact with draughtsmen, builders and instrument-makers. These people taught me many a new way of doing things. Illiterate, they relied on the evidence of their five senses, in most cases regardless of where such evidence might lead them . . .

THE PHILOSOPHER: Oho!

GALILEO: Very like our mariners, who a hundred years ago left our shores without knowing what sort of other shores they might reach, if any at all. It seems that today, in order to find that high curiosity which made the true greatness of ancient Greece, one has to resort to the shipyards.

THE PHILOSOPHER: After all that we have heard here, I have no longer any doubt that Signor Galilei will find admirers in the shipyards.

THE CHAMBERLAIN: Your Highness, to my dismay I find that this extraordinarily   instructive conversation has become somewhat long drawn out. Your Highness must rest a while before the Court Ball.
(At a sign the Grand Duke bows to GALILEO. The COURT rapidly begins to leave.)

SIGNOR SARTI (*places herself in front of the Grand Duke and offers him a plate of pastries*):   A biscuit, your Highness?
   (*The older court lady leads the Grand Duke out.*)

GALILEO (*running after them*):   But really, you gentlemen need only look through the instrument!

THE CHAMBERLAIN: His Highness will not fail to obtain an opinion on your claims from the greatest living astronomer, Father Christopher Clavius, Astronomer-in-Chief at the Papal College in Rome.

————————— • —————————

5

UNDAUNTED EVEN BY THE PLAGUE, GALILEO CONTINUES HIS RESEARCHES

SCENE 5a: GALILEO'S STUDY IN FLORENCE

Early morning. GALILEO over his notes, at the telescope. Enter VIRGINIA with a travelling bag.

GALILEO: Virginia! Has something happened?

VIRGINIA: The convent has closed; we have been sent straight home. There are five cases of plague in Arcetri.

GALILEO (*calls out*):   Sarti!

VIRGINIA: The market-street has been closed off since this morning. In the Old Town there are said to be two dead and three dying in hospital.

GALILEO: Once again they've kept everything secret till the last moment.

SIGNORA SARTI (*enters*):   What are you doing here?

VIRGINIA: The plague.

SIGNORA SARTI: My God! I'll pack. (*She sits down.*)

GALILEO: Pack nothing. Take Virginia and Andrea. I'll collect my notes.
   (*He runs quickly back to his table and shovels papers together in great haste. SIGNORA SARTI puts a cloak on to ANDREA, who has come running in, and fetches some bedding and food. Enter a grand-ducal lackey.*)

LACKEY: His Highness, on account of the prevailing sickness, has left the city for Bologna. But he insists that Signor Galilei be offered the opportunity of being brought to safety as well. The carriage will be at the door in two minutes.

SIGNORA SARTI (*to VIRGINIA and ANDREA*):   Go, go quickly. Here, take that with you.

ANDREA: But why? If you don't tell me why, I shan't go.

SIGNORA SARTI: It's the plague, my child.

VIRGINIA: We will wait for father.

SIGNORA SARTI: Signor Galilei, are you ready?

GALILEO *(who is wrapping the telescope in the table-cloth):* Put Virginia and Andrea in the carriage. I'll come immediately.

VIRGINIA: No. We won't go without you. You'll never be ready if you once start packing your books.

SIGNORA SARTI: The coach is here.

GALILEO: Be sensible, Virginia; if you two don't get in, the coachman will drive away. The plague — that's no light matter.

VIRGINIA *(protesting, as SIGNORA SARTI shepherds her and ANDREA out):* Help him with his books, otherwise he'll never come.

SIGNORA SARTI *(calls from the front door):* Signor Galilei, the coachman refuses to wait!

GALILEO: Signora Sarti, I do not think I should leave. Everything is in disorder, you know; I might as well throw away the last three months' notes if I cannot go on with them for one or two more nights. And this pestilence is everywhere, after all.

SIGNORA SARTI: Signor Galilei! Come down at once. You are out of your mind!

GALILEO: You must go on with Virginia and Andrea. I'll follow later.

SIGNORA SARTI: In another hour no one will be allowed to leave the city. You must come! *(She listens.)* He is driving off! I must stop him!
(Exit.
GALILEO walks backwards and forwards. SIGNORA SARTI returns, very pale, without her bundle of luggage.)

GALILEO: Why are you standing about? The carriage with the children will go off without you.

SIGNORA SARTI: They have gone. They had to hold Virginia in. Someone will look after the children in Bologna. But who would prepare your food here?

GALILEO: You are out of your mind. To stay in the city for the sake of cooking . . .! *(He picks up his notes.)* Don't think I am a fool, Signora Sarti. I cannot abandon my observations. I have powerful enemies and must collect my proofs for certain theories.

SIGNORA SARTI: You don't need to apologise. But it's not sensible.

———————— • ————————

SCENE 5b: OUTSIDE GALILEO'S HOUSE IN FLORENCE

GALILEO steps out and looks down the street. Two nuns walk past.

GALILEO *(addresses them):* Can you tell me, sisters, where I can buy some milk? This morning the milk-woman did not come and my housekeeper is out.

A NUN: Shops are open only in the Lower Town now.

ANOTHER NUN: Have you come out of there? *(GALILEO nods.)* This is the street!

(Both nuns cross themselves, murmur a Hail Mary and hurry away. A man comes along.)

GALILEO *(addresses him):* Aren't you the baker who brings us white bread? *(The man nods.)* Have you seen my housekeeper? She must have gone out yesterday evening. She wasn't in the house this morning.
(The man shakes his head.
A window opposite opens and a woman looks out.)

THE WOMAN *(shouting):* Run! They have the plague over there!
(The man runs away in terror.)

GALILEO: Do you know anything about my housekeeper?

THE WOMAN: Your housekeeper collapsed down the street. She must have known it. That's why she left. Such inconsiderateness! *(She slams the window shut.)*
(Some children come down the street. They see GALILEO and run away screaming. GALILEO turns and two soldiers covered from head to foot in armour come running in.)

SOLDIERS: Back into your house immediately!
(With their long lances they push GALILEO back into his house. Behind him they barricade the door.)

GALILEO *(at the window):* Can you tell me what has happened to my housekeeper?

SOLDIERS: They are all being taken to the meadows.

THE WOMAN *(appears at her window again):* The whole of that side of the street is plagued. Why don't you close it off?
(The soldiers tie a rope across the street.)

THE WOMAN: But now no one can get into our house either! There's no need to shut *us* off! Everyone is healthy here. Stop! Stop! Listen to me. My husband is still in the town, and he won't be able to get back to us. You brutes, you brutes!
(She can be heard inside sobbing and screaming. The soldiers go off. At another window appears an old woman.)

GALILEO: There must be a fire over there.

THE OLD WOMAN: They no longer put a fire out where plague is suspected. No one thinks of anything but plague.

GALILEO: How like them that is! That's their whole system of government. They lop us off like the infected branch of a fig-tree that can no longer bear fruit.

THE OLD WOMAN: You mustn't say that. They are just helpless.

GALILEO: Are you alone in the house?

THE OLD WOMAN: Yes. My son sent me a note. Thank God, he discovered yesterday evening that someone had died over here, and he didn't come home. There were eleven cases last night in this district.

GALILEO: I reproach myself for not having sent my housekeeper away in time. I had urgent work, but she had no reason to stay.

THE OLD WOMAN: We can't go either, now. Who would take us in? You mustn't reproach yourself. I saw her. She went out this morning early, about seven o'clock. She was ill, for when she saw me come out of the door to take in my bread, she gave me a wide berth. She probably didn't want them to close your house. But they find out everything.

(There is the sound of a rattle.)

GALILEO: What is that?

THE OLD WOMAN: They make those noises to try and disperse the clouds that harbour the plague seeds.

(GALILEO laughs loudly.)

And you can laugh!

(A man comes down the street and finds it barred by the rope.)

GALILEO: Hi, you! I am locked in here and there is nothing to eat in the house.

(The man has already run away.)

GALILEO: But you can't leave us to starve here! Hi! Hi!

THE OLD WOMAN: Perhaps they will bring something. Otherwise, but only after dark, I can leave a jug of milk outside your door if you are not afraid.

GALILEO: Hi! Hi! Someone must hear us!

(ANDREA suddenly stands by the rope. His face is stained with tears.)

GALILEO: Andrea! How did you get here?

ANDREA: I was here earlier. I knocked, but you didn't open. The people told me that . . .

GALILEO: Didn't you leave in the carriage?

ANDREA: Yes, but on the way I managed to jump off. Virginia has gone on. Can't I come in?

THE OLD WOMAN: No, that you can't. You must go to the Ursulines. Your mother may be there.

ANDREA: I've been there. But they wouldn't let me see her. She is so ill.

GALILEO: Have you walked all the way here? It is three days since you left.

ANDREA: It took me that long; don't be angry with me. They caught me once.

GALILEO *(helplessly):* Stop crying now. Look, I have discovered all sorts of things in the meanwhile. Shall I tell you? *(ANDREA nods, sobbing.)* Well, listen carefully or you won't understand. Do you remember when I showed you the planet Venus? Don't listen to that noise, that's nothing. Can you remember? Do you know what I have seen? It is like the moon! I have seen it as a hemisphere and I have seen it as a crescent. What do you say to that? I can show it all to you with a little ball and a candle. It proves that that planet, too, has no light of its own. And it revolves round the sun, in a simple circle. Isn't that wonderful?

ANDREA *(sobbing):* Yes, and it's a fact.

GALILEO *(softly):* I didn't keep her here.

(ANDREA is silent.)

GALILEO: But of course if I hadn't stayed, it wouldn't have happened.

ANDREA: Will they have to believe you now?

GALILEO: I have assembled all my proofs now. Do you know, when this is all over, I shall go to Rome and show them.
(Down the street come two men, muffled up and carrying long poles with buckets on the end. They pass bread, first to GALILEO and then to the old woman, through the windows.)

THE OLD WOMAN: And over there is a woman with three children. Put in something for them, too.

GALILEO: But I have nothing to drink. There is no water in the house. *(The two men shrug their shoulders.)* Will you be coming again tomorrow?

ONE OF THE MEN *(in a smothered voice as he has a cloth over his mouth):* Who knows today what tomorrow will bring?

GALILEO: If you do come could you also hand me a little book that I need for my work?

THE MAN *(laughs hollowly):* As if a book mattered now! Be thankful if you get your bread.

GALILEO: But that boy, my pupil, will be here to give it to you for me. — It's the map with the period of rotation of Mercury, Andrea; I've mislaid it. Will you get one from the school?
(The two men have already walked away.)

ANDREA: Of course. I'll fetch it, Signor Galilei. *(Exit.)*
(GALILEO withdraws from the window. From the house opposite the old woman steps out and places a jug by GALILEO's door.)

———————— • ————————

6

1616: THE COLLEGIUM ROMANUM, THE VATICAN'S INSTITUTE OF RESEARCH, CONFIRMS GALILEO'S DISCOVERIES

Things take indeed a wondrous turn
When learned men do stoop to learn.
Clavius, we are pleased to say,
Upheld Galileo Galilei

SCENE 6: HALL OF THE COLLEGIUM ROMANUM IN ROME

It is night. High church dignitaries, monks and scholars in groups. To one side stands GALILEO — alone. The atmosphere is very boisterous. Before the scene begins one hears roars of thunderous laughter.

THE FAT PRELATE *(clutching his stomach with mirth):* Oh stupidity! Oh stupidity! I wish someone would tell me one proposition that would *not* be believed!

THE SCHOLAR: For example, that you have an unconquerable aversion to dining, monsignor!

THE FAT PRELATE: They'd believe it! They'd believe it! Only the reasonable is not believed. That a Devil exists — that's doubted. But that the earth spins round like a marble in the gutter — that's believed! Sancta simplicitas!

A MONK (play-acting): I feel dizzy. The earth's turning too fast. Permit me to hold on to you, professor. (He pretends to sway and clings to one of the scholars.)

THE SCHOLAR (joining in the game): Yes, she's drunk again today, our dear old Mother Earth. (He clutches at another.)

THE MONK: Stop, stop! We're slipping off. Stop, I say!

A SECOND SCHOLAR: Venus is quite crooked already. I can only see half of her behind! Help!
(A group of monks collects. Laughing, they act as if trying to save themselves from being thrown off a ship in a storm.)

A SECOND MONK: If only we don't get flung on to the moon. Brothers, they say it's got horribly sharp mountain peaks!

THE FIRST SCHOLAR: Steady yourself with your feet.

THE FIRST MONK: And don't look down. I get giddy.

THE FAT PRELATE (intentionally loud, in GALILEO's direction): Impossible! Giddiness in the Collegium Romanum!
(Loud laughter.
Through the door at the back enter two astronomers of the College.
Silence falls.)

A MONK: Are you still investigating? Scandalous!

THE FIRST ASTRONOMER (angrily): We are not!

THE SECOND ASTRONOMER: Where will this lead? I cannot understand Clavius . . . If one had accepted as sterling truth everything claimed during the past five years! In the year 1572, in the highest sphere, the eighth, the sphere of fixed stars, a new constellation blazes, far brighter and larger than all its neighbours, and before eighteen months have passed it vanishes again and returns to oblivion. Might one ask: what of the eternal duration and immutability of the Heavens?

THE PHILOSOPHER: If one let them, they would demolish our whole universe.

THE FIRST ASTRONOMER: Yes, what are we coming to? Five years later the Dane, Tycho Brahe, determines the track of a comet. It started up above the moon and broke through one after another of the crystal spheres, the solid carriers of the moving constellations! It meets with no resistance, it suffers no refraction of its light. Should one ask: where are the spheres?

THE PHILOSOPHER: Quite out of the question! How can Christopher Clavius, Italy's and the Church's great astronomer, even investigate such a thing?

THE FAT PRELATE: Scandalous!

THE FIRST ASTRONOMER: But he *is* investigating it! He's sitting in there and peering through that devil's tube!

THE SECOND ASTRONOMER: Principiis obsta! It all began by our calculating so many things from the tables of Copernicus, who is a heretic! The length of the solar years, the dates of eclipses of the sun and moon, the positions of the celestial bodies for years ahead.

A MONK: I ask you which is better: to experience an eclipse three days after it appears in the calendar, or eternal salvation never?

A VERY THIN MONK *(steps forward with an open Bible, pointing his finger frantically at a passage):* What is said in the Holy Writ? 'Sun, stand thou still upon Gibeon; and thou, Moon, in the Valley of Ajalon.' How can the sun stand still if it never moves, as these heretics aver? Does Holy Writ lie?

THE FIRST ASTRONOMER: No — and that is why we are leaving.

THE SECOND ASTRONOMER: There are phenomena which present difficulties to us astronomers, but does man have to understand everything?
(Both exeunt.)

THE VERY THIN MONK: They equate the home of the human race to a wandering star. They pack men, animals, plants, and the earth itself on to a cart and trundle it in a circle through an empty sky. Earth and Heaven exist no more according to them. The earth no more, because it is a star in Heaven; and Heaven no more, because it is made up of earths. There is no longer any difference between the Upper and the Lower. Between the Eternal and the Temporal. That we pass away, we know. That Heaven too passes away, they now inform us. There are sun, moon and stars, and we live on the earth; so it was said, and so it is written. But now the earth, too, is a star according to them. There is nothing but stars! We shall yet live to see the day when they will say: there are no longer men and animals, man is an animal, there is nothing but animals!

THE FIRST SCHOLAR *(to GALILEO):* Signor Galilei, you have dropped something on the floor.

GALILEO *(who during the foregoing has taken his stone out of a pocket, played with it, and finally let it fall to the ground, as he stoops to pick it up):* No, Monsignor. It fell up to me.

THE FAT PRELATE *(turning away):* Impudent rascal.
(Enter a very old cardinal supported by a monk. Everyone respectfully makes way for him.)

THE VERY OLD CARDINAL: Are they still in there? Can they really not dispose of this triviality more quickly? Clavius ought to understand his own astronomy. I hear that this Signor Galilei banishes mankind from the centre of the universe to somewhere at the edge. He is, therefore, plainly an enemy of the human race. And he should be treated as such. Man is the crown of creation, every child knows that, God's highest and most beloved creature. How could He place such a miracle, such a masterpiece, on a little remote and for ever wandering star? Would He have sent His Son to such a place? How can there be people so perverse as to believe in these slaves of their own mathematical tables? Which of God's creatures would submit to such a thing?

THE FAT PRELATE *(sotto voice):* The gentleman is present.

THE VERY OLD CARDINAL *(to GALILEO):* So you are the person? I no longer see very well, but what I can see is enough to show me that you are remarkably like that man we burnt here in his time. What was his name?

THE MONK: Your Eminence should not excite himself. The doctor . . .

THE VERY OLD CARDINAL *(shaking him off, to GALILEO):* You wish to degrade the earth, although you live on it and receive everything from it. You would foul your own nest! But I at least will have none of it! *(He pushes the monk away and begins proudly pacing up and down.)* I an not just any being on just any little star circling round somewhere for a short time. I tread the firm earth, with a sure step; it is at rest; it is the centre of the universe; I am at the centre, and the eye of the Creator rests on me and on me alone. Around me revolve, attached to eight crystalline spheres, the fixed stars and the mighty sun which was created to shed light upon my surroundings. And upon me too, in order that God may see me. And so, visibly and irrefutably, everything depends on me, on Man, the masterpiece of God, the centre of Creation, the very image of God, immortal and . . . *(He collapses.)*

THE MONK: Your Eminence has overstrained himself.
(At this moment the door at the back opens and the great CLAVIUS enters at the head of his astronomers. He walks through the hall hurriedly and in silence, not looking to right or left. Just as he is leaving the hall he speaks to a monk.)

CLAVIUS: He is right.
(He goes out, followed by the astronomers. The door at the back remains open. A dead silence falls. The very old cardinal revives.)

THE VERY OLD CARDINAL: What is it? Have they reached a decision?
(No one dares to tell him.)

THE MONK: Your Eminence must be taken home.
(The old man is helped out. All leave the hall bewildered. A little monk from CLAVIUS' commission of investigation stops beside GALILEO.)

THE LITTLE MONK *(surreptitiously):* Signor Galilei, Father Clavius said before he left: Now let the theologians see how they can put their heavenly rings together again! You have won. *(Exit.)*

GALILEO *(tries to hold him back):* It has won! Not I but commonsense has won!
(The little monk has already gone. GALILEO leaves too. In the doorway he encounters a tall priest, the CARDINAL INQUISITOR. An astronomer accompanies him. GALILEO bows. Before he goes out, he whispers a question to the lackey at the door.)

THE LACKEY *(whispering back):* His Eminence, the Cardinal Inquisitor. *(The astronomer leads the CARDINAL INQUISITOR to the Telescope.)*

———————— • ————————

7

BUT THE INQUISITION PUTS THE COPERNICAN TEACHINGS ON THE INDEX
(MARCH 5th, 1616)

When Galileo was in Rome
A Cardinal asked him to his home
He wined and dined him as his guest
And only made one small request.

SCENE 7: CARDINAL BELLARMIN'S HOUSE IN ROME

A ball is in progress. In the vestibule, where two clerks in holy orders are playing chess and making notes about the guests, GALILEO is received with applause by a little group of masked ladies and gentlemen. He arrives in the company of his daughter, VIRGINIA, and her betrothed, LUDOVICO MARSILI.

VIRGINIA: I shall dance with no one else, Ludovico.

LUDOVICO: Your shoulder-strap is loose.

GALILEO: 'Fret not, daughter, if perchance
You attract a wanton glance.
The eyes that catch a trembling lace
Will guess the heartbeat's quickened pace.
Lovely women still may be
Careless with felicity.'

VIRGINIA: Feel my heart.

GALILEO *(lays his hand on her heart):* It's beating.

VIRGINIA: I want to look beautiful.

GALILEO: You must, or people will soon start wondering once more whether the earth really goes round.

LUDOVICO: But it doesn't. *(GALILEO laughs.)* All Rome talks of nothing but you. But after this evening, Signor, it's your daughter they'll be talking about.

GALILEO: They say it is easy to look beautiful in the Roman springtime. Even I must resemble a slightly corpulent Adonis. *(To the two young clerks.)* I am supposed to await the Cardinal here. *(To the young couple.)* Go and enjoy themselves.
(Before they go off to join the ball, VIRGINIA comes running back once more.)

VIRGINIA: Father, the hairdresser in the Via del Trionfo took me first and let four other ladies wait. He knew your name immediately. *(Exit.)*

GALILEO *(to the clerks playing chess):* How can you still play that old-fashioned chess? Narrow, narrow. Nowadays people play with the important pieces moving all over the board. The rook like that — *(he demonstrates)* — and the bishop like that, and the queen here and here. That gives room, and you can lay your plans.

A CLERK: That is not commensurate with our small salaries, you know. We can only afford moves like this. *(He makes a tiny move.)*

GALILEO: On the contrary, my friend, on the contrary. Who takes big steps is given big boots. One must move with the times, gentlemen. No hugging the coast; sometimes you must put out to sea.

(The very old CARDINAL from the previous scene crosses the stage, accompanied by his monk. He catches sight of GALILEO, walks past him, then turns uncertainly and greets him. GALILEO sits down. From the ballroom can be heard boys' voices singing the beginning of LORENZO DE' MEDICI's famous poem on fugacity:)

'I, who have seen the summer's roses die
And all their petals pale and shrivelled lie
Upon the chilly ground, I know the truth:
How evanescent is the flower of youth.'

GALILEO: Rome. — Great celebrations?

FIRST CLERK: The first carnival since the plague years. All the great families in Italy are represented here this evening. The Orsinis, the Villanis, the Nuccolis, the Soldanieris, the Canes, the Lecchis, the Estes, the Colombinis . . .

SECOND CLERK *(interrupts):*   Their Eminences the Cardinals Bellarmin and Barberini.
(Enter CARDINAL BELLARMIN and CARDINAL BARBERINI. In front of their faces they each hold a mask of a lamb and a dove respectively on the end of a stick.)

BARBERINI *(pointing his index finger at GALILEO):*   'The sun also ariseth, and the sun goeth down, and hasteneth to his place where he arose.' So saith Ecclesiastes, the Preacher. And what says Galileo?

GALILEO: When I was so high, your Eminence — *(he indicates with his hand)* — I stood on a ship and I cried out: the shore is moving away! Today I know that the shore stood still and the ship moved away.

BARBERINI: Shrewd, shrewd. What one sees, Bellarmin, namely the constellations revolving, need not be true; think of the ship and the shore. But what is true, namely that the earth rotates, cannot be seen! Shrewd. But his moons of Jupiter are hard nuts for our astronomers to crack. Unfortunately, I too read some astronomy at one time, Bellarmin. It sticks to one like a burr.

BELLARMIN: Let us move with the times, Barberini. If star-charts based on a new hypothesis simplify navigation for our sailors, then let them use these charts. We only dislike teachings which contradict the Bible. *(He waves in greeting towards the ballroom.)*

GALILEO: The Bible. — 'He that withholdeth corn, the people shall curse him.' Proverbs.

BARBERINI: 'Wise men lay up knowledge'. Proverbs.

GALILEO: 'Where no oxen are, the crib is clean; but much increase is by the strength of the ox.'

BARBERINI: 'He that ruleth his spirit is better than he that taketh a city.'

GALILEO: 'But a broken spirit drieth the house.' *(Pause.)* 'Doth not truth cry aloud?'

BARBERINI: 'Can one go upon hot coals and his feet not be burned?' Welcome in Rome, friend Galileo. You know her origin? Two little boys, so runs the legend, received milk and shelter from a she-wolf. From that hour on, all children have had to pay for the she-wolf's milk. But in return the she-wolf provides all sorts of pleasures, heavenly and earthly, ranging from conversations with my learned friend Bellarmin to the company of three or four ladies of international reputation. May I display them to you?

(He leads GALILEO to the rear, in order to show him the ballroom. GALILEO follows reluctantly.)

BARBERINI: No? He insists on a serious conversation. All right. Are you sure, friend Galileo, that you astronomers are not simply concerned with making your astronomy more manageable? *(He leads him to the front again.)* You think in terms of circles and ellipses and equal velocities, simple movements that your mind can grasp. But what if it had pleased God to make his stars move like this? *(With his finger moving at varying speeds he describes in the air an extremely complicated track.)*

GALILEO: Your Eminence, if God had constructed the universe like that — *(he repeats BARBERINI's track)* — then he would also have constructed our grains like that — *(he repeats the same track)* — so that they would recognise these very tracks as the simplest possible. I believe in reason.

BARBERINI: I hold reason to be inadequate. — He is silent. He is too polite to say now that he holds me to be inadequate. *(He laughs and returns to the balustrade at the back.)*

BELLARMIN: Reason, my friend, does not reach very far. All around we see nothing but crookedness, crime and weakness. Where is truth?

GALILEO *(angrily):* I believe in reason.

BARBERINI *(to the clerks):* There is no need to take this down. This is a scientific conversation between friends.

BELLARMIN: Consider for a moment all the trouble and thought it cost the Fathers of the Church, and so many after them, to bring a little sense into this world (is it not a little repellent?). Consider the brutality of the landlords in the Campagna who have their peasants whipped half-naked over their estates, and the stupidity of these poor people who kiss their feet in return.

GALILEO: Horrible! On my journey here I saw . . .

BELLARMIN: We have placed the responsibility for the meaning of such happenings as we cannot comprehend — life consists of them — on a higher Being, and we have explained that such things are the result of certain intentions, that all this happens according to one great plan. Not that this has brought about complete reassurance; but now you have to accuse this supreme Being of not knowing for certain how the stars move, a matter on which *you* are perfectly clear. Is that wise?

GALILEO *(preparing to explain):* I am a true son of the Church . . .

BARBERINI: He is incorrigible. In all innocence he tries to prove God a complete fool on the subject of astronomy! Do you mean that God did not study astronomy sufficiently before he indited the Holy Scriptures? My dear friend!

BELLARMIN: Does it not appear probable to you that the Creator knows more about His own handiwork than does the handiwork itself?

GALILEO: But, gentlemen, man can misinterpret not only the movements of the stars, but the Bible too.

BELLARMIN: But the interpretation of the Bible is, after all, the business of the theologians of the Holy Church, eh?

(GALILEO is silent.)

BELLARMIN: You see. You are silent now. *(He makes a sign to the clerks.)* Signor Galilei, tonight the Holy Office has decided that the teachings of Copernicus, according to which the sun is the centre of the universe and motionless, while the earth is not the centre of the universe and is moving, are futile, foolish and heretical. I have been entrusted with the duty of informing you of this decision. *(To the first clerk):* Repeat that.

FIRST CLERK: His Eminence Cardinal Bellarmin to the aforementioned Galileo Galilei: The Holy Office has decided that the teachings of Copernicus, according to which the sun is the centre of the universe and motionless, while the earth is not the centre of the universe and is moving, are futile, foolish and heretical. I have been entrusted with the duty of informing you of this decision.

GALILEO: What does that mean?

(From the ballroom can be heard boys' voices singing another verse of the poem):
'I said: the lovely season flieth fast;
So pluck the rose — it still is May.'
(BARBERINI gestures GALILEO to be silent while the song lasts. They listen.)

GALILEO: But the facts? I understood that the astronomers of the Collegium Romanum had accepted my observations.

BELLARMIN: With the expression of the deepest satisfaction, which does you the greatest honour.

GALILEO: But the satellites of Jupiter, the phases of Venus . . .

BELLARMIN: The Holy Congregation has made its decision without considering these details.

GALILEO: That means that all further scientific research . . .

BELLARMIN: Is well assured, Signor Galilei. And that, in conformity with the Church's view that we cannot know, but we may research. *(He again greets a guest in the ballroom.)* You are at liberty to expound even this teaching through mathematical hypotheses. Science is the legitimate and dearly beloved daughter of the Church, Signor Galilei. Not one of us seriously believes that you desire to undermine the authority of the Church.

GALILEO *(angrily):* Authority grows feeble from being abused.

BARBERINI: Does it? *(He claps him on the shoulder, laughing loudly. Then he looks sharply at him and says, not unkindly):* Don't throw out the baby with the bath-water, friend Galileo. We don't do that either. We need you, more than you need us.

BELLARMIN: I am burning to present the greatest mathematician in Italy to the President of the Holy Office, who regards you with the utmost admiration.

BARBERINI *(catching hold of GALILEO's other arm):* Whereupon he is once more transformed into a lamb. You too, my dear friend, would have done better to appear here costumed as the worthy doctor of school tradition. It is my mask that permits me a little freedom today. In such a get-up you might hear me murmuring: if there were no God, one would have to invent one. Good, let us put up our masks again. Poor Galilei has none. *(They take GALILEO between them and lead him into the ballroom.)*

FIRST CLERK: Did you get the last sentence?

SECOND CLERK: I did. *(They write industriously.)* Have you got down the bit where he says that he believes in reason.
    (Enter the CARDINAL INQUISITOR.)

THE INQUISITOR: Did the conversation take place?

FIRST CLERK *(mechanically):* At first Signor Galilei came in with his daughter. Today she became engaged to Signor . . . *(The INQUISITOR stops him impatiently.)* Signor Galilei then instructed us in the new manner of playing chess in which the pieces move all over the board contrary to the rules of the game.

THE INQUISITOR *(gestures him to silence):* The transcript.
    (A clerk hands it to him, and he sits down to glance through it. Two young ladies, masked, cross the stage. They curtsey in front of the cardinal.)

ONE YOUNG LADY: Who is that?

THE OTHER: The Cardinal Inquisitor.
    (They giggle and go off. Enter VIRGINIA, looking round in search of something.)

THE INQUISITOR *(from his corner):* Well, my daughter?

VIRGINIA *(starts, for she has not seen him):* Oh, your Eminence!
    (Without looking up, the INQUISITOR stretches out his right hand. She approaches, kneels and kisses his ring.)

THE INQUISITOR: A superb night! Permit me to congratulate you on your engagement. Your bridegroom comes from a noble family. You will remain with us in Rome?

VIRGINIA: Not at first, your Eminence. There is so much to prepare for a wedding.

THE INQUISITOR: Ah. — So you will return with your father to Florence. I am glad of that. I can imagine that your father needs you. Mathematics is a cold companion, is it not? A creature of flesh and blood in such surroundings makes all the difference. If one is a great man it is so easy to lose oneself in the world of stars which are so very vast.

VIRGINIA *(breathlessly):* You are most kind, your Eminence. Really, I understand almost nothing of such matters.

THE INQUISITOR: No? *(He laughs.)* In the fisherman's house they never eat fish, eh? It will amuse your father when he hears that you have in fact learnt from *me* all you know about the constellations, my child. *(Leafing through the transcript):* I read here that our innovators regard our present conceptions of the importance of our dear earth as somewhat exaggerated. Now, from the days of Ptolemy, a sage of antiquity, up to the present day, it has been agreed that the width of the universe — that is the whole crystal sphere of which the earth is the centre — is about twenty thousand earth diameters. A pretty space, but too small, far too small for the innovators. According to them, so we hear, space is quite unbelievably extended. And the distance from the earth to the sun — a very considerable distance, it has always seemed to us — has become so infinitesimally small in comparison to the distance of our poor earth from the fixed stars which are attached to the very outermost sphere that it need not be taken into our calculations at all! Who could now say that the innovators do not live in a large way?

(VIRGINIA laughs. The INQUISITOR laughs too.)

THE INQUISITOR: In fact some gentlemen of the Holy Office have recently been almost shocked by this new picture of the universe, compared to which our accepted one is only a miniature such as could be hung round the enchanting necks of certain young ladies. They are worried because, in the case of such enormous distances, a prelate and even a cardinal might easily go astray. Even a Pope might lose the eye of the Almighty. Yes, it is funny, but I am happy to know that you will continue to be close to your father whom we all esteem so much, my dear child. I wonder whether I know your Father Confessor . . .?

VIRGINIA: Father Christophorus from Saint Ursula.

THE INQUISITOR: Ah, yes. I am glad that you will be with your father. He will need you. You may not be able to imagine it, but it will be so. You are so young and really so very much flesh and blood, and greatness is not always easy to bear for those on whom God has bestowed it; not always. No one among mortals is so great that he cannot be included in a prayer. But now I am keeping you, dear child, and I shall be making your betrothed jealous and perhaps even your dear father, since I have been telling you something about the stars which is maybe outmoded. Now go quickly to the dancing, but do not forget to greet Father Christophorus from me.

(VIRGINIA makes a deep curtsey and goes quickly.)

———————— • ————————

8

A CONVERSATION

> Galileo, feeling grim,
> A young monk came to visit him.
> The monk was born of common folk
> It was of science that they spoke.

SCENE 8: IN THE PALACE OF THE FLORENTINE AMBASSADOR IN ROME

GALILEO listens to the little monk who, after the session of the Collegium Romanum, whispered to him the verdict of the Papal astronomers.

GALILEO: Speak, speak! The habit you wear gives you the right to say whatever you wish.

THE LITTLE MONK: I have studied mathematics, Signor Galilei.

GALILEO: That might be a help, if it could induce you to admit that twice two now and again make four!

THE LITTLE MONK: Signor Galilei, for the last three nights I have been unable to sleep at all. I didn't know how to reconcile the decree which I have read and the satellites of Jupiter which I have seen. I decided to say Mass early today and then come to you.

GALILEO: In order to inform me that Jupiter has no satellites?

THE LITTLE MONK: No. I have succeeded in fathoming the wisdom of that decree. It has revealed to me the danger to mankind that lurks in too much uncontrolled research, and I have decided to give up astronomy. However, it is still my duty to put before you the reasons which should cause even an astronomer to desist from further work on that particular teaching.

GALILEO: I may say that such reasons are already known to me.

THE LITTLE MONK: I understand your bitterness. You are thinking of certain exceptional powers which the Church can command.

GALILEO: Just say instruments of torture.

THE LITTLE MONK: But I would mention other reasons. Let me speak for a moment of myself. I grew up as a son of peasants in the Campagna. They were simple people. They knew all about olive-trees, but very little else. While observing the phases of Venus, I can see my parents, sitting by the hearth with my sister, eating their cheese. I see above them the beams blackened by centuries of smoke, and I see clearly, their old, work-worn hands and the little spoons they hold. They are not rich, but even in their misfortune there lies concealed a certain invisible order of things. There are those various rounds of duties, from scrubbing the floor, through the seasons in the olive grove, to the payment of taxes. There is even regularity in the disasters that befall them. My father's back becomes bent, not suddenly, but more and more each spring among the olive-trees, just as the childbearings which have made my mother less and less a woman have followed one another at regular intervals. But they call up the strength to sweat up the stony paths with their baskets, to bear children, yes, even to eat, from the feeling of continuity and necessity which is given them by the sight of the soil, of the trees springing with new green foliage every year, of the little church, and by listening every Sunday to the Bible texts. They have been assured that the eye of God rests upon them; searchingly, yes, almost anxiously — that the whole universe has been built up round them in order that they, the actors, can play their greater or lesser parts. What would my people say if they learned from me that they were really on a little bit of rock that ceaselessly revolves in empty space round another star, one among very many, a comparatively unimportant one? Why is such patience, such acceptance of their misery, either necessary or good today? Why is there still virtue in Holy Writ, which explains everything and has established the necessity of toil, endurance, hunger, resignation, and which now is found to be full of errors? No, I see their eyes grow frightened! I see them dropping their spoons on the hearth-stone, I see how they feel cheated and betrayed. So there is no eye resting upon us, they say. We must look after ourselves, untaught, old and worn out as we are? No one has provided a part for us on this earthly, miserable, tiny star which is not independent and round which nothing revolves? There is no meaning in our misery, hunger is simply not-having-eaten, and not a test of strength; exertion is just stooping and tugging — with nothing to show. So do you understand that in that decree of the Holy Congregation I perceive true maternal compassion, great goodness of soul?

GALILEO: Goodness of soul! What you probably mean is — there's nothing there, the wine's drunk up, their lips are parched, so let them kiss the cassock! And why is nothing there? Why is the orderliness in this country merely the order of an empty cupboard, and the necessity merely that of working oneself to death? Among bursting vineyards, beside the ripening cornfields! Your Campagna peasants are paying for the wars which the representative of gentle Jesus is waging in Spain and Germany. Why does he put the earth at the hub of the universe? So that the throne of Saint Peter can stand at the hub of the earth. That's why! You are right; it's nothing to do with the planets, it's to do with the peasants in the Campagna. And don't come talking to me about the beauty of phenomena to which age has given a golden patina! Do you know how Margaritifera oysters produce their pearls? When suffering from a deadly disease they envelop an unbearable foreign body — a grain of sand for example — in a nacreous secretion. They nearly die in the process. To the devil with the pearls. I prefer a healthy oyster. Virtues are not linked with misery, my friend. If your people were prosperous and happy, they could develop the virtues derived of prosperity and happiness. But now these virtues come from exhausted men on exhausted acres, and I reject them. Sir, my new water-pumps can work more miracles than your ridiculous superhuman slave-driving. — 'Be fruitful and multiply', for fields are unfruitful and wars are decimating you. Should I lie to your people?

THE LITTLE MONK *(in great agitation):*   The very highest reasons keep us silent — the peace of mind of our unfortunate people.

GALILEO: Would you like to see a Cellini clock which Cardinal Bellarmin's coachman delivered here this morning? My friend, as a reward for leaving undisturbed the peace of mind of, shall we say, your worthy parents, the authorities offer me wine pressed with the sweat of their brows, which are said to have been created in the image of God. Were I prepared to keep silence, it would doubtless be for the basest of reasons: comfort, freedom from persecution, etc.

THE LITTLE MONK: Signor Galilei, I am a priest.

GALILEO: You are also a physicist. And you see that Venus has phases. Look through there! *(He points through the window.)* Do you see that little Priapus there on the well beside the laurel? The god of gardens, of birds and thieves — rustic, obscene, two-thousand-years-old! He told fewer lies. — All right, I'm a son of the Church too. But do you know the eight satires of Horace? I've just been reading him again; he gives one a sense of balance. *(He reaches out for a little book.)* He lets Priapus speak, a little statue which was put up in the Esquiline Gardens. It begins like this:
'A fig-tree log, a useless piece of wood
Was I, when the carpenter, uncertain
Whether to carve a Priapus or a stool
Decided on the god . . .'
Do you think Horace would have forgone the stool and let a table be put into the poem? Sir, my sense of beauty is wounded if Venus appears in my universe without phases. We cannot invent machinery for pumping up the water from the river if we may not study the greatest machinery that lies before our eyes, the machinery of the stars. The sum of the angles in a triangle cannot be changed according to the requirements of the Curia. I cannot calculate the paths of freely moving bodies in such a way as to explain the rides of witches upon broomsticks.

THE LITTLE MONK: And do you not believe that the truth — if it be the truth — will triumph even without us?

GALILEO: No, no, no. Truth will triumph only in so far as we triumph; the victory of reason can only be the victory of reasonable people. You describe your Campagna peasants just like the moss on their huts! How can anyone assume that the sum of the angles in a triangle could contradict *their* requirements? But if they never stir themselves and start to think, the most beautiful irrigation schemes will be no of use to them. Damnation, I perceive the divine patience of your people, but where is their divine anger?

THE LITTLE MONK: They are tired.

GALILEO *(throws a bundle of manuscript to him):* Are you a physicist, my son? Here you will find the reasons why the ocean moves in ebb and flood. But you mustn't read it, do you hear. Oh, you're already reading it? So you are a physicist?

(The little monk is engrossed in the papers.)

GALILEO: An apple from the tree of knowledge! He's already cramming it in. He's eternally damned, but he must cram it in, an unhappy guzzler! Sometimes I think I'll have myself shut in a dungeon ten fathoms under the ground where no light penetrates, if I could thereby discover what it is — light. And the worst is that what I know I must repeat. Like a lover, like a drunkard, like a traitor. It's nothing but a sin and leads to disaster. How long shall I be able simply to shout it at the fireplace — that's the question.

THE LITTLE MONK *(pointing to a passage in the papers):* I cannot understand this sentence.

GALILEO: I'll explain it to you. I'll explain it to you.

———————————— • ————————————

9

AFTER EIGHT YEARS OF SILENCE, THE ENTHRONEMENT OF A NEW POPE,
HIMSELF A MATHEMATICIAN, ENCOURAGES GALILEO TO RESUME HIS
RESEARCHES INTO THE FORBIDDEN SUBJECT OF SUN-SPOTS

> Eight long years with tongue in cheek
> Of what he knew he did not speak.
> Then temptation grew too great
> And Galileo challenged fate.

SCENE 9: GALILEO'S HOUSE IN FLORENCE

GALILEO's pupils, FEDERZONI, the little monk and ANDREA SARTI, now a young man, are assembled for a practical lecture. GALILEO himself reads a book, standing up. VIRGINIA and SIGNORA SARTI are sewing the trousseau.

VIRGINIA: Sewing a trousseau is fun. This is for a long dining table, Ludovico loves entertaining. It has to be very neat; his mother notices every thread. She doesn't agree with father's books. Like Father Christophorus.

SIGNORA SARTI: He hasn't written a new book for years.

VIRGINIA: I think he's realised he was mistaken. In Rome a very high church dignitary explained to me a lot about astronomy. The distances are too great.

ANDREA *(as he writes up the lesson for the day on a blackboard):* 'Thursday afternoon. Floating bodies.' Ice again; a pail with water; scales; iron needle; Aristotle.

(He fetches out the various objects. The others follow what he says in their books. Enter FILIPPO MUCIUS, a scholar of middle age. He has a rather agitated manner.)

MUCIUS: Can you tell Signor Galilei that he must receive me? He damns me without hearing me.

SIGNORA SARTI: But he will *not* receive you.

MUCIUS: God will reward you if you ask him once again. I *must* speak to him.

VIRGINIA *(goes to the stairs):* Father!

GALILEO: What is it?

VIRGINIA: Signor Mucius.

GALILEO *(standing up abruptly, goes to the top of the stairs, his pupils behind him):* What do you want?

MUCIUS: Signor Galilei, I beg you will permit me to explain to you those passages in my book where there appears to be disproof of the Copernican teaching about the rotation of the earth. I have . . .

GALILEO: What are you trying to explain? You are in agreement with the decree of the Holy Congregation of 1616. You are entirely within your rights. You have certainly studied mathematics here, but that imposes on us no obligation to hear from you that twice two makes four. You are, on the other hand, perfectly entitled to say that this stone — *(he takes a little stone from his pocket and throws it on the floor)* — has just flown up into the roof.

MUCIUS: Signor Galilei, I . . .

GALILEO: Don't talk about difficulties! I didn't let the plague stop me from continuing with my researches.

MUCIUS: Signor Galilei, the plague is not the worst thing.

GALILEO: I say to you: he who does not know the truth is merely an idiot. But he who knows it and calls it a lie, is a criminal. Get out of my house!

MUCIUS *(tonelessly):* You are right. *(He goes.)*
(GALILEO goes back to his study.)

FEDERZONI: Unfortunately, that's the trouble. He is not a great man and would be of no importance were it not that he has been your pupil. But now, of course, people will say: he's heard everything that Galilei teaches and he has to admit that it is all false.

SIGNORA SARTI: I am sorry for the gentleman.

VIRGINIA: Father was too fond of him.

SIGNORA SARTI: I would like to talk to you about your marriage, Virginia. You're still such a young thing, and you have no mother, and your father floats these bits of ice on water. Anyway, I wouldn't advise you to ask *him* anything about your marriage. He'd take a whole week-end and at mealtime and when young people are at table he'd say the most shocking things, not having half a scudo's worth of modesty — he never had. And I don't mean things like that; simply, what the future holds for you. I can't know such things; I'm an uneducated person. But one doesn't go blindly into a serious situation like marriage. I mean, really you ought to go to a proper astronomer at the University, so that he can cast your horoscope, when you'll know where you are. What are you laughing at?

VIRGINIA: Because I did go to him.

SIGNORA SARTI *(very curious):* What did he say?

VIRGINIA: For three months I must be careful because the sun will be in Capricorn, but after that I'll have an extremely favourable ascendent and the clouds will part. If I don't let Jupiter out of sight, I can undertake any journey I fancy, since I'm a Capricorn.

SIGNORA SARTI: And Ludovico?

VIRGINIA: He's a Leo. *(After a slight pause.)* His nature is sensual. *(A pause.)* I know that step. It is the Rector, Signor Gaffone.
  (Enter SIGNOR GAFFONE, Rector of the University.)

GAFFONE: I'm only bringing a book that may interest your father. Please, for Heaven's sake, don't disturb Signor Galilei. I cannot help it, but I always feel that every minute stolen from that great man is a minute stolen from Italy. I'll put the book, in mint condition, into your hands and steal away on tip-toe.
  (He leaves. VIRGINIA gives the book to FEDERZONI.)

GALILEO: What's it about?

FEDERZONI: I don't know. *(He spells it out.)* 'De Maculis in Sole.'

ANDREA: On sun-spots. Another one!
  (FEDERZONI hands it over to him crossly.)

ANDREA: Listen to the dedication! 'To the greatest living authority on physics, Galileo Galilei.'
  (GALILEO has already immersed himself again in his book.)

ANDREA: I've already read the sun-spot treatise by Fabricius of Holland. He believes they are swarms of stars passing between the earth and the sun.

THE LITTLE MONK: Isn't that rather doubtful, Signor Galilei?
  (GALILEO does not answer.)

ANDREA: In Paris and Prague they believe they are vapours from the sun.

FEDERZONI: Hm.

ANDREA: Federzoni doubts that.

FEDERZONI: Please leave me out of it. I have said 'Hm', that's all. I'm a lens-grinder. I grind lenses, and you look through them and observe the heavens, and what you see are not spots but 'maculis'. How could I ever doubt anything? How often must I keep saying to you that I can't read books, they're all in Latin.
  (In fury he gesticulates with the scales. A pan falls to the floor. GALILEO goes across and silently picks it up.)

THE LITTLE MONK: There is joy in doubt. I wonder why?

ANDREA: For the last two weeks, on every sunny day, I've climbed up into the attic under the roof. Through a tiny crack in the shingles falls just a thin ray of light. And that way one can get a reversed image of the sun on a sheet of paper. I have seen a spot, as big as a fly, swept away like a cloudlet. It wandered, too. Why don't we investigate the spots, Signor Galilei?

GALILEO: Because we are working on floating bodies.

ANDREA: Mother has wash-baskets full of letters. All Europe is asking for your opinion. Your reputation has grown so great that you cannot remain silent.

GALILEO: Rome has permitted my reputation to grow because I have remained silent.

FEDERZONI: But now you can no longer afford to be silent.

GALILEO: Neither can I afford to allow myself to be smoked over a wood-fire like a ham.

ANDREA: Do you think these spots have anything to do with this matter? *(GALILEO does not answer.)*

ANDREA: All right, let's keep to our bits of ice; they can't do you any harm.

GALILEO: Correct. — Our thesis, Andrea!

ANDREA: As far as the property of floating is concerned, let us assume that it is not the shape of a body that matters, but whether it is lighter or heavier than water.

GALILEO: What does Aristotle say?

THE LITTLE MONK: 'Discus latus platique . . .'

GALILEO: Translate, translate!

THE LITTLE MONK: 'A broad and flat disc of ice is able to float on water, whereas an iron needle sinks.'

GALILEO: Why, according to Aristotle, does the ice not sink?

THE LITTLE MONK: Because it is broad and flat and so is unable to divide the water.

GALILEO: Good. *(He takes up a lump of ice and places it in the pail of water.)* Now I press the ice forcibly down to the bottom of the vessel. I remove the pressure of my hands. And what happens?

THE LITTLE MONK: It rises to the surface again.

GALILEO: Right. Apparently it can divide the water when rising. — Fulganzio!

THE LITTLE MONK: But then why does it float at all? It is heavier than water because it is condensed water.

GALILEO: What if it were thinned water?

ANDREA: It must be lighter than water, otherwise it wouldn't float.

GALILEO: Aha!

ANDREA: Just as an iron needle won't float. Everything that's lighter than water floats, and everything that's heavier sinks. Quod erat demonstrandum.

GALILEO: Andrea, you must learn to think carefully. Give me the needle. A sheet of paper. Is iron heavier than water?

ANDREA: Yes.
(GALILEO lays the needle on the sheet of paper and then gently slides the needle on to the surface of the water. A pause.)

GALILEO: What has happened?

FEDERZONI: The needle is floating! Holy Aristotle, they've never put him to the test! *(They laugh.)*

GALILEO: One of the chief causes of poverty in science is usually imaginary wealth. The aim of science is not to open a door to infinite wisdom, but to set a limit to infinite error. — Make your notes.

VIRGINIA: What is it?

SIGNORA SARTI: Every time they laugh, it gives me a little shudder. What are they laughing at, I wonder.

VIRGINIA: Father says: the theologians have their bell-ringing, and the physicists have their laughter.

SIGNORA SARTI: But I'm glad that at least he no longer looks through his telescope so often.

VIRGINIA: Now he's only putting pieces of ice into water; not much harm can come of that.

SIGNORA SARTI: I don't know.
(Enter LUDOVICO in travelling clothes, followed by a servant carrying pieces of luggage. VIRGINIA runs over to him and embraces him.)

VIRGINIA: Why didn't you write to me that you were coming?

LUDOVICO: I was near by, visiting our vineyards at Bucciole, and I couldn't keep away from you.

GALILEO *(as if short-sighted):* Who is that?

VIRGINIA: Ludovico.

THE LITTLE MONK: Can't you see him?

GALILEO: Oh, yes, Ludovico. *(He walks toward him.)* How are the horses?

LUDOVICO: They are doing well, signor.

GALILEO: Sarti, we'll have a celebration. Fetch a jug of that Sicilian wine, the old wine.
(Exit SIGNORA SARTI with ANDREA.)

LUDOVICO *(to VIRGINIA):* You look pale. Living in the country will suit you. Mother is expecting you in September.

VIRGINIA: Wait — I'll show you my wedding-dress. *(She runs out.)*

GALILEO: Sit down.

LUDOVICO: I hear you have more than a thousand students at your lectures in the University, signor. What are you working on at the moment?

GALILEO: The same sort of thing, day after day. Have you come through Rome?

LUDOVICO: Yes. — Before I forget it, Mother congratulates you on your admirable tact over the new sun-spot orgies of the Dutch.

GALILEO *(drily):* Thank you.
(SIGNORA SARTI and ANDREA bring in wine and glasses. All settle round the table.)

LUDOVICO: Rome's already got its topic of conversation for February. Father Christopher Clavius has expressed a fear that the whole earth-round-the-sun hullabaloo may be started up again by these sun-spots.

ANDREA: No need to worry.

GALILEO: Any further gossip in the Holy City, apart from hopes of new sins on my part?

LUDOVICO: You know, of course, that the Holy Father is dying?

THE LITTLE MONK: Oh!

GALILEO: Who is mentioned as his successor?

LUDOVICO: Most people say Barberini.

GALILEO: Barberini.

ANDREA: Signor Galilei knows Barberini.

THE LITTLE MONK: Cardinal Barberini is a mathematician.

FEDERZONI: A man of science on the Papal Throne!

GALILEO: Well, nowadays they need men like Barberini, who have read a bit of mathematics. Things are starting to move, Federzoni; we may yet live to see the day when we no longer have to look over our shoulders like criminals when we say that twice two is four. *(To LUDOVICO):* I admire this wine, Ludovico. What do you think of it?

LUDOVICO: It's good.

GALILEO: I know the vineyard. The slope is steep and stony, the grapes almost blue. I love its wine.

LUDOVICO: Yes, signor.

GALILEO: It has little shadows in it. And it is almost sweet, but one mustn't forget the 'almost'. — Andrea, clear that stuff away, the ice, the pail and the needle. — I enjoy the consolations of the flesh. I have no patience with cowardly souls who call them little weaknesses. I say: enjoyment is an accomplishment.

THE LITTLE MONK: What are you proposing to do?

FEDERZONI: We'll begin again with the earth-round-the-sun hullabaloo.

ANDREA *(humming):* The Bible says the earth stands still, my dears
A fact which every learned doctor proves:
The Holy Father grabs it by the ears
And holds it hard and fast. — And yet it moves.
(ANDREA, FEDERZONI and the little monk hurry across to the experimental table and clear it.)

ANDREA: We might find out that the sun itself revolves. How would you like that, Marsili?

LUDOVICO: Why the excitement?

SIGNORA SARTI: You aren't going to start again with all that devil's stuff, Signor Galilei?

GALILEO: I know now why your mother sent you to me. Barberini in the ascendent! Knowledge will become a passion, and research a pleasure. Clavius is right; these sun-spots interest me. Do you like my wine, Ludovico?

LUDOVICO: I've told you so, signor.

GALILEO: You really like it?

LUDOVICO *(stiffly):* I like it.

GALILEO: Would you go so far as to accept a man's wine or his daughter without demanding that he abandons his calling? What has my astronomy to do with my daughter? The phases of Venus don't affect her curves.

SIGNORA SARTI: Don't be so vulgar. I'll fetch Virginia right away.

LUDOVICO *(holds her back):* Marriages in families like mine are not made only from the sexual point of view.

GALILEO: Did they restrain you from marrying my daughter for eight years, while I had to serve a probation period?

LUDOVICO: My wife will also have to cut a figure in our place in the village church.

GALILEO: You mean, your peasants will make it dependent upon the godliness of their squire's wife whether they pay their rents or not.

LUDOVICO: In a manner of speaking.

GALILEO: Andrea, Fulganzio, fetch the brass reflector and the screen. We'll throw the picture of the sun on to it to spare our eyes; that's your method, Andrea.
(ANDREA and the little monk fetch the reflector and screen.)

LUDOVICO: In Rome, at that time, you signed that you wouldn't meddle any more in that earth-round-the-sun business, signor.

GALILEO: Oh, then! Then we had a reactionary Pope!

SIGNORA SARTI: Had! And His Holiness isn't yet dead!

GALILEO: Almost, almost. — Lay a squared grid over the screen. We'll proceed methodically. And then we'll be able to answer their letters, won't we, Andrea?

SIGNORA SARTI: 'Almost!' Fifty times the man re-weighs his lumps of ice, but when it's something that suits his stomach he swallows it blind.
(The screen is set up.)

LUDOVICO: Should His Holiness die, Signor Galilei, the next Pope, whoever he may be and however great his love for science, will also have to pay due regard to the extent of the love which the foremost families in the land feel towards him.

THE LITTLE MONK: God made the physical world, Ludovico; God made the human brain; God will permit physics.

SIGNORA SARTI: Galileo, now I'll tell *you* something. I have seen my son fall into sin over these 'Experiments' and 'Theories' and 'Observations', and I haven't been able to do anything. You have set yourself up against the authorities and they have already warned you once. The most eminent cardinals have talked to you like a sick beast. It worked for a time, but two months ago, soon after the Annunciation, I caught you again, starting up secretly with those 'Observations'. In the attic! I didn't say much, but I knew all right. I ran out and lit a candle to Saint Joseph. It was beyond me. When I'm alone with you, you show signs of sense and tell me that you know you must control yourself because it's dangerous, but two days' experimenting and you're as bad as ever. If I have to give up my eternal salvation for sticking to a heretic, that's my business, but you've no right to trample on your daughter's happiness with your great flat feet.

GALILEO *(peevishly):*   Bring the telescope.

LUDOVICO: Giuseppe, put my luggage back in the coach.
(Exit the servant.)

SIGNORA SARTI: She won't get over that! You can tell her yourself!
(She runs off, still holding the jug.)

LUDOVICO: I see you have already made your preparations. Signor Galilei, my mother and I spend three quarters of the year on our estate in the Campagna, and we can assure you that your treatises on the satellites of Jupiter in no way disturb our peasants. Their work in the fields is too arduous. Yet it could disturb them to learn that frivolous attacks on the sacred doctrines of the Church now go unpunished. Don't entirely forget that these unfortunates, in their animal-like condition, get everything confused. They really *are* animals. You can scarcely conceive it. At the rumour that an apple-tree's bearing pears they'll run away from the fields to gossip about it.

GALILEO *(interested):*   Will they?

LUDOVICO: Animals. When they come to our house to complain about some trivial thing, mother's compelled to have a hound whipped before their eyes; that's the only thing that will remind them of breeding and behaviour and civility. You, Signor Galilei, occasionally see from a travelling coach fruitful fields of maize; absent-mindedly you eat our olives and our cheese; and you have no idea what trouble, what supervision it takes to grow these things.

GALILEO: Young man, I do not eat my olives absent-mindedly. *(Angrily.)* You're detaining me. *(He calls upstairs.)* Have you got the screen?

ANDREA: Yes. Are you coming?

GALILEO: It's not only hounds you whip to keep them under control, eh Marsili?

LUDOVICO: Signor Galilei. You have a wonderful brain. A pity.

THE LITTLE MONK *(amazed):*   He's threatening you.

GALILEO: Yes. I might stir up his peasants into thinking new thoughts. And his servants and his stewards.

FEDERZONI: How? None of them reads Latin.

GALILEO: I could write for the many in the language of the people, instead of in Latin for the few. For these new ideas we need people who work with their hands. Who else wants to learn about the origins of things? Those who see only the bread on the table don't want to know how it is baked; that lot would rather thank God above than the baker. But those who make the bread will understand that nothing moves which isn't moved. Your sister at the olive-press, Fulganzio, will not be greatly amazed, but will probably laugh when she hears that the sun is not a golden coat of arms but a lever; the earth moves, because the sun moves it.

LUDOVICO: You will always be the slave of your own infatuations. Excuse me to Virginia; I think it is better not to see her now.

GALILEO: The dowry is at your disposal at any time.

LUDOVICO: Good day. *(He goes.)*

ANDREA: And give our regards to all the Marsilis!

FEDERZONI: Who command the earth to stand still so that their castles don't come tumbling down!

ANDREA: And the Cencis and the Villanis!

FEDERZONI: The Cervillis!

ANDREA: The Lecchis!

FEDERZONI: The Pirleonis!

ANDREA: Who are only willing to kiss the Pope's feet if he'll trample down the people with them.

THE LITTLE MONK *(now at the apparatus):*   The new Pope will be an enlightened man.

GALILEO: So now we start on our observation of these spots on the sun, which interest us, at our own risk and without counting too much on the protection of a new Pope.

ANDREA *(interrupting):*   But with full confidence in dispersing the star-shadows of Signor Fabricius and the sun-vapours of Prague and Paris, and of proving the rotation of the sun.

GALILEO: With some confidence in proving the rotation of the sun. My intention is not to prove that hitherto I have been right; but to discover whether I am right. I say: abandon all hope, you who enter the realm of observation. Perhaps they are clouds, perhaps they are spots, but before we assume that they are spots, which would be most opportune for us, let us rather assume that they are fishes' tails. Yes, we will question everything, everything once again. And we shall advance not in seven-league boots, but at a snail's pace. And what we find today we shall strike out from the record tomorrow, and only write it in again when we

have once more discovered it. And what we wish to find, if we do find it, we shall regard with especial distrust. So we shall start our observations of the sun with the inexorable determination to prove that the earth *stands still*. Only when we are defeated, utterly and hopelessly defeated, and are licking our wounds in the most miserable dejection, shall we begin to ask ourselves whether we may be right after all and perhaps the earth does move! *(With a wink.)* And if every conception but this one goes up in smoke, then there can be no more mercy for those who have not searched and yet speak. Take the cloth off the telescope and turn it to the sun.
(He sets up the brass reflector.)

THE LITTLE MONK: I knew that you had already begun your work. I knew it when you didn't recognise Signor Marsili.
(Silently they begin their observations. When the flaming image of the sun appears on the screen, VIRGINIA comes running in her wedding-dress.)

VIRGINIA: You sent him away, father!
(She faints. ANDREA and the little monk run over to her.)

GALILEO: I've got to know the truth.

———————————— • ————————————

10

DURING THE FOLLOWING DECADE GALILEO'S TEACHING SPREADS AMONG THE PEOPLE. PAMPHLETEERS AND BALLAD-SINGERS EVERY-WHERE TAKE UP THE NEW IDEAS. IN 1632, DURING CARNIVAL TIME, MANY CITIES IN ITALY CHOOSE ASTRONOMY AS THE THEME FOR THE GUILDS' PROCESSIONS

On April Fool's Day, 'thirty two,
Of science there was much ado,
People had learned from Galilei:
They used his teaching in their way.

SCENE 10: A MARKETPLACE

A half-starved pair of strolling players with a five-year-old girl and a baby enter a marketplace where a crowd, many masked, are waiting for the carnival procession. Both carry bundles, a drum and assorted utensils.

THE BALLAD-SINGER *(drumming):*   Esteemed citizens, ladies and gentlemen! Before the great carnival procession of the guilds arrives, we bring you the latest song from Florence, a song which is being sung throughout the whole of Upper Italy and which we have imported here at great cost. It is entitled: *The Terrible Teachings and Views of Court Physicist Signor Galileo Galilei, or a Foretaste of the Future.*
(He sings:)
When the Almighty ordered his great Creation,
He told the sun that it, at his command,
Must circle round the earth for illumination
Just like a little maiden, lamp in hand.

For it was His desire each thing inferior
Should henceforth circle round its own superior.
And things began to turn for all their worth
The lesser ones around the greater
And round the earlier the later,
As it is in Heaven so on earth.
And round the Pope revolve the cardinals
And round the cardinals revolve the bishops
And round the bishops revolve the secretaries
And round the secretaries revolve the magistrates
And round the magistrates revolve the craftsmen
And round the craftsmen revolve the servants
And round the servants revolve the dogs, the chickens and the beggars.
That, good people, is the Great Order, ordo ordinum as the Signori theologians
say, regular aeternis, the Rule of Rules — but what, dear people, happened?
   (He sings:)
Then up got Doctor Galilei
(Threw the Bible away, caught up his telescope,
   Took a look at the universe.)
   'Stand still!' to the sun he said,
   'For now the Creatio Dei
   Shall turn the opposite way.
   Now the mistress must obey
   And turn around her maid.'
You say that's scandalous? Good people, that's no jest.
The serving folk grow bolder every day. — Disaster!
Yet one thing's true: life's dull for you. And hand on breast,
Who wouldn't rather be his own liege lord and master?

Worthy citizens, such teachings are quite impossible.
   (He sings:)
An idle lad, a cheeky lass
The hounds all overfed —
The choirboy comes no more to Mass
The apprentice lies abed.
No, no, no! With the Bible do not jest!
If the rope round our neck isn't thick it'll break. — Disaster!
Yet one thing's true: life's dull for you. And hand on breast:
Who wouldn't be his own liege lord and master?

Good people, cast a glance into the future as the learned
Doctor Galileo Galilei predicts it:
   (He sings:)
Two housewives stand in the market square
Not knowing which way to turn;
The fishwife pulls out a loaf right there
And eats her fish alone!
The mason digs his plot with care
And takes the builder's stone
And when the house is finished and fair
Why! he moves in on his own!
But can this be allowed? No, no, it is no jest.
If the rope around our neck isn't thick it'll break. — Disaster!

Yet one thing's true; life's dull for you. And hand on breast:
Who wouldn't rather be his own true lord and master?
   The farmer kicks the landlord
   And attacks him with his scythe
   While the farmer's wife gives her children
   Milk from the parson's tithe.
No, no, good people, with the Bible do not jest!
If the rope round our neck isn't thick it'll break. — Disaster!
Yet one thing's true: life's dull for you. And hand on breast:
Who wouldn't be his own liege lord and master?

THE SINGER'S WOMAN: I've just kicked over the traces
For I said to my man, said I:
A fixed star from other places
Might do better than you. — I'll try.

THE SINGER: No, no, no, no! Stop, Galileo, stop it all!
Unmuzzle a mad dog and he'll bite. — Disaster!
Of course it's true: fun and games are too few and duties call:
Who wouldn't rather be his own lord and master?

BOTH: All you who live on earth in wretchedness
Arise! Stir up your feeble spirits faster
And learn from worthy Doctor Galuliss
The wondrous A.B.C. of earthly bliss
Only obedience holds us back from this!
Who wouldn't rather be his own liege lord and master?

THE SINGER: Esteemed citizens, behold Galileo Galilei's phenomenal discovery: The earth circling round the sun!
   (He pounds fiercely on his drum. The woman and the child step forward. The woman carries a crude representation of the sun, and the child, holding a pumpkin above its head to represent the earth, circles round the woman. The singer points triumphantly at the child, as if it were executing some perilous death-defying feat as it walks jerkily, step by step, in time to single taps on the drum. There is a roll of drums from the back.)

A DEEP VOICE *(calls out):*   The procession.
   (Enter two men in rags, pulling a little cart. On a ridiculous throne sits 'The Grand Duke of Florence', a figure in a pasteboard crown and clothed in sacking and peering through a telescope. Above the throne is a signboard: 'Looking out for Trouble'. Then four masked men march in, carrying a huge baldachin. They stop and toss into the air a dummy representing a cardinal. A dwarf has established himself at one side with a board bearing the words 'The New Age'. In the crowd a beggar raises himself on his crutch and stamps on the ground, dancing, until he falls down with a crash. Enter an over-life-size dummy, Galileo Galilei, who bows to the public. In front of it a child carries a gigantic Bible, open, with the pages crossed out.)

THE BALLAD-SINGER: Galileo Galilei, the Bible-buster!
   (Tremendous laughter from the crowd.)

———————— • ————————

11

1633: THE INQUISITION SUMMONS THE WORLD-FAMOUS SCHOLAR
TO ROME

> The depths are hot, the heights are chill
> The streets are loud, the court is still.

SCENE 11: LOBBY AND STAIRCASE OF THE MEDICI PALACE IN FLORENCE

GALILEO and his daughter are waiting to be admitted to the Grand Duke.

VIRGINIA: It's taking a long time.

GALILEO: Yes.

VIRGINIA: There's that man again, the one who followed us here.
(She points to an individual who passes without looking at them.)

GALILEO *(whose sight has deteriorated):* I do not know him.

VIRGINIA: But I have often seen him during the last few days. He makes me uneasy.

GALILEO: Nonsense. We are in Florence and not among Corsican bandits.

VIRGINIA: Here comes Rector Gaffone.

GALILEO: He's the one I'm afraid of. The fool will involve me in another hour-long conversation.
(Down the stairs comes SIGNOR GAFFONE, the Rector of the University. He is visibly alarmed when he sees GALILEO and, with his head sharply averted, he walks past the pair, scarcely nodding.)

GALILEO: What has got into him? My eyes are bad again today. Did he greet us at all?

VIRGINIA: Hardly. — What is in your book? Is it possible they think it heretical?

GALILEO: You hang around in churches too much. All this getting up early and going to Mass is completely ruining your complexion. You pray for me, don't you?

VIRGINIA: Here is Signor Vanni, the iron-founder you designed the smelting plant for. Don't forget to thank him for the quails.
(A man is coming down the staircase.)

VANNI: Did you enjoy the quails I sent you, Signor Galilei?

GALILEO: The quails were excellent, Master Vanni. Again, my best thanks.

VANNI: They were talking about you upstairs. They are holding you responsible for those pamphlets against the Bible which have lately been on sale everywhere.

GALILEO: I know nothing about pamphlets. The Bible and Homer are my favourite reading.

VANNI: And even if that were not so, I should like to take this opportunity of assuring you that we manufacturers are on your side. I am not a man who knows much about the movements of the stars, but to me you are the man who fights for the freedom to teach new things. Take that mechanical cultivator from Germany which you described to me. Last year alone five books on agriculture were published in London. We here would be only too thankful for a book on Dutch canals. The very same circles that are making difficulties for you will not permit the doctors of Bologna to dissect corpses for purposes of research.

GALILEO: Your opinion carries weight, Vanni.

VANNI: I hope so. Do you know that in Amsterdam and London they have money markets? Also trade schools. And papers appearing regularly with the latest news. Here we haven't even the liberty to make money. They are against iron-foundries because they believe too many workers together in one place will encourage immorality! I stand and fall with men like you, Signor Galilei. If they ever try to do anything against you, I beg you to remember that you have friends throughout the world of commerce. Behind you stand the cities of Upper Italy, Signor Galilei.

GALILEO: So far as I know, nobody intends to do anything against me.

VANNI: No?

GALILEO: No.

VANNI: In my opinion you would be better off in Venice. Fewer blackcoats. From there you could take up the fight. I have a travelling-coach and horses, Signor Galilei.

GALILEO: I cannot see myself as a refugee. I value my comfort.

VANNI: Of course. But after what I've heard upstairs here, it's a matter of haste. I have the impression they would rather you weren't in Florence just now.

GALILEO: Nonsense. The Grand Duke is my pupil, and besides, the Pope himself would counter any attempt to entrap me with a forceful No!

VANNI: You seem unable to distinguish your friends from your enemies, Signor Galilei.

GALILEO: I know the difference between power and impotence.
(He walks brusquely away.)

VANNI: Very well. I wish you luck.
(Exit.)

GALILEO *(returns to VIRGINIA):* Every Tom, Dick and Harry here with any sort of grievance picks me for his spokesman, particularly in places where it's not likely to do me any good. I have written a book about the mechanics of the universe, that's all. What is made or not made of it is no concern of mine.

VIRGINIA *(loudly):* If only people knew how you condemned what happened everywhere last carnival.

GALILEO: Yes. Give a bear honey, and you'll lose your arm if the beast is hungry!

VIRGINIA *(softly):* Did the Grand Duke actually summon you here today?

GALILEO: No, but I had myself announced. He wants to have the book; he has paid for it. Ask that official, and complain about them keeping us waiting here.

VIRGINIA *(followed by the individual, goes over to speak to an official):* Signor Mincio, has his Highness been informed that my father wishes to speak with him?

THE OFFICIAL: How should I know?

VIRGINIA: That is no answer.

THE OFFICIAL: No?

VIRGINIA: It is your business to be polite.
(The official half turns his back on her and yawns, looking at the individual.)

VIRGINIA *(returns):* He says the Grand Duke is still busy.

GALILEO: I heard you say something about 'polite'. What was it?

VIRGINIA: I thanked him for his polite reply, that was all. Can't you leave the book here? You are only wasting your time.

GALILEO: I am beginning to ask myself what my time is worth. Possibly I might accept Sagredo's invitation to go to Padua for a few weeks. My health is not too good.

VIRGINIA: You couldn't live without your books.

GALILEO: I could take a cask or two of the Sicilian wine in the coach.

VIRGINIA: You've always said it won't stand travelling. And the Court still owes you three months' salary. They won't send it after you.

GALILEO: That's true.
(The CARDINAL INQUISITOR comes down the stairs.)

VIRGINIA: The Cardinal Inquisitor.
(In passing he bows deeply to GALILEO.)

VIRGINIA: What is the Cardinal Inquisitor doing in Florence. Father?

GALILEO: I don't know. He behaved not unrespectfully. I knew what I was doing when I came to Florence and kept silence all those years. They praised me so highly that now they must accept me as I am.

THE OFFICIAL *(calls out):* His Highness the Grand Duke!
(COSIMO DE' MEDICI comes down the stairs. GALILEO goes up to him. COSIMO stops, slightly embarrassed.)

GALILEO: I wish to show your Highness my dialogues on the two greatest astronomical systems . . .

COSIMO: Aha, aha! How are your eyes?

GALILEO: Not at their best, your Highness. If your Highness permits, I have the book . . .

COSIMO: The condition of your eyes worries me. Really, it worries me. It shows that you are perhaps using your excellent telescope a little too zealously, eh?

(He walks on without accepting the book.)

GALILEO: He didn't take my book, eh?

VIRGINIA: Father, I'm afraid.

GALILEO *(sotto voce and firmly):*   Don't show your feelings. From here we will not go home, but to Volpi, the glasscutter. I have an arrangement with him that, in the tavern yard next door to him, there will always be a waggon with empty wine-casks waiting to take me out of the city . . .

VIRGINIA: You knew . . .

GALILEO: Don't look round . . .
(They start to leave.)

A HIGH OFFICIAL *(comes down the stairs):*   Signor Galilei, it is my duty to inform you that the Florentine Court is no longer able to refuse the request of the Holy Inquisition to examine you in Rome. The coach of the Holy Inquisition awaits you, Signor Galilei.

12

THE POPE

SCENE 12: AN APARTMENT IN THE VATICAN

POPE URBAN VIII, formerly Cardinal Barberini, has received the CARDINAL INQUISITOR. During the audience he is being robed. Outside is the sound of many shuffling feet.

THE POPE *(very loudly):*   No! No! No!

THE INQUISITOR: Your Holiness, there are assembled here doctors of all faculties, representatives of all the holy orders and of the whole priesthood who have come, with their childlike faith in the Word of God as revealed in the Scriptures, to receive from your Holiness the confirmation of their faith. Will your Holiness now tell them that the Scriptures can no longer be regarded as true?

THE POPE: I will not have the mathematical tables destroyed. No!

THE INQUISITOR: That it is the mathematical tables and not the spirit of denial and doubt — so say *these* people. But it is not the tables. A terrible unrest has come into the world. It is this unrest in their own minds which these men would impose on the motionless earth. They cry: the figures compel us! But whence come their figures? They come from doubt, as everyone knows. These men doubt everything. Are we to establish human society on doubt and no longer on faith? 'You are my master, but I doubt if that is a good thing.' 'That is your house and your wife, but I doubt whether they should not be mine.' On the other hand, your Holiness's love of art, which we have to thank for such beautiful collections, is treated to abusive remarks daubed on the walls of Roman houses, such as: 'What the barbarians left in Rome, the Barberinis have plundered.' And abroad? It has pleased God to beset the Holy See with heavy trials. Your Holiness's Spanish policy is not understood by men who, lacking insight, regret our rupture with the Emperor. For the last fifteen years Germany has been a slaughterhouse where men have butchered one another with Biblical texts on their lips. And now, when plague, war and the Reformation have reduced Christianity to a few small outposts, the rumour is spreading through Europe that you have made a secret alliance with the Lutheran Swedes in order to weaken the Catholic Emperor. And these worms of mathematicians turn their telescopes to the skies and tell the world that your Holiness here too — in the one domain where no one has yet contested you — is ill informed. One might think: what sudden interest in such an obscure science as astronomy! Is it not all the same how these spheres move? But no one in the whole of Italy — where everyone down to the stable-boys chatters about the phases of Venus as a result of the wicked example of this Florentine — there is no one in Italy who does not think at the same time of so many things which the schools and other authorities have declared to be beyond question, and which have become a burden. What would happen if all these people, so weak in the flesh and inclined towards every excess, were to believe only in their own commonsense which this madman declares to be the sole court of appeal! From first questioning whether the sun stood still over Gibeon, they might then practise their filthy doubts upon the Collects! Since they have been sailing over the ocean — I have nothing against that — they have put their faith in a brass ball they call a compass, instead of in God. Even as a young man this Galilei wrote about machines. With machines they would perform miracles. What sort of miracles? At all events, they no longer have any need of God, so what sort of miracles could these be? For example, they say there is to be no more Upper and Lower. They no longer need it. Aristotle, who in all other respects is a dead dog to them, has said — and they quote this — 'When the weaver's shuttle weaves on its own and the zither plays of itself, then the masters will need no apprentices and the rulers no servants'. And they think they have got that far. This wicked man knows what he is doing when he writes his astronomical works, not in Latin, but in the language of the fishwives and wool merchants.

THE POPE: That shows very bad taste; I will mention it to him.

THE INQUISITOR: He incites the former and bribes the latter. The seaport cities of Upper Italy are more and more insistent on having Galilei's star-charts for their ships. One will have to accede to them in this, for there are material interests at stake.

THE POPE: But these star-charts are based on his heretical assertions. It is precisely a matter of those very star-movements which are *not* possible if we reject his teachings. One cannot damn the teachings and keep the star-charts.

THE INQUISITOR: Why not? One cannot do otherwise.

THE POPE: Those footsteps make me nervous. Forgive me if I am always listening to them.

THE INQUISITOR: Perhaps they say more to you than I can, your Holiness. Are all these to leave here with doubt in their hearts?

THE POPE: After all, the man is the greatest physicist of the age, the glory of Italy, and not just some scatter-brained fool. He has friends. There is Versailles. There is the Court at Vienna. They will call the Holy Church a sink of decayed prejudices. Hands off him!

THE INQUISITOR: In practice one would not have to go very far with him. He is a carnal man. He would succumb immediately.

THE POPE: He knows more pleasures than any other man I have met. He even thinks from sensuality. To an old wine or a new idea, he cannot say no. And I want no condemnation of physical facts, no battle-cries like: 'Here the Church, there Reason!' I have permitted him his book, so long as in conclusion it states that the last word is not with science but with faith. And he has kept to that.

THE INQUISITOR: But how? In his books a stupid man, who naturally represents the views of Aristotle, argues with a clever man, who equally naturally puts forward the opinions of Galileo; and who speaks the conclusion, your Holiness?

THE POPE: What is it now? Well, who speaks for us?

THE INQUISITOR: Not the clever man.

THE POPE: That is certainly an impertinence. This tramping in the corridors is intolerable. Is the whole world coming here?

THE INQUISITOR: Not the whole world, but its best part.
(Pause. The POPE is now in his full robes.)

THE POPE: The very most that may be done is to show him the instruments.

THE INQUISITOR: That will suffice, your Holiness. Signor Galilei is an expert on instruments.

———————————— • ————————————

13

ON THE 22nd OF JUNE, 1633, BEFORE THE INQUISITION, GALILEO GALILEI RECANTS HIS TEACHING ABOUT THE MOVEMENT OF THE EARTH

> June twenty-second, sixteen thirty-three.
> A momentous date for you and me.
> Of all the days that was the one
> An age of reason could have begun.

SCENE 13: IN THE PALACE OF THE FLORENTINE AMBASSADOR IN ROME

GALILEO's pupils are waiting for news. The little monk and FEDERZONI are playing the new form of chess with its extended moves. In a corner VIRGINIA is kneeling and praying.

THE LITTLE MONK: The Pope has not received him. No more scientific discussions.

FEDERZONI: He was his last hope. It was true what he said years ago in Rome, when he was still Cardinal Barberini: 'We need you.' Now they have him.

ANDREA: They will destroy him. The Discorsi will never be finished.

FEDERZONI *(looks at him furtively):* Do you think so?

ANDREA: Because he will never recant.
(Pause.)

THE LITTLE MONK: You always get distracted with trivial thoughts when you lie awake at nights. Last night, for example, I kept thinking: he should never have left the Republic.

ANDREA: He could not write his book there.

FEDERZONI: And in Florence he could not publish it.
  (Pause.)

THE LITTLE MONK: I also wondered whether they would leave him his little stone which he always carries round with him in his pocket. His touch-stone.

FEDERZONI: To that place where they are taking him, one goes without pockets.

ANDREA *(shouting):* They won't dare! And even if they do it to him, he would never recant. 'He who does not know the truth is merely an idiot, but he who knows it and calls it a lie, is a criminal.'

FEDERZONI: I do not think he will, either; and I would rather not live if he did; but they have force on their side.

ANDREA: Not everything can be accomplished by force.

FEDERZONI: Perhaps not.

THE LITTLE MONK *(softly):* He has been in prison for twenty-three days. Yesterday was the great cross-examination. And today is the sitting. *(Loudly, since ANDREA is listening.)* The time when I visited him here two days after the decree, we sat over there, and he pointed out to me the little figure of Priapus by the sundial in the garden — you can see it from here — and he compared his work to a poem by Horace in which nothing can be changed either. He spoke of his feeling for beauty, which made him search for the truth. And he quoted a motto: hieme et aestate, et prope et procul, usque dum vivam et ulra. And he meant the truth.

ANDREA *(to the little monk):* Have you told him how he stood in the Collegium Romanum when they were testing his telescope? Tell him. *(The little monk shakes his head.)* He behaved just as usual. He stood with his hands on his buttocks, stuck out his stomach and said: 'I ask only for commonsense, gentlemen!' *(Laughing, he imitates GALILEO.)*
  (Pause.)

ANDREA *(speaking of VIRGINIA):* She is praying that he will recant.

FEDERZONI: Leave her. She is almost out of her mind since they spoke to her. They have summoned her Father Confessor from Florence.
  (Enter the individual from the Grand Duke's Palace in Florence.)

THE INDIVIDUAL: Signor Galilei will soon be here. He may require a bed.

FEDERZONI: Has he been released?

THE INDIVIDUAL: It is expected that, at five o'clock at a session of the Inquisition, Signor Galilei will recant. The great bell of St. Mark's will be rung and the wording of the recantation will be publicly proclaimed.

ANDREA: I don't believe it.

THE INDIVIDUAL: Because of the crowds collecting in the streets, Signor Galilei will be brought here through the garden door at the back of the palace.
  (Exit.)

ANDREA *(suddenly shouting):*   The moon is an earth and has no light of its own. Neither has Venus its own light and like the earth it revolves round the sun. And four moons revolve round the planet Jupiter, which is in the region of the fixed stars and is not attached to any crystal sphere. And the sun is the centre of the universe and motionless in its place, and the earth is *not* the centre and is *not* motionless. And he is the one who showed it to us.

THE LITTLE MONK: And force cannot make unseen what has already been seen.
  (Silence.)

FEDERZONI *(looks at the sundial in the garden):*   Five o'clock.
  (VIRGINIA prays louder.)

ANDREA: I cannot wait any longer. They are killing the truth.
  (He stops up his ears, as does the little monk. But the bell does not toll. After a pause, filled by VIRGINIA's murmured prayers, FEDERZONI shakes his head in negation. The others let their hands drop.)

FEDERZONI *(hoarsely):*   Nothing. It is three minutes past five.

ANDREA: He resists.

THE LITTLE MONK: He does not recant.

FEDERZONI: No! Oh, we blessed ones!
  (They embrace. They are overjoyed.)

ANDREA: Well! Force has not prevailed! It cannot do everything! Therefore, stupidity is conquered; it is not invulnerable! Therefore, man is not afraid of death!

FEDERZONI: Now the age of science has really begun. This is the hour of its birth. And think, if he had recanted!

THE LITTLE MONK: I did not say it, but I was filled with fear. I, of so little faith!

ANDREA: But I knew it.

FEDERZONI: It would have been as if night had fallen again just after the sun rose.

ANDREA: As if the mountain had said: I am a sea.

THE LITTLE MONK *(kneels down, crying):*   Lord, I thank Thee!

ANDREA: But everything has been changed today! Man, tortured man, lifts up his head and says: I can live. So much is gained when only one man stands up and says 'No'.
  (At this moment the bell of St. Mark's begins to toll. All stand rigid.)

VIRGINIA *(stands up):*   The bell of Saint Mark's. He is not damned!
  (From the street outside can be heard the voice of the crier reading GALILEO's recantation.)

VOICE OF THE CRIER: 'I, Galileo Galilei, teacher of mathematics and physics at the University of Florence, renounce what I have taught, that the sun is the centre of the universe and motionless in its place, and that the earth is not the centre and not motionless. I renounce, abhor and curse, with all my heart and with sincere faith, all these falsehoods and heresies, as well as every other falsehood and every other opinion which is contrary to the teachings of the Holy Church.'

(The stage grows dark.
When it grows light again the bell is still tolling, and then stops.
VIRGINIA has gone. GALILEO's pupils are still there.)

FEDERZONI: He never paid you properly for your work. You could neither buy hose nor publish your own work. You suffered because it was 'working for science.'

ANDREA *(loudly):* Unhappy the land that has no heroes!
(Enter GALILEO — completely altered by his trial, almost to the point of being unrecognizable. He has heard ANDREA's last sentence. For a moment he pauses at the door for someone to greet him. As no one does, for his pupils shrink back from him, he goes, slowly and unsteadily because of his failing eyesight, to the front where he finds a stool and sits down.)

ANDREA: I cannot look at him. He must go.

FEDERZONI: Be calm.

ANDREA *(screams at GALILEO):* Winebag! Snail-eater! Have you saved your precious skin? *(He sits down.)* I feel sick.

GALILEO *(calmly):* Give him a glass of water.
(The little monk goes outside and fetches ANDREA a glass of water. The others take no notice of GALILEO, who sits listening upon a stool. From far off can be heard the voice of the crier.)

ANDREA: I can walk all right, if you help me a bit.
(They help him to the door. At this moment GALILEO starts to speak.)

GALILEO: No. Unhappy the land that is in need of heroes.
(Written up in front of the curtain:
Is it not clear that a horse which falls from a height of three or four ells can break its legs, whereas a dog receives no harm; nor does a cat from the height of eight or ten ells, nor a cricket from the top of a tower, nor an ant if it fell from the moon? And just as smaller animals are proportionately stronger and more sturdy than large ones, so too, smaller plants survive better; an oak-tree two hundred ells high could not support branches which were in exact proportion to those of a smaller oak, and Nature could not allow a horse to be as large as twenty horses, nor a giant to be ten times the size of an ordinary man, without changing the proportions of all the members, particularly the bones, which would have to be strengthened out of all proportion to the original enlargement. — The common assumption that large and small machines are equally effective is plainly erroneous.

Galileo, 'Discorsi'.

———————— • ————————

14

1633-1642. GALILEO GALILEI LIVES IN A COUNTRY HOUSE NEAR FLORENCE, A PRISONER OF THE INQUISITION UNTIL HIS DEATH. THE 'DISCORSI'

> Sixteen hundred and thirty-three till
> Sixteen hundred and forty-two
> Galileo Galilei remains a prisoner of the Church
> Up to the day of his death.

SCENE 14: A LARGE ROOM WITH TABLE, LEATHER CHAIR AND GLOBE

GALILEO, now old and half blind, is experimenting carefully with a little wooden ball on a curved wooden rail. In the ante-room sits a monk on watch. There is a knock at the door. The monk opens it and a peasant enters, carrying two plucked geese. VIRGINIA comes out of the kitchen. She is now about forty.

THE PEASANT: I've been told to deliver these.

VIRGINIA: Who are they from? I haven't ordered any geese.

THE PEASANT: I've been told to say: 'They are from someone passing through.' *(Exit.)*
   (VIRGINIA looks at the geese in amazement. The monk takes them from her and examines them suspiciously. Then, reassured, he hands them back to her, and she carries them by their necks to GALILEO in the large room.)

VIRGINIA: Someone passing through has sent us a present.

GALILEO: What is it?

VIRGINIA: Can't you see?

GALILEO: No. *(He walks over.)* Geese. Is there a name on them?

VIRGINIA: No.

GALILEO *(takes one goose out of her hand):*   Heavy. I could eat a bit of that now.

VIRGINIA: You can't be hungry so soon; you've just finished supper. And what's wrong with your eyes again? You ought to have been able to see them from your table.

GALILEO: You are standing in the shadow.

VIRGINIA: I am not standing in the shadow.
   (She carries the geese out.)

GALILEO: Cook them with thyme and apples.

VIRGINIA *(to the monk):*   We must send for the eye-doctor. Father couldn't see the geese from his table.

THE MONK: I shall first have to have the permission of Monsignor Carpula. Has he been writing again himself?

VIRGINIA: No. He has been dictating his book to me; you know that. You have got pages 131 and 132, and they were the last.

THE MONK: He is an old fox.

VIRGINIA: He does nothing against the rules. His repentance is genuine. I watch over him. *(She hands him the geese.)* Tell them in the kitchen to roast the livers with an apple and an onion. *(She goes back to the large room.)* And now we'll have a little thought for our eyes and leave that ball alone immediately and dictate a little more of our weekly letter to the archbishop.

GALILEO: I don't really feel well enough. Read me some Horace.

VIRGINIA: Only last week Monsignor Carpula, to whom we owe so much — more vegetables again the other day — said to me that the archbishop asks him every time how you like the questions and quotations he sends you. *(She has sat down to take dictation.)*

GALILEO: How far had I got?

VIRGINIA: Paragraph four: As regards the attitude of the Holy Church towards the disturbances in the Arsenal at Venice, I am entirely in agreement with the position taken up by Cardinal Spoletti towards the mutinous rope-makers . . .

GALILEO: Yes. *(He dictates):* . . . I am entirely in agreement with the position taken up by Cardinal Spoletti towards the mutinous rope-makers, namely, that it is better to dole out soup in the name of Christian brotherly love than to pay them more for their hawsers and bell-ropes. For surely it must be wiser to fortify their faith rather than their greed. The Apostle Paul said: Charity aboundeth. — How does that sound?

VIRGINIA: It's wonderful, father.

GALILEO: You don't think any irony could be read into it?

VIRGINIA: No, the archbishop will be delighted. He is so practical.

GALILEO: I rely on your judgment. What is the next thing?

VIRGINIA: A beautiful saying: 'If I am weak, then I am strong.'

GALILEO: No comment.

VIRGINIA: But why not?

GALILEO: What's the next thing?

VIRGINIA: 'And to know the love of Christ which passeth knowledge.' Epistle to the Ephesians, iii, 19.

GALILEO: I would particularly thank your Eminence for the wondrous text from the Epistle to the Ephesians. Stimulated by it, I discovered in our inimitable Imitatio the following. *(He quotes from memory):* 'He to whom the eternal work speaketh, is relieved of much questioning.' May I take this opportunity to speak of myself? I am still being reproached with having once written a book about the heavenly bodies in the language of the marketplace. In doing so it was not my intention to suggest or even to approve that books on subjects so much more important, as for example theology, should be written in the jargon of pastrycooks. The argument in favour of the Latin liturgy — namely that because of the universality of this tongue, the Holy Mass can be heard in the same way by all peoples — seems to me less happy, since the blasphemers, who are never at a loss, could object that *no* people can understand the text. I heartily reject cheap lucidity in sacred matters. The Latin of the pulpit, which protects the eternal verities of the Church against the inquisitiveness of the ignorant, evokes confidence when spoken by the priestly sons of the lower classes in the accents of their local dialect. — No, cross that out.

VIRGINIA: The whole lot?

GALILEO: Everything after 'pastrycooks'.
(There is a knock at the door. VIRGINIA goes into the anteroom. The monk opens the door. It is ANDREA SARTI. He is now a middle-aged man.)

ANDREA: Good evening. I am about to leave Italy in order to take up scientific work in Holland, and have been asked to look him up on my way through, so that I can give them news of him.

VIRGINIA: I don't know whether he will see you. You have never come.

ANDREA: Ask him.
(GALILEO has recognised the voice. He sits motionless. VIRGINIA goes in to him.)

GALILEO: Is that Andrea?

VIRGINIA: Yes, shall I send him away?

GALILEO *(after a pause):*   Bring him in.
(VIRGINIA shows ANDREA in.)

VIRGINIA *(to the monk):*   He is harmless. He was once his pupil. So now he's his enemy.

GALILEO: Leave him alone with me, Virginia.

VIRGINIA: I want to hear what news he brings. *(She sits down.)*

ANDREA *(coldly):*   How are you?

GALILEO: Come closer. What are you doing now? Tell me about your work. I hear it's to do with hydraulics.

ANDREA: Fabricius in Amsterdam has charged me to enquire after your health.

GALILEO: My health is all right. They pay a great deal of attention to me.

ANDREA: I am glad I shall be able to report that you are in good health.

GALILEO: Fabricius will be pleased to hear it. And you can inform him that I live in suitable comfort. By the depth of my repentance I have been able to retain the favour of my superiors so far as to be permitted to engage in scientific work — within certain limits and under the supervision of the Church.

ANDREA: Yes. We, too, have heard that the Church is satisfied with you. Your complete submission has had its effect. It has ensured, as the authorities will have noted with satisfaction, that in Italy no further work containing new ideas has been published since you submitted.

GALILEO *(listening):* Unfortunately there are countries which refuse the protection of the Church. I fear that the condemned teachings may be disseminated there.

ANDREA: There, too, as a result of your recantation, there has been a set-back most gratifying to the Church.

GALILEO: Really? *(Pause.)* Nothing of Descartes? Nothing from Paris?

ANDREA: Yes. At the news of your recantation he stuffed his treatise on the Nature of Light into a drawer.
(A long pause.)

GALILEO: I am anxious about certain scientific friends whose feet I have set upon the path of error. Have they been enlighted by my recantation?

ANDREA: In order to be able to do scientific work, I intend to go to Holland. The bull is not permitted to do what Jupiter does not permit himself.

GALILEO: I understand.

ANDREA: Federzoni is once again grinding lenses in some shop in Milan.

GALILEO *(laughs):* He knows no Latin.
(Pause.)

ANDREA: Fulganzio, our little monk, has given up research and has returned to the bosom of the Church.

GALILEO: Yes.
(Pause.)

GALILEO: My superiors are looking forward to my spiritual recuperation. I am making better progress than might have been expected.

ANDREA: Ah!

VIRGINIA: The Lord be praised.

GALILEO *(harshly):* Go and see to the geese, Virginia.
(VIRGINIA goes out angrily. As she passes, the monk speaks to her.)

THE MONK: I don't trust that man.

VIRGINIA: He's harmless. You can hear what they say. *(As she goes):* We've got some fresh goat's cheese.
(The monk follows her out.)

ANDREA: I shall travel through the night in order to be able to cross the frontier tomorrow morning. May I leave?

GALILEO: I don't know why you came, Sarti. In order to upset me? I live cautiously and I think cautiously, ever since I've been here. But in spite of that I have my relapses.

ANDREA: I'd rather not excite you, Signor Galilei.

GALILEO: Barberini called it the itch. He himself was never quite free of it. I've been writing again.

ANDREA: Oh?

GALILEO: I have finished writing the 'Discorsi'.

ANDREA: What? 'The Conversations between two Branches of Science: Mechanics and the Laws of Falling Bodies'? Here?

GALILEO: Oh, they give me paper and quills. My superiors are no fools. They know that ingrained vices cannot be cured overnight. They protect me from unfortunate results by locking it away page by page.

ANDREA: Oh God!

GALILEO: Did you say anything?

ANDREA: They're making you plough water! They give you paper and quills just to soothe you! How could you ever write anything with that prospect before your eyes?

GALILEO: Oh, I am the slave of my habits.

ANDREA: The 'Discorsi' in the hands of the monks! And Amsterdam and London and Paris hungry for them!

GALILEO: I can hear Fabricius wailing, insisting on his pound of flesh, while he sits safely in Amsterdam.

ANDREA: Two new branches of science as good as lost!

GALILEO: It will doubtless cheer him and some others to hear that I risked the last miserable remains of my peace of mind by making a copy, behind my own back so to speak, using up the last ounce of light of the bright nights for the last six months.

ANDREA: You have a copy?

GALILEO: My vanity has hitherto restrained me from destroying it.

ANDREA: Where is it?

GALILEO: 'If thine eye offend thee, pluck it out.' Whoever wrote that knew more about comfort than I. I call it the height of stupidity to hand it over. But since I have never managed to keep myself away from scientific work you might as well have it. The copy is in the globe. If you were to risk taking it to Holland, you would of course have to shoulder full responsibility. In that case you would have bought it from someone who had access to the original in the Holy Office.
(ANDREA walks across to the globe and takes out the manuscript.)

ANDREA: The 'Discorsi'!
(He thumbs through the pages.)

ANDREA *(reads):* 'My project is to establish an entirely new science dealing with a very old subject — Motion. Through experiments I have discovered some of its properties which are worth knowing.'

GALILEO: I had to do something with my time.

ANDREA: This will found a new science of physics.

GALILEO: Stuff it under your coat.

ANDREA: And we thought you had become a renegade! My voice was raised loudest against you!

The Life of Galileo

GALILEO: And quite right, too. I taught you science and I denied the truth.

ANDREA: This changes everything, everything.

GALILEO: Yes?

ANDREA: You concealed the truth. From the enemy. Even in the field of ethics you were a thousand years ahead of us.

GALILEO: Explain that, Andrea.

ANDREA: In common with the man in the street, we said: he will die, but he will never recant. — You came back: I have recanted, but I shall live. — Your hands are tainted, we said. — You say: better tainted than empty.

GALILEO: Better tainted than empty. Sounds realistic. Sounds like me. New science, new ethics.

ANDREA: I of all people ought to have known. I was eleven years old when you sold another man's telescope to the Venetian Senate. And I saw you make immortal use of that instrument. Your friends shook their heads when you bowed before a child in Florence, but science caught the public fancy. You always laughed at our heroes. 'People that suffer bore me,' you said. 'Misfortune comes from insufficient foresight.' And: 'Taking obstacles into account, the shortest line between two points may be a crooked one.'

GALILEO: I recollect.

ANDREA: Then, in 1633, when it suited you to retract a popular point in your teachings, I should have known that you were only withdrawing from a hopeless political squabble in order to be able to carry on with your real business of science.

GALILEO: Which consists in . . .

ANDREA: . . . The study of the properties of motion, mother of machines, which will make the earth so inhabitable that heaven can be demolished.

GALILEO: Aha.

ANDREA: You thereby gained the leisure to write a scientific work which only you could write. Had you ended in a halo of flames at the stake, the others would have been the victors.

GALILEO: They are the victors. And there is no scientific work which only one man can write.

ANDREA: Then why did you recant?

GALILEO: I recanted because I was afraid of physical pain.

ANDREA: No!

GALILEO: I was shown the instruments.

ANDREA: So there was no plan?

GALILEO: There was none.
(*Pause.*)

ANDREA (*loudly*): Science knows only one commandment: contribute to science.

GALILEO: And that I have done. Welcome to the gutter, brother in science and cousin in treachery! Do you eat fish? I've got fish. What stinks is not fish but me. I sell cheap; you are a buyer. Oh irresistible sight of a book, the sacred goods! Mouths water, and curses drown. The Great Babylonian, the murderous cow, the scarlet woman, opens her thighs and everything is different! Hallowed be our haggling, white-washing, death-fearing society!

ANDREA: Fear of death is human! Human weaknesses are no concern of science.

GALILEO: No! My dear Sarti, even in my present situation I still feel capable of giving you a few tips about science in general, in which you have involved yourself.
   (A short pause.)

GALILEO *(academically, his hands folded over his stomach):*   During my free hours, of which I have many, I have gone over my case and have considered how the world of science, in which I no longer count myself, will judge it. Even a wool-merchant, apart from buying cheaply and selling dear, must also be concerned that trade in wool can be carried on unhindered. In this respect the pursuit of science seems to me to require particular courage. It is concerned with knowledge, achieved through doubt. Making knowledge about everything available for everybody, science strives to make sceptics of them all. Now the greater part of the population is kept permanently by their princes, landlords and priests in a nacreous haze of superstition and outmoded words which obscure the machinations of these characters. The misery of the multitude is as old as the hills, and from pulpit and desk is proclaimed as immutable as the hills. Our new device of doubt delighted the great public, which snatched the telescope from our hands and turned it on its tormentors. These selfish and violent men, who greedily exploited the fruits of science to their own use, simultaneously felt the cold eye of science turned on a thousand-year-old, but artificial misery which clearly could be eliminated by eliminating them. They drenched us with their threats and bribes, irresistible to weak souls. But could we deny ourselves to the crowd and still remain scientists? The movements of the stars have become clearer; but to the mass of the people the movements of their masters are still incalculable. The fight over the measurability of the heavens has been won through doubt; but the fight of the Roman housewife for milk is ever and again lost through faith. Science, Sarti, is concerned with both battle-fronts. A humanity which stumbles in this age-old milky mist of superstition and outmoded words, too ignorant to develop fully its own powers, will not be capable of developing the powers of nature which you reveal. What are you working for! I maintain that the only purpose of science is to ease the hardship of human existence. If scientists, intimidated by self-seeking people in power, are content to amass knowledge for the sake of knowledge, then science can become crippled, and your new machines will represent nothing but new means of oppression. With time you may discover all that is to be discovered, and your progress will only be a progression away from mankind. The gulf between you and them can one day become so great that your cry of jubilation over some new achievement may be answered by a universal cry of horror. — I, as a scientist, had a unique opportunity. In my days astronomy reached the marketplaces. In these quite exceptional circumstances, the steadfastness of one man could have shaken the world. If only I had resisted, if only the natural scientists had been able to evolve something like the Hippocratic oath of the doctors, the vow to devote their knowledge wholly to the benefit of mankind! As things now stand, the best one can hope for is for a race of inventive dwarfs who can be hired for anything. Moreover, I am now convinced, Sarti, that I never was in real danger. For a few years I was as strong as the authorities. And I surrendered my knowledge to those in power, to use, or not to use, or to misuse, just as suited their purposes. *(VIRGINIA has entered with a dish and stops still.)* I have betrayed my profession. A man who does what I have done cannot be tolerated in the ranks of science.

VIRGINIA: You have been received into the ranks of the faithful.
  (She walks forward and places the dish upon the table.)

GALILEO: Right. — I must eat now.
  (ANDREA holds out his hand. GALILEO looks at his hand without taking it.)

GALILEO: You yourself are a teacher, now. Can you bring yourself to take a hand such as mine? *(He walks over to the table.)* Someone passing through sent me geese. I still enjoy my food.

ANDREA: So you are no longer of the opinion that a new age has dawned?

GALILEO: I am. Take care when you go through Germany. — Hide the truth under your coat.

ANDREA *(incapable of leaving):* With regard to your estimation of the author we were talking about, I don't know how to answer you. But I cannot believe that your murderous analysis will be the last word.

GALILEO: Many thanks, signor. *(He begins to eat.)*

VIRGINA *(showing ANDREA out):* We do not care for visitors from the past. They excite him.
  (ANDREA leaves. VIRGINIA returns.)

GALILEO: Have you any idea who could have sent the geese?

VIRGINIA: Not Andrea.

GALILEO: Perhaps not. What is the night like?

VIRGINIA *(at the window):* Clear.

———————— • ————————

15

1637. GALILEO'S BOOK, THE 'DISCORSI', CROSSES THE ITALIAN BORDER

> The great book o'er the border went
> And, good folk, that was the end.
> But we hope you'll keep in mind
> He and I were left behind.
>
> May you know guard Science' light
> Kindle it and use it right
> Lest it be a flame to fall
> Downward to consume us all.

SCENE 15: A SMALL ITALIAN FRONTIER TOWN

Early morning. At the frontier turnpike, children are playing. ANDREA, a coachman beside him, is waiting for his papers to be examined. He is sitting on a little chest and reading GALILEO's manuscript. The travelling-coach stands at the far side of the barrier.

THE CHILDREN *(singing):*   Mary, Mary sat her down
Had a little old pink gown
Gown was shabby and bespattered
But when chilly winter came
Gown went round her just the same
Bespattered don't mean tattered.

THE FRONTIER GUARD: Why are you leaving Italy?

ANDREA: I am a scholar.

THE FRONTIER GUARD *(to the clerk):*   Write under 'reason for journey': scholar. I must search your luggage. *(He does so.)*

THE FIRST BOY *(to ANDREA):*   You shouldn't sit there. *(He points to the hut outside which ANDREA is sitting.)* A witch lives inside.

THE SECOND BOY: Old Marina is *not* a witch.

THE FIRST BOY: Do you want me to twist your arm?

THE THIRD BOY: She *is* a witch. She flies through the air every night.

THE FIRST BOY: And why can't she get so much as a jug of milk anywhere in town if she isn't a witch?

THE SECOND BOY: How can she fly through the air? No one can do that. *(To ANDREA):* Can one?

THE FIRST BOY *(referring to the second):*   That's Giuseppe. He doesn't know a thing because he doesn't go to school because he hasn't a proper pair of breeches.

THE FRONTIER GUARD: What's that book?

ANDREA *(without looking up):*   It's by the great philosopher Aristotle.

THE FRONTIER GUARD *(suspiciously):*   What sort of a fellow's he?

ANDREA: He's dead.
   (The boys, to mock ANDREA as he reads, prance round pretending to read books at the same time.)

THE FRONTIER GUARD *(to the clerk):*   See whether there's anything about religion in it.

THE CLERK *(leafing through it):*   I can find nothing.

THE FRONTIER GUARD: There's little enough point in all this searching! Nobody's going to show us openly things that he wants to hide. *(To ANDREA.)* You must sign that we've searched everything.
   (ANDREA stands up hesitantly and goes, still reading, into the house with the frontier guard.)

THE THIRD BOY *(to the clerk, pointing at the chest):*   Look, there's something else, look!

THE CLERK: Wasn't that there before?

THE THIRD BOY: The Devil put it there. It's a chest.

THE SECOND BOY: No, it belongs to the stranger.

THE THIRD BOY: I wouldn't go in there. She's bewitched the coachman's old nags. I looked through that hole in the roof which the snowstorm made and heard them coughing.

THE CLERK *(who has almost reached the chest, hesitates and turns back):* Devil's work, eh? Well, we can't examine everything. Or where would we be?
  (ANDREA returns with a jug of milk. He sits down again on the chest and continues to read.)

THE FRONTIER GUARD *(following him with papers):* Close up the boxes again. Have we everything?

THE CLERK: Everything.

THE SECOND BOY *(to ANDREA):* You're a scholar. You tell us — can one fly through the air?

ANDREA: Wait a moment.

THE FRONTIER GUARD: You can pass.
  (The luggage is collected by the coachman. ANDREA picks up the chest and is about to go.)

THE FRONTIER GUARD: Stop! What's that chest?

ANDREA *(resuming his book):* It's books.

THE FIRST BOY: It's bewitched.

THE FRONTIER GUARD: Nonsense. How could she bewitch a chest?

THE THIRD BOY: She can if the Devil helps her!

THE FRONTIER GUARD *(laughs):* That won't work here. *(To the clerk):* Open it up. *(The chest is opened.)*

THE FRONTIER GUARD *(morosely):* How many are there?

ANDREA: Thirty-four.

THE FRONTIER GUARD *(to the clerk):* How long will you take over them?

THE CLERK *(who has begun to rummage superficially in the chest):* All printed already. You can certainly say goodbye to your breakfast; when am I going to have time to get over to the coachman and collect these arrears of toll money from the selling up of his house if I have to wade through all these books?

THE FRONTIER GUARD: Yes, we must have the money. *(He pushes the books with his foot.)* Well, what a lot of stuff there must be in them! *(To the coachman):* Get on!
  (ANDREA, carrying the chest, goes with the coachman across the frontier. On the other side he puts GALILEO's manuscript in his travelling bag.)

THE THIRD BOY *(points at the jug which ANDREA has left behind):* Look!

THE FIRST BOY: And the chest has gone! You see, it *was* the Devil.

ANDREA *(turning round):* No, it was me. You must learn to open your eyes. The milk is paid for and so is the jug. The old woman can have it. Yes, and I haven't yet answered your question, Giuseppe. One cannot fly through the air on a broomstick. It must at least have a machine on it. And as yet there is no such machine. Perhaps there never will be, for man is too heavy. But, of course, one cannot tell. We don't know nearly enough, Giuseppe. We are really only at the beginning.

———————————— • ————————————

Consider the Play

1. The first scene of a drama must give the audience a chance to absorb some of the background of place, time, and events and to be put in touch with the general situation as quickly and briefly as possible. In your opinion, is the first scene of *The Life of Galileo* effective in giving the audience antecedent action? Support your point of view.

2. Why does Galileo find the idea of the earth not being the centre of the universe an exciting one?

3. "For where belief has prevailed for a thousand years, doubt now prevails." What does this statement tell us about Galileo's character and approach to life?

4. What is the Curator's attitude towards Galileo in Scene 1? Is this attitude held by some people towards scientists today? Would you agree or disagree with the Curator's view? Why?

5. What does the quatrain, which opens Scene 2, suggest about Galileo's invention of the telescope? What further evidence later in the scene substantiates the suggestion made in the quatrain?

6. When Ludovico says that he is beginning to understand something about science, what does he mean?

7. In Scene 3, the Curator rants at Galileo. Why? Is this passage humorous? Why?

8. Why is Sagredo upset and worried about Galileo's idea that the earth is a star like any other?

9. What happened to Giordano Bruno? Why?

10. In Scene 4, Galileo argues with the Philosopher and the Mathematician. About what do they argue? Does Galileo succeed in his efforts to persuade them to accept his point of view?

11. Why do you think the young duke is prevented from looking through the telescope?

12. In Scene 6, several characters show their lack of appreciation for Galileo's theories. Why is this scene necessary?

13. To what do the Cardinals Barberini and Bellarmin want Galileo to agree? Do you find their arguments convincing? Explain your position.

14. In Scene 8, the Little Monk tries to persuade Galileo to renounce his findings. In the end, who wins the argument? Explain.

15. In Scene 9, Ludovico reveals new aspects of his character. What does he value? Do you approve of the action he takes? Discuss.

16. Why do you think Brecht chose to present much of Scene 10 in the form of verse? Is this technique effective? Explain the satire in the scene.

17. In Scene 12, the Pope becomes nervous at the sound of feet shuffling in the corridor outside his robing chamber. Why? How does he respond to the stress? If you had been in his position, how would you have reacted? Why?

18. How does Brecht create suspense in Scene 13? What is ironic about this scene?

19. One theme of *The Life of Galileo* is the theme of betrayal. In your opinion, is betrayal inevitable in human relationships? Can you recall a time when you were betrayed by someone or when you betrayed someone? Why did it happen? How did you feel at the time? How do you feel now, looking back on the incident?

20. Galileo lived the last nine years of his life under house arrest, supervised by the Roman Catholic Church. In 1639, John Milton, the renowned English poet, visited Galileo and wrote: "I found and visited the famous Galileo, grown old, a prisoner to the Inquisition for thinking in Astronomy otherwise than the Franciscan and Dominican and Jesuit licensers thought." On his deathbed, Galileo muttered, "Eppur si muove" ("Yet it does turn"), a reference to the earth's turning around the sun. Select three other famous people whose last years were tragic ones. Discuss the contribution to humanity made by each, and comment on the problems they faced in life.

———————————— • ————————————

Inook and the Sun

by Henry Beissel

The Playwright

Henry Beissel was born in Cologne, Germany, in 1929. He came to Canada in 1951 after studying philosophy in England. In 1956, he resumed his studies at the University of Toronto, where he earned his Masters in English literature. At present, he is Professor of English at Concordia University in Montreal.

Beissel is well known as a poet, playwright, translator, and editor. His works have been translated into many languages, including French, Spanish, German, Serbo-Croatian, Hungarian, Rumanian, and Japanese. He has also received many awards, including the Epstein Award in 1958, the Davidson Award in 1959, and several grants from the Canada Council and the Quebec Ministry of Culture.

Beissel's first play was a translation and adaptation of *The Double Take* by Pirandello, which was broadcast on CBC radio in 1958. Since then he has translated and adapted many works, including plays by Tankred Dorst, Louis-Dominique Lavigne, and André Simard.

Inook and the Sun was written and staged for the first time in 1973. It is a mythological, epic play written for both children and adults and designed for Bunraku marionettes, a Japanese style of puppetry. It has been translated into and staged in three languages (French, German, and Japanese). It is produced frequently in Canada and abroad.

The Play

Inook and the Sun deals with the life of a boy in a land which is different from that of most Canadians. It is appropriate, therefore, to consider the play in the light of its setting.

The Eskimo language has more than a hundred words to describe various types of snow and nearly the same number to describe the various types of ice formations. The plant growing season in the high Arctic is 40 days or fewer. On the Arctic mainland, it is about 80 days. Certain lichens survive in areas so cold and rugged that they may be able to grow during only one day of the year. A small patch of lichen may be hundreds of years old.

The ability to survive these long periods of cold is one of the most important features of the plants and animals which inhabit the Arctic regions. The ultimate test is surviving the combination of high winds and deep cold. For example, a 38 km/h wind at 0°C produces a greater heat loss than a temperature of − 40°C with no wind. Yet muskoxen, which may have a mass of up to 400 kg, survive in the Arctic where the average January temperature is − 35°, where temperatures can drop to as low as − 45°C or even − 55°C, and where blinding blizzards can last for days.

The Arctic sun sets on October 22 and does not rise above the horizon again until March 1. But rather than seek shelter in the valleys, the muskoxen move to the windy slopes where the thin snow cover makes it easier to reach the sparse vegetation on which they feed. The muskoxen are protected from heat loss and death from exposure by a thick, silky layer of wool under an immense cloak of coarse guard hair, so long that the hairs nearly reach the ground.

The aquatic mammals of the Arctic face a special environmental challenge. Although the winter water temperature remains fairly constant at about $-2°C$, heat conduction is about 250 times greater than in the air. They protect themselves against the sapping chill by an excellent insulating medium, a layer of fat, or blubber. On the smaller seals, this layer may be from 5 cm to 10 cm thick. On the great Greenland whale, this layer may be up to 60 cm thick.

Other animals protect themselves in other ways. For example, Arctic birds ruffle their feathers to trap more air, which acts as an insulating layer. Land mammals fluff out their fur for the same reason.

As descendants of warmer climate anthropoids, human beings seemed unsuited for the Arctic. Yet, the Eskimo and Inuit made remarkable adaptations. These adaptations are cultural, rather than physiological. Their knowledge of how to protect themselves from the harsh winter climate has made the Eskimo and Inuit masters of it.

One adaptation was in clothing, such as the double-layered suit of caribou skin which took advantage of the basic principle that air acts as an insulating barrier. A complete winter outfit had a mass of about 4.5 kg and kept the wearer comfortable at temperatures as low as $-40°C$.

Another adaptation, based on the principle that warm air rises, was in housing. When igloos were the main form of shelter, they were built with a low entrance leading through a low passage, which acted as a cold trap, into the main house. The warmth in the main room was created by the body heat of the inhabitants and the heat from lamps fuelled by seal oil. This warm air did not escape through the low entrance passage because warm air is lighter than cold air.

When southerners wrote stories about the Arctic, they often dwelt on the cold as the enemy. Traditional Eskimo and Inuit tales, however, rarely dealt with it except in the context of preventing the hunt. The more common focus was food or the lack of it. Heaven was pictured as a place where "caribou graze in great herds, and they are easy to hunt" and hell was pictured as a place where people "are always hungry, for their food is butterflies."

In the dead of winter, when the caribou had migrated elsewhere, the Eskimo and Inuit would hunt sea animals and use every part of the body for some useful purpose. For example, blubber provided lamp oil and food. The raw skin of the white whale and narwhal, called *muktuk* by the Eskimo, provided food rich in Vitamin C (as much per unit of mass as a fresh orange). The rubbery seal intestines and stomachs often held partly digested shrimp, which tastes like lobster paste. Both the seal organs and the shrimp are rich in vitamins.

To those who live in warmer climates, the Arctic may seem a harsh, hostile, barren, and forbidding land. But to those who have adapted themselves, such as the Eskimo and Inuit, the Arctic is home. In *Inook and the Sun,* Henry Beissel shows one such individual, Inook. As Beissel wrote in his introduction to his play:

"Years ago I studied Eskimo life and culture, and what I encountered there never lost its hold over my imagination. In the Arctic, I saw fundamental patterns of life and death and quest lying open to the mind that are buried in our urban civilization. The stark realities of the conflict between summer and winter, light and dark, heat and cold, and the struggle to survive between them, seemed to call out for dramatic treatment, though it was some time before the shape of the play emerged."

The shape that emerged eventually was a puppet performance. Puppetry has a long tradition as a theatrical medium. One of its fascinations is that it combines many of the arts — sculpture, painting, design, and theatre. Beissel was fascinated by the potential, as he explained in his introduction:

"The particular form of *Inook and the Sun* grew out of a presentation by the Bunraku National Puppet Company of Japan. I was moved by the subtlety and sophistication of Bunraku puppetry, and by the complexity and profundity of human experience which they were able to embody. In Bunraku the manipulators are on stage, all dressed and hooded in black so as to obliterate themselves in the drama of puppets. It occurred to me that the manipulators could wear masks and interact with the puppets, and that such a technique would be particularly appropriate to the two basic dimensions of the Eskimo experience as I saw it — the one natural, the other supernatural. The spirit figures might be effectively enacted through masks, and the Eskimo, principally Inook himself, through puppets."

Inook and the Sun has been presented in many different ways since its first presentation in 1973. Although most have been in puppet form, the play has also been performed by actors wearing masks (without puppets). Some productions have used ballet and mime.

Henry Beissel

Inook and the Sun by Henry Beissel. Copyright © Henry Beissel, 1974. Reprinted by permission of Gage Publishing Limited.

Inook and the Sun

Henry Beissel

The First Production Was Staged
On August 1, 1973
At the Third Stage
In Stratford, Ontario

With This Cast

Cast of Marionettes: Inook, Father, Mother, Raven, Dog-Team, Polar Bear, Musk Oxen, Arctic Fox, Seals, Sea-Monster, Two Sharks

Masks: Spirit of the Caribou, Spirit of the Moon (male), Spirit of the Wind (male), Spirit of the Dream (female), Sumna, Goddess of the Sea, Spirit of the Ice (male), Spirit of the Sun (female)

Director: Jean Herbiet, in collaboration with the puppeteer Felix Mirbt

A stark flat snowscape. A few igloos at the edge of an Eskimo village. The sun is setting; its warm orange glow fades slowly and is replaced by the silvery ice-blue light of the rising moon. The music evokes the bleak harshness of the land. A flock of wild geese departs noisily as the blustering wind increases in intensity; wolves howl at close distance.

With a sinister cackle, a jet-black RAVEN appears and circles the stage, chanting in a cracked voice:

RAVEN

White is black, and black is white
Arctic winter, arctic night.
Snow wind, ice wind, wolves at bay
Man and beast are winter's prey.

Gull and goose have followed the sun
Moose and caribou have gone
Whitefish, flatfish, whale and shark —
All have fled the howling dark.

Snow wind, ice wind, wolves at bay
Man and beast are winter's prey
White is black, and black is white
Arctic winter, arctic night.

EPISODE 1

The RAVEN settles on an igloo. A light goes on inside — yellow glow in the sombre polar night. The wind. When INOOK and his FATHER emerge from the igloo, dogs bark and yelp wildly.

INOOK: Quiet! . . . Nippaitit! . . . Down! . . . Nipjarnak! *(ad lib.)*

FATHER: The dogs are frantic to be off on the hunt. They are hungry.

INOOK: I am hungry too.
(The dogs yelp again.)
Quiet! . . . Down! *(ad lib.)* We are all hungry.
(Wolves howl. At once the dogs are quiet.)

FATHER: Even the wolves are hungry.

INOOK: We must find game.

FATHER: It will not be easy. Most of the animals have followed the sun.

INOOK: We shall track down those that stayed behind.

FATHER: A killer wind is blowing. It jumps on the back of animals and forces them to the ground. Then it covers them with a thick fur of snow. We should wait till the wind is out of breath and tires.

INOOK: The wind has a long breath and we need food. For seven days we waited out the snow storm. I cannot wait any longer. I want to prove myself a man, Father, and a man is a hunter.

FATHER: A hunter knows how to wait.

INOOK: Wait? What for? A hunter stalks and kills his prey.

FATHER: Ayorama. Everything happens as the spirits have decreed. That is why we must know how to wait. Wait for the right moment to shoot the arrow. Wait with the harpoon over the ice-hole for the seal. Wait in the igloo for the storm to pass. Wait for the return of the caribou and the sun. Winter is the season of waiting.

INOOK: Where does the sun go, Father, when she leaves us?

FATHER: No one knows for sure. She leaps over the edge of the world. Some say, into the sea to warm the fish. Others say she goes to shine for the spirits of the dead. There are even rumours that she is under the curse of an evil spirit. But no one knows.

INOOK: Has no one ever followed the sun to see where she goes?

FATHER: We must let the secrets of the world be. It is as the spirits have decreed, Ayorama.

INOOK: Can the spirits be trusted, Father?

FATHER: There are good spirits and bad ones.

INOOK: Most of them are bad, aren't they? They make things difficult for us. Sometimes they even kill us.

FATHER: But the good ones help us and with their help we can overcome all difficulties.

INOOK: Then I want to go and find the sun.

FATHER: You are impatient and reckless, Inook.

INOOK: If the good spirits help us we can travel right to the edge of the world and hunt for the sun.

FATHER: There is no return from beyond the edge of the world.

INOOK: The animals follow the sun there every year and they return.

FATHER: And it is animals we must hunt, not the sun. We need food and clothing.

INOOK: But if we hunt the sun and capture her and bring her back here, then all the geese and hares and caribou and seals will come back too, and we shall have lots of food.

SPIRIT OF THE MOON: *(shaking with laughter)* He wants to hunt the sun!
   (The RAVEN starts up and circles the stage with his sinister cackle.)

INOOK: *(frightened)* Who is that?

SPIRIT OF THE MOON: *(now serious)* You are bold, my boy. What is your name?

Inook and the Sun

INOOK: I am Inook.

SPIRIT OF THE MOON: You bear a proud name, Inook. Do you know who I am?

INOOK: You are the Spirit of the Moon.

SPIRIT OF THE MOON: Yes, I am the moon. I rule this land of the long night. The black sky is my dominion and the stars are spirits in my service. I make a glittering feast of the night.

INOOK: But you are so cold, Moon, so bitter cold.

SPIRIT OF THE MOON: Is that why you want to bring back the sun and drive me out of my land?

FATHER: Inook is young and foolish.

SPIRIT OF THE MOON: Teach him then that all things have their season. I paint your igloos and your hunting-grounds as white as my face so that you should know your way in the long winter night. What more do you want?

INOOK: The sun is brighter and warmer.

SPIRIT OF THE MOON: O yes, my sister, the sun. Everybody loves her. Foolish creatures that do not know that her love is deadly. Love her then! But me, me you must respect and admire because I shall outlast her. She consumes herself with fiery passion, but I am immutable and at peace.

INOOK: But you wax and wane —

SPIRIT OF THE MOON: . . . illusions, deceptions! I am who I am. I never change.

INOOK: All the animals follow the sun.

SPIRIT OF THE MOON: They too will be consumed. And so will you! *(laughs uproariously)* A boy hunting the sun to banish me!
   (The RAVEN circles with cackling laughter and flies off.)
Your father knows to call the spirits for the hunt. Music and dance triumph where rebellion comes to a bad end. Remember that, Inook, remember that. . . . *(withdraws)*

FATHER: He's gone.

INOOK: Where?

FATHER: Back into the igloo of his clouds.

INOOK: Let's go after the sun, Father.

FATHER: Get such foolish and dangerous notions out of your head. We shall go on a hunt, and we shall hunt for food. That's all. Let's call the Spirit of the Caribou to help us find game. Start the drums, Inook!

———————————— • ————————————

EPISODE 2

Music. The MOTHER emerges from the igloo. INOOK and his parents perform a ritual dance enacting the stalking, hunting and killing of the caribou. INOOK is the caribou and wears an antlered headgear. He carefully imitates the movements and the sounds of a caribou. His FATHER is the hunter, the MOTHER assists. Drums, rattles, and clappers. Authentic Eskimo rhythms. The climax is reached with the mock-killing of INOOK, the caribou. His FATHER and MOTHER then dance around the "dead body" chanting:

FATHER: Great Spirit of the Caribou,
The Eskimo are calling you.

MOTHER: When we're by snow and wind pursued
You give us fur and oil and food.

FATHER: We Eskimo must hunt to live
And owe our life to what you give.

MOTHER: Great Spirit of the Caribou,
We sing and dance in praise of you.

FATHER, MOTHER: *(chorus)* The Eskimo are calling you,
Great Spirit of the Caribou,
Please visit our igloo.
   (A bone rattle accompanies the appearance of the SPIRIT OF THE CARIBOU. The music stops.
   INOOK leaps up and withdraws into the igloo.)

SPIRIT OF THE CARIBOU: You called me.

FATHER: O Great Spirit of the Caribou!

MOTHER: We have not eaten for many days.

FATHER: We need your help, Great Spirit. For seven days we waited in the igloo for the blizzard to pass. Our stores of food were low. For four days we have eaten nothing but the snowladen wind that strangled the bark in the throat of our dogs.

MOTHER: Help us, great and powerful Spirit. We need food.

SPIRIT OF THE CARIBOU: I am the protector of the caribou.

FATHER: We are setting out on a hunt. Help us find game.

SPIRIT OF THE CARIBOU: Why should I help you who kill many caribou each year?

FATHER: We honour the caribou and help you against foxes and wolves. We never kill more than we need to live. That is the law of the north.

MOTHER: We celebrate the grace and courage of the caribou in our songs and dances. Who will praise you when we die?

SPIRIT OF THE CARIBOU: How can I help? My caribou herds are grazing in the sun. Here, under the moon, the wind holds sway. Nothing moves without his consent while he rides the hounds of snow.

FATHER: Speak for us to the wind.

SPIRIT OF THE CARIBOU: The wind never listens. When he is awake he raises his voice so that nothing else can be heard. And when he's asleep he is deaf.
   (Unnoticed by the others, INOOK has emerged from the igloo with bow and arrow. He shoots an arrow at the SPIRIT OF THE CARIBOU.)

I cannot he-e-ellp! *(He is struck by INOOK's arrow, and disappears with a scream in a flash of light.*
The RAVEN returns with his sinister cackle.)

FATHER: *(choking with laughter)* Inook, you fool! . . . You tried to kill a spirit! Don't you know the spirits are immortal?

MOTHER: A spirit never forgets insult or injury until he is revenged.

RAVEN: *(circling throughout song)*
White is black and black is white,
Arctic winter, arctic night.

MOTHER: Gull and goose have followed the sun,
Moose and caribou have gone.

FATHER: Whitefish, flatfish, whale and shark —
All have fled the freezing dark.

RAVEN: Snow wind, ice wind, wolves at bay,
Man and beast are winter's prey.

————————— • —————————

EPISODE 3

Arctic winter. Arctic night. There is no moon. The wind is howling. We hear the barking dog team before it whisks the sled with INOOK and his FATHER into sight.

FATHER: Ho-o-o-h!
(The sled halts. The dogs bark and jump.)
Quiet!

INOOK: Down! . . . Nippaitit! . . . Quiet! . . . *(ad lib.)*

FATHER: It is too dark to read the map the wind has drawn into the snow.

INOOK: Have you lost your way?

FATHER: The moon will tell us. Let's build a shelter here and rest.
(They do so using the sleigh as protection against the wind.)

INOOK: We have no food.

FATHER: You need no food while you sleep.

INOOK: I am hungry.
(like a prayer)

Animals of the long night
Where are you?
Animals of the long night
Why do you flee from us?
We are your friends
We need you.
Animals of the long night
Come bring us your flesh.

FATHER: They cannot hear you in this wind. Lie down and sleep. We must wait for the moon.

(There is a spectacular display of Northern Lights.)

INOOK: Look, Father! Northern Lights! How beautiful they are! They look like many-coloured streamers. And the sky is like a big black igloo all decorated for a happy dance. Maybe that's the glittering feast the moon was talking about.

FATHER: No. Inook. It's giant spirits playing with the skulls of our dead ancestors. The souls of our fathers and mothers have returned to earth, but their bodies are up in the sky or down in the sea, and sometimes the spirits play games with their skulls to while away the time.

INOOK: I wish I could join them. It would be one way to keep warm.

FATHER: You are too reckless, Inook. One day the spirits will fetch you. Sleep now. The moon will be up soon. *(He sleeps.)*

INOOK: *(Gets up stealthily and talks to the Northern Lights in the sky.)*

Help me, o Spirits.
I am a shadow
in a land of shadows.
The wind plays with me
the moon plays with me
I am fair game for the dark.
Help me become a man.

Help me conquer my fear
of the moon, of the wind.
Give me the strength
of the polar bear
the foxes' speed
and the skill of wolves
for I want to hunt the sun.

Help me, Good Spirits.
I am a shadow
in a land of shadows.
I am a boy
at the mercy of the wind
at the mercy of the moon.
Help me become a man.

(The wind now howls at full force. Abruptly the SPIRIT OF THE WIND swoops down from the sky and all is still.)

SPIRIT OF THE WIND: So you are afraid of me, Inook? I am the Spirit of the Wind.

INOOK: Yes, I am afraid of you — but I stand up to you all the same.

SPIRIT OF THE WIND: Good for you. Only the brave stand up to me and I favour the brave.

INOOK: Will you help me then?

SPIRIT OF THE WIND: Perhaps. Are you willing to follow me?

INOOK: Where?

SPIRIT OF THE WIND: I will show you the way to the sun. Just follow me!

Inook and the Sun

INOOK: I cannot leave my father alone.

SPIRIT OF THE WIND: You want to become a man, don't you, Inook?

INOOK: Yes.

SPIRIT OF THE WIND: All you have to do is follow me, follow the wind. When the moon rises everything will be arranged. Now lie down and sleep. It will be a long journey to the sun.

INOOK: *(lies down)* I wish you too would lie down and sleep, Spirit of the Wind, so that we can find some game. My father and I are hungry. Our dogs are hungry too.

SPIRIT OF THE WIND: Leave it to me, Inook, leave it to the wind. Leave it to the wind. *(disappears in a swoop that brings back the wind's howl)*
(INOOK and his FATHER sleep.)

---------------•---------------

EPISODE 4

When the SPIRIT OF THE DREAM appears the wind falls silent. The story she tells is accompanied by an appropriate play of shadow puppets.

SPIRIT OF THE DREAM: Sleep, Inook, sleep. You will need all your strength when you wake. I am the Spirit of the Dream and I can see into the future. You are still a boy, but you will be a man soon. In between lies a dangerous journey. There! That is the giant sea-monster. He is blind and ferocious. All the fish, even the whale and the shark, are afraid of him. He is so powerful that once upon a time he climbed out of the sea to break a large piece out of the sky. He wanted to have it for a ceiling in his underwater cave. But the sun blinded him and he fell back into the sea. Now, in revenge, he snatches the beautiful sun from the sky every year. The wild geese always try to stop him, but he makes an arrow of them and shoots them way . . . way into the air until they disappear in the clouds. He wants to keep the golden sun imprisoned in his cave until she gives him back his sight. But . . . you will soon find out what happens.
(The shadow of INOOK himself appears in the shadow play.)

SPIRIT OF THE DREAM: Beware, Inook! The giant sea-monster knows no mercy. He cannot see you, but he feels and senses you from the slightest movement in the water. Watch out, Inook! If he catches you he will tear you apart and the sharks will have a feast.
(The shadow play shows INOOK confronting the SEA-MONSTER. Sharks are closing in. INOOK throws his harpoon, but the monster snaps it like a twig and his silent sinister laughter metamorphoses into the wild barking of the dogs. The SPIRIT OF THE DREAM vanishes. INOOK wakes up —)

---------------•---------------

EPISODE 5

INOOK wakes up to find himself face to face with a POLAR BEAR beset by the dogs who have surrounded and are attacking him.

INOOK: Father! A polar bear!
(In a flash INOOK's FATHER is up and ready, harpoon in hand, to meet the BEAR who has begun to kill the dogs one by one.)

FATHER: Stay behind me, Inook. *(to the Bear)* Come on, Pride of Beasts, it is your life or mine.
(Having killed all the dogs the BEAR now attacks the humans. INOOK's FATHER fights him with the harpoon. INOOK circles to attack him from behind. He is about to throw his harpoon.)
Don't! It takes more than one harpoon to kill a bear. Without it you're defenceless! Stab him with it!
(In the ensuing life-and-death struggle the BEAR kills INOOK's FATHER but is himself killed by INOOK.)

FATHER: *(with difficulty)* I'm proud of you, Inook. You've killed your first bear. You're a man now.

INOOK: *(his dying FATHER in his arms)* O Good Spirits, do not let my father die.

FATHER: Don't grieve. Ayorama. All is decreed. I'm not sorry to leave the world. I'm tired of struggling. In the Land of the Dead I shall find peace at last. Perhaps the sun shines there forever. Warmth and peace.
(He dies.)

INOOK: Listen, Father! You'll be all right. I'll build you an igloo here and go for help. You'll be all right. You hear me?
(The MOON appears and harshly lights the scene.)

SPIRIT OF THE MOON: Your father is dead.
(INOOK cries.)
Yes, weep, Inook. A man must know how to weep. And you're a man now — albeit a little man. Tears are the price of living. There is much weeping in the mutable world. Every snowflake is a frozen tear.
(The WIND swoops down from the sky.)

SPIRIT OF THE WIND: *(angry)* Don't listen to him, Inook! He hates the living because he is dead. Your sorrow will pass. Life is full of joy.

SPIRIT OF THE MOON: O Wind, you envy me my peace because you must be forever on the move. You roam the world without rest. Joy, Inook, passes quickly — like your father.

SPIRIT OF THE WIND: You, Moon, are forever on the move too — except you are locked into the monotony of your prescribed circles. You are jealous of our freedom to come and go as we please. Life means change, Inook, and change brings joy.

SPIRIT OF THE MOON: Weep not for your father, Inook, for he is at peace now. Weep for yourself!

SPIRIT OF THE WIND: Bury your father, Inook, and move on. There is laughter over the horizon.

INOOK: Must you quarrel at my father's grave?

SPIRIT OF THE WIND: Your father's spirit lives on, for the soul never dies.

INOOK: Yes, that's right. What I bury is only his body, isn't it? But where has his spirit gone? His soul — where can I find it? I want to go there and speak with it. Please, Great Spirits, help me!

SPIRIT OF THE WIND: You must travel beyond the edge of the world.

Inook and the Sun

SPIRIT OF THE MOON: Travel? How do you propose that he travel? His dogteam is dead. Will he pull his own sleigh?

INOOK: I'm young and I've lots of bear meat now to give me strength. Yes, I'll go over the edge of the world to the Land of the Dead. My father said the sun was there too.

SPIRIT OF THE MOON: There is only one way to the Land of the Dead.

INOOK: Will you show me the way?

SPIRIT OF THE MOON: I can't.

SPIRIT OF THE WIND: I know where you can find the sun. I can show you the way there.

Follow the wind, follow me.
Though heaven is my place of birth
I know every corner of the earth
from the mountains across the tundra to the sea.

I blow from the east
I blow from the west
I breathe and whisper
and howl without rest.

I blow from the west
I blow from the east
I can comfort or kill
both man and beast.

I blow from the north
I blow from the south
I blow the very words
right out of your mouth.

I blow from the south
I blow from the north
and if I don't have my way
I have my will by force.

Follow the wind, follow me.
Though heaven is my place of birth,
I know every corner of the earth
from the mountains across the tundra to the sea.

SPIRIT OF THE MOON: Empty boasts! Empty promises! You listen to the wind and you're lost.

INOOK: *(to the SPIRIT OF THE WIND)* Will I find the spirit of my father where you take me?

SPIRIT OF THE WIND: You ask too many questions. Just follow me. Follow the wind!

SPIRIT OF THE MOON: You are a fool to trust the wind, Inook. He is gentle as a summer breeze now to hide that he is a killer at heart.

INOOK: I'm a man now and I trust my own strength.

SPIRIT OF THE MOON: I'll light up the whole length of my long night to watch the wind lead you astray. *(laughs uproariously)*
(The MOON's laughter is taken up by the RAVEN who suddenly returns and circles with his sinister cackle while INOOK prepares to bury his FATHER.)

RAVEN: White is black and black is white
Arctic winter, arctic night.
Man kills beast and beast kills man
thus it was since time began.
Snow wind, ice wind, wolves at bay
man and beast are winter's prey.
(Intermission)

———————————— • ————————————

EPISODE 6

Three days later. INOOK is stumbling across the icy wasteland. His feet are sore now and he is approaching exhaustion.

INOOK: How much further is it to the Land of the Sun?
(Silence.) Can you hear me, Great Spirit of the Wind?
(Silence.) I have walked three days now. The knife-edged ice has cut my boots and my feet are cold and sore. I have eaten the last of the bear meat I carried, and the edge of the world is as far away as ever.
(Silence.) What shall I do, Great Spirit of the Wind?
(Silence.) Why don't you answer me? *(Silence.)*

I am a shadow
in a land of shadows.
The wind plays with me
the moon plays with me.
I am fair game for ice and snow
I am fair game for the dark.
Help me, Spirits in the sea and in the sky!
I did not come this far to die.

(The MOON breaks into prolonged uproarious laughter.)

SPIRIT OF THE MOON: You see, Inook, the wind has abandoned you. *(laughs again)* You wouldn't listen to me. You should have gone home.

INOOK: I couldn't go home to my mother empty-handed. And my father dead.

SPIRIT OF THE MOON: You are lost now, aren't you? You don't know where to go. *(laughs)*

INOOK: I know the direction. There — where the light is the colour of blood! *(He points to the horizon where a faint glow of sunlight stains the darkness.)*

SPIRIT OF THE MOON: You don't need my help then.

INOOK: My feet are sore and it seems still so far to go.

SPIRIT OF THE MOON: You blind young fool — to run after my dazzling sister! Don't you know that her fire is fatal? Her golden rays are nothing but a flaming net in which to trap you and burn you up.

Inook and the Sun

INOOK: O Moon, you are jealous of the sun, because she is more beautiful than you. Her fire is the fire of life. When she comes the ice runs away, the animals return, and the rocks burst into flower. Why do you always speak ill of her?

SPIRIT OF THE MOON: Time will tell, my boy. I have no more to say. Speak to the musk-oxen. Perhaps they will help you.

Ice-light brittle
shadows crunch
moonbeam skittle
back and hunch.

Skull-faced silence
crack-crazed loon
snow-crust islands
knife the moon.

Black blood river
sickle-starred
glaciers shiver
bonebite-scarred.

Ice-clot spittle
frost harpoon
snow-night brittle
hail the moon.

    (The SPIRIT OF THE MOON withdraws laughing.)

MUSK-OX: *(picking up the MOON's last line)*

Hail the moon!
bone-face spirit
ice-crack horn
silver hoof-print
shadow born.

Flaming snow torch
night beast eye
shag-fur frost-scorch
praise the sky!

    (During this speech five MUSK-OXEN enter to the rhythm of a dark, slow drum. INOOK waits till their dance is finished before he approaches them. The bull comes forward menacingly.)

INOOK: Peace, mighty musk-ox! I'm hungry but I come not to kill you.

MUSK-OX: You — little man — kill me? *(He laughs and the other MUSK-OXEN join in.)*

INOOK: I've killed my first polar bear. I'm a big hunter.

MUSK-OX: My respects. But you are still little to me. I could run you into the ground quicker than a blizzard.

INOOK: I don't want to fight you. I've come for help.

MUSK-OX: Lay down your harpoon then, and we shall talk in peace.

INOOK: I'm hunting the sun. The wind promised to show me the way, but he has abandoned me. I've travelled for three days and I am lost now.

MUSK-OX: What do you want of the sun?

INOOK: I want to bring her back here to the Land of the Aivilik, my people. Winter is long and cruel to us. Often we Eskimo suffer hunger and many starve to death. And always we suffer from the cold, the bitter cold. Our bodies do not grow the shaggy furs that keep you warm.

MUSK-OX: I know. You kill us to save your skin.

INOOK: The moon says that is the law of the north, and man and beast have to live by it. But I prefer to live under the rule of the sun. Under the sun the land is bright and happy, and there's plenty of food for us all. And everyone is nice and warm.

MUSK-OX: Well, for us musk-oxen it gets a little too warm under our thick fur in the summer. But still, you're right, it's a happier time.

INOOK: That's why I want to find the sun and bring her back here.

MUSK-OX: Why don't you wait? She'll come back. She always comes back every year.

INOOK: There's no game and the Eskimo are starving. Winter is too long. Besides, I'm looking for the spirit of my father. The polar bear I killed first killed my father, and I want to find his spirit to know when and where he returns to the world.

MUSK-OX: I understand. But I cannot help you. We don't know exactly where the Land of the Sun lies. We see the sun roll along the horizon till she falls over the rim of darkness and disappears. My grandfather told me that's where the Land of the Dead is, but how to get there . . . Why don't you ask the arctic fox over there? He has relatives in the Land of the Sun. He should know. But beware! He's sly.
(A FOX is sleeping curled up in the snow.
INOOK picks up his harpoon and bows to the MUSK-OX. The MUSK-OXEN
depart. INOOK jumps the FOX and holds the harpoon to his throat.)

INOOK: Don't move or you'll die! Listen! I'm in search of the sun. You must show me the quickest way to her or I'm going to kill you.

ARCTIC FOX: I don't know the way. Please don't kill me.

INOOK: I count to three. You have relatives in the Land of the Sun, isn't that right? — One!

ARCTIC FOX: Yes, that's true, but I don't know where they live.

INOOK: If you have relatives there you must know how to get there. — Two!!

ARCTIC FOX: But I've never been there, honest.

INOOK: There is no such thing as an honest fox. You're lying. — Three!!!

ARCTIC FOX: Wait! I know who can show you the way — the whistling swan! He goes there every year. There is one up there. *(He points behind INOOK's back and, when INOOK turns to look, he slips away and is gone in a flash.)*
(The SPIRIT OF THE MOON reappears, convulsed with laughter.)

Inook and the Sun

SPIRIT OF THE MOON: Ha, he tricked you. You still have a lot to learn, Inook, before you can take on a fox. A whistling swan indeed! *(laughs)* There's not a whistling swan left in all the Arctic lands. They've all gone with the sun before the long night came and I took over.

INOOK: I deserve your mockery, Spirit of the Moon. It's not honourable to be cheated by a fox.

SPIRIT OF THE MOON: And what are you going to do now? You're tired, hungry and lost. Perhaps you'll reach the Land of the Dead sooner than you think.
(The SPIRIT OF THE WIND swoops down from the sky.)

SPIRIT OF THE WIND: Don't listen to him. His light is the colour of the cruel polar bear and his heart is a chip of ice. Follow me, follow the wind!

INOOK: Where have you been, Spirit of the Wind? You left me here without food or directions. I called and you did not come.

SPIRIT OF THE WIND: I am busy raising huskies of snow and driving them southward across the tundra toward the sun. I've taken a short break to come here and help you. Now look. Right here is a seal-hole. Tie your harpoon-line around your waist and stand here with your harpoon ready. When the seal comes up, throw your harpoon. If you hit it, the seal will show you the way to the sun.

INOOK: And if I miss?

SPIRIT OF THE WIND: Then you must wait for it to come back. There's no other way. I must be off again. Never lose heart, Inook. I'll protect you. I have a long arm. *(The SPIRIT OF THE WIND departs swiftly.)*
(INOOK ties the harpoon-line around his waist and stands over the seal-hole, harpoon at the ready.)

SPIRIT OF THE MOON: Inook, I have to admire your courage — you, a little boy, defying me, the grand Ruler of the Night! I like that. Perhaps you will grow up to be a man after all. But so long as you put your trust in the wind. . . .
(At this moment a SEAL comes up for air. INOOK hurls the harpoon and hits it. The SEAL dives quickly and pulls the struggling INOOK into the sea and under.)

INOOK: Help, Good Spirit of the Moon, help! I'm drowning.

SPIRIT OF THE MOON: For you the way to the fire leads through the water, Inook, but I remain behind, immutable and at peace.

———————— • ————————

EPISODE 7

The action of this episode, and of the two that follow, takes place under water. I suggest black lighting until INOOK enters the Hall of the Iceberg. The action continues from Episode 6. INOOK is being dragged by the SEAL to an underwater cave where he is quickly surrounded by other SEALS and tied up with his harpoon line. The SEALS then perform a ritual dance around him.

SEALS: *(chorus)*

We are the seals,
the cheerful seals.

We sleep on ice
and eat codfish and eels.

All winter we live
under the sea
under the ice
flipper-de-lee.

We are the seals
with flippers and tail
we are hunted by man
by shark and by whale.

We are nowhere safe
so we live with fear
but all the same
we are full of cheer.

We caught a little man
from the Land of the Moon
and pulled him down
by his own harpoon.

We are the seals
the cheerful seals —
shall we try and see
if the little man squeals?

(SUMNA, Goddess of the Sea, appears. She is ugly and imperious. The SEALS scatter.)

SUMNA: What is going on here? *(to INOOK)* Who are you? What are you doing here?

INOOK: I'm Inook. I think I've drowned.

SUMNA: Have you ever heard a drowned man talk?

INOOK: Well, no, but . . .

SUMNA: Don't talk nonsense then. You're out to find the sun. That's a serious matter.

INOOK: *(startled)* How do you know about that?

SUMNA: *I* ask the questions here, *you* answer them.

INOOK: But who are you?

SUMNA: That shall be the first riddle you must solve.

INOOK: I don't understand.

SUMNA: As a special favour to the Spirit of the Wind, and because he asked me to, I am prepared to help you find the sun — on three conditions. First, you must discover who I am.

INOOK: You must be one of the sea-witches.

SUMNA: Are you trying to insult me?
(The SEALS are giggling in the background.)

INOOK: No, but you're so ugly.

SUMNA: Think before you speak, Inook, or I shall feed you to the sharks.

INOOK: No, please, don't do that. I'll try my best. — What's the second riddle?

SUMNA:
Wind or moon —
who is the groom?
Who is the bride
crying in the tide?

INOOK: *(repeats)*

'Wind or moon —
who is the groom?
Who is the bride
crying in the tide?'
That's very difficult.

SUMNA: The sea-monster knows the answer.

INOOK: The sea-monster? I can't ask him. I don't even know where he is.

SUMNA: The seals will take you to his cave.

INOOK: But he isn't going to tell me anything.

SUMNA: It's up to you to make him tell you the secret.

INOOK: But the sea-monster is a terrible giant. I dreamed of him. He'll kill me.

SUMNA: A man is known by his trials, Inook. Don't you want to know your third and final task?

INOOK: Yes, but please make it something easy.

SUMNA: You must get past the two ferocious sharks that guard the entrance to the Great Hall of the Iceberg.

INOOK:
O Good Spirits!
You have forsaken me.
I am a shadow among shadows
at the bottom of the sea
at the mercy of a monster
at the mercy of sharks
O why is the world —
so cold and so dark?

SUMNA: There is no darkness in the Iceberg. Once you are inside the Great Hall, everything will be bright and clear.

INOOK: Will I find the spirit of my father there?

SUMNA: I told you, *I* ask the questions here, *you* answer them. Now tell me — who am I?

INOOK: Please, can I be untied first? I cannot think bundled up in my harpoon-line.

SUMNA: *(motioning the SEALS who have remained in the background.)*
Untie him!
    (The SEALS come forward. While they untie INOOK, they furtively exchange signs and gestures with him until he realizes what the song is meant to tell him.)

SEALS: *(chorus)*

We are the seals,
the cheerful seals!
We sleep on ice
and eat codfish and eels.

We are happy in winter,
we are happy in summer,
because we serve
the Goddess Sumna . . .
because we serve
the Goddess Sumna . . .
Sumna, Goddess of the Sea . . .
Goddess of the Sea . . .

    (Till INOOK comprehends, then the SEALS withdraw into the background again.)

INOOK: I'm ready.

SUMNA: Answer me then — who am I?

INOOK: *(play-acting)* You are . . . you are . . .

SUMNA: Yes, I am . . .

INOOK: You are not a sea-witch.

SUMNA: I'm not.

INOOK: You are . . . you are . . .

SUMNA: Yes . . .

INOOK: You are . . . not a sea-fairy.

SUMNA: I'm not.

INOOK: Then you are . . . you must be . . .

SUMNA: I must be . . .

INOOK: Sumna, the Goddess of the Sea!

SUMNA: *(furious)* O hurricane-and-tidal-wave! How did you guess? Someone must have betrayed me.

INOOK: I am Inook, and Inook uses his head.

SUMNA: Alright. I am Sumna, Goddess of the Sea. You have solved the first riddle. Now let's see if your head is a match for the grim sea-monster. Remember. . .

Wind or moon —
who is the groom?

Who is the bride
crying in the tide?

(motions to the SEALS) Take him to the cave of the monster! *(to INOOK)* If you pass all your tests, we shall meet again. Farewell, Inook. *(She disappears.)*

INOOK: If the monster doesn't kill me and the sharks don't eat me, we shall meet again. Farewell.
(The SEALS move off with him.)

——————————— • ———————————

EPISODE 8

Continue black lighting. INOOK arrives in the cave of the MONSTER OF THE SEA. He is terrified by the huge blind octopus-like creature, but he is determined to get what he wants.

SEA-MONSTER: *(menacing)* I sense a presence. *(He probes the air with one of his many tentacles but INOOK eludes him.)*

I'm the Monster of the Sea.
With my many tentacles
I choke my enemy.
I choke the whale
and I choke the shark.
I'm as mean as can be
because I live in the dark
and I cannot see.

But I can sense and I can feel
every movement in the water
whether it's creature or ship's keel.
Someone's entered my cave
and I know it's not a seal
not a whale and not a shark
but some creature from afar
that can penetrate the dark
reckless as a shooting star.

SEA-MONSTER: *(During the song he tries to snatch INOOK, but INOOK eludes him every time.)*
Who or what thing are you? Are you a giant crab? Or a sea urchin? Or a sting-ray? *(Each time he waits for an answer, and when he gets none, he tries in vain to lay hold of INOOK.)*
Are you fish, flesh or fowl? No one enters my cave uninvited and lives. *(Now he charges INOOK furiously and a pursuit ensues until INOOK strikes off one of the MONSTER's tentacles with his harpoon.)*

INOOK: I am Inook, the mighty Eskimo hunter.

SEA-MONSTER: You have cut off one of my tentacles. You must die.

INOOK: Beware! I have killed a polar bear with my magic harpoon.

SEA-MONSTER: *(laughs)* Are you trying to frighten me? I have polar bear for breakfast and I shall have you for lunch. *(He attacks.)*

INOOK: I shall cut off your tentacles one by one till you are powerless.

SEA-MONSTER: For every tentacle you cut off I grow two new ones. Sooner or later I'll catch you.

SEA-MONSTER: *(The fight between them continues. INOOK cuts off another tentacle and two new ones sprout at once to replace it. Eventually the MONSTER catches INOOK.)*
Ha! I've got you. Now you must die.

INOOK: *(in desperation)*

Wind or moon —
who is the groom?
Who is the bride
crying in the tide?

SEA-MONSTER: *(taken aback)* Who told you that?

INOOK: Sumna.

SEA-MONSTER: You know her name!

INOOK: The Goddess of the Sea.

SEA-MONSTER: Did she send you?

INOOK: Yes, she did.

SEA-MONSTER: What does she want?

INOOK: The answer. The answer to the riddle.

SEA-MONSTER: Never, never! I hate the Goddess of the Sea. It is she who banishes me to this black cave. Every year I snatch the sun from the sky, but Sumna takes her away from me and gives her to her son, the Spirit of the Ice, who keeps her in the Great Hall of his Iceberg. I hate Sumna, and since you are one of her servants, all the more reason that you should die.

INOOK: I'm not one of her servants. I'm Inook, an Eskimo boy. I'm looking for the sun.

SEA-MONSTER: You are looking for the sun?

INOOK: Yes. And the Goddess of the Sea is an ugly witch. She has set me three difficult and dangerous tasks before I get inside the Iceberg. One of them is to get the answer to her riddle from you.

SEA-MONSTER: What do you want of the sun?

INOOK: I want to take her back to the Land of the Aivilik.

SEA-MONSTER: Where is this Land of the Aivilik?

INOOK: It's the land of my people — up above the ice and by the edge of the sea. A land cold and barren without the sun.

SEA-MONSTER: And you want to take the sun there?

INOOK: Yes. Because when the sun comes to us, our land is full of colour and life and beauty . . . I tell you what I'll do. If you give me the answer to the riddle I promise you a piece of the sun in exchange. You have always wanted one to put in the ceiling of your cave, haven't you?

Inook and the Sun

SEA-MONSTER: Ye-es.

INOOK: Then you'll be able to see again. Because you are not really blind. It's because of the darkness in your cave that you cannot see.

SEA-MONSTER: And what guarantee do I have that you'll keep your promise once I let you go?

INOOK: Cross my heart.

SEA-MONSTER: I shall come and get your heart if you deceive me.

INOOK: I won't deceive you.

SEA-MONSTER: I shall know where to find you, you hear me?

I'm the Monster of the Sea.
With my many tentacles
I choke my enemy.
I choke the whale
and I choke the shark.
I'm as mean as can be,
because I live in the dark
and I cannot see.

INOOK: I shall keep my promise. And you'll be able to see again.

SEA-MONSTER: Alright then. *(He whispers at length with INOOK and then lets him go.)*

INOOK: Thank you, monster. You shall have your piece of the sun — if I survive the sharks! *(He departs.)*

SEA-MONSTER: I shall tear him from limb to limb if he has tricked me.

————————— • —————————

EPISODE 9

Continue black lighting. Outside the entrance to the Great Hall of the Iceberg guarded by two fierce sharks. INOOK arrives in the company of the SEALS.

INOOK: There is the entrance to the Iceberg. But how will I ever get in? How will I get past these savage sharks? They'll tear me to pieces.

O Good Spirits
I am a shadow
in a sea of shadows
at the mercy of the sea
at the mercy of the dark.
Please help me
conquer these sharks.

SEALS: *(chorus)*

Listen to the seals
with flippers and tail.
You will get past the sharks
disguised as a whale.

INOOK: That's a good idea. I'll disguise myself as a killer whale.

SEALS: *(chorus)*

Pretend to chase us
and they'll soon join in
and when their backs are turned
you quickly slip in.

INOOK: Thank you, good seals. You have been a great help.
(INOOK disguises himself as a whale and pretends to chase the swarm of SEALS back and forth before the very noses of the sharks until they can no longer resist the temptation and join in the hunt.)

SEALS: *(chorus)*

We are the seals
the cheerful seals
we sleep on ice
and eat codfish and eels.

We are the seals
with flippers and tail
we are hunted by man
by shark and by whale.

We are nowhere safe
so we live with fear
but all the same
we are full of cheer.

SEALS: *(chorus) (When the sharks are engrossed in the hunt and have their backs turned, INOOK disappears in the entrance to the Iceberg. Too late, the sharks realize they have been tricked. As they swim furiously back and forth in front of the entrance, the SEALS depart laughing at them.)*

You were tricked by a boy
you silly shark —
your teeth are bright
but your brains are dark.

You were tricked by a boy
and by the cheerful seals,
who sleep on ice
and eat codfish and eels.
  (Off.)

———— • ————

EPISODE 10

The Great Hall in the Iceberg. Everything glistens and sparkles in white and silver and turquoise. The SPIRIT OF THE ICE sits in a frozen position on a block of ice which glitters golden because the sun is evidently locked in it; what movements he makes must be slow and stiff. INOOK's FATHER lies frozen inside another block of ice. INOOK enters in his whale disguise. Once inside he takes off his disguise and stares in amazement at all the sparkling magnificence around him.

INOOK: O Spirits of the Sea and of the Sky!
You have pulled me down
over the edge of the world
without telling me why.
I am a shadow now
all sparkling and bright
in this crystal hall of light.

(He discovers his FATHER in the ice.)
Father, Father! I've found you. It's me — Inook!
(He tries to shake and break the ice-block.)

INOOK: Can you hear me? Wake up, Father! Come on out! It's Inook, your son!
(He looks about distraught and discovers the sun in another ice-block. He rushes over to it and shakes it wildly.)
The sun! If I could chip a piece off the sun I would melt the ice and free my father.

O Spirits, good and bad!
I know I'm in your hands,
toy and harpoon.
You play with me a little in the sun
but all too soon
you hurl me back
into the dark dominion of the moon.

(He raises his harpoon and prepares to throw it at the frozen sun.)
But I defy you, Spirits.
While I live
I'll have the sun.

SPIRIT OF THE ICE: *(sharp, hard, loud)* You're undone!
(Startled, INOOK looks about and only now discovers the SPIRIT OF THE ICE.)
You dare raise your harpoon against me, the Spirit of the Ice, in my Great Hall?

SPIRIT OF THE ICE: *(INOOK lowers his harpoon.)* What impudent creature are you?

INOOK: I am . . .

SPIRIT OF THE ICE: *(thundering)* Silence! Do you think I don't know who you are, Inook? Prepare to die! I shall turn you into a block of ice.

INOOK: I didn't aim my harpoon at you, great Spirit of the Ice, I aimed at the sun.

SPIRIT OF THE ICE: The sun?!
(SPIRIT OF THE SUN enters, but INOOK does not notice her.)
You aimed your harpoon at the sun?

INOOK: I've travelled the whole length of the winter earth to find the sun. My people are starving. Our land is dark and cold. We need the sun to survive.

SPIRIT OF THE ICE: Yet you raised your harpoon against the sun.

INOOK: I wanted to capture her to take her back to the Land of the Aivilik.

SPIRIT OF THE ICE: You forfeited your life!

SPIRIT OF THE SUN: *(coming forth, to the SPIRIT OF THE ICE.)*
I pardon him.
   (to INOOK.)
I am the Spirit of the Sun. I like you, Inook. *(looks closely at him.)* I like the fire in your eyes.

INOOK: It is your fire
that burns in my eyes
as it is your light
that flushes our skies.
O Great Spirit of the Sun
I did not know
you were so beautiful
and still so young.
Now I understand
why the animals follow you
and joy colours the land
wherever you go.
Come back with me
drive our night away
tear the ice-sheet off the sea
and wake the lavish day!
Scatter your flowers
bring back the beasts —
so that in your honour
we may sing and dance and feast.

SPIRIT OF THE ICE: Enough! How dare you, impudent little boy?

SPIRIT OF THE SUN: He is not a little boy any longer. Only a man would have the courage and the knowledge to enter here.

SPIRIT OF THE ICE: How did you get in here?

INOOK: Sumna, the Goddess of the Sea, told me to go here and showed me the way.

SUMNA: *(rushing in)* . . . on three conditions! Two you have fulfilled. You discovered my identity and you've got past the ferocious sharks. But by the third condition shall be determined whether you'll be turned into ice or returned to earth.

Wind or moon —
who is the groom?
Who is the bride
crying in the tide?

INOOK: The moon is the groom.

SUMNA: And who is the bride?

INOOK: You, Goddess of the Sea, are the bride.

SUMNA: And why am I crying in the tide?

INOOK: Because you are betrothed to the moon, but month after month the moon puts off the wedding. You cry because you fear you may never be married to him.

(To the accompaniment of a bone rattle SUMNA quickly changes from an ugly bag into a beautiful woman. The SPIRIT OF THE ICE puts his hands over his eyes as if he were blinded.)

How you've changed! You're almost as beautiful as the Spirit of the Sun.

SUMNA: It's you who's changed. Understanding has changed you, and courage. The better you understand and the braver you are, the more beautiful I and all things shall be.

INOOK: I don't understand that.

SUMNA: Some day perhaps. Now go . . . You may return to your people.

SPIRIT OF THE SUN: I will go with you as your bride — if you want me.

INOOK: Inook, the mighty Eskimo hunter — married to the sun?!

SUMNA: But let me warn you. The sun is betrothed to the Spirit of the Ice in the same way that I, Goddess of the Sea, am betrothed to her brother, the moon. She will never be wholly yours.

INOOK: But why?

SUMNA: Every year she must return for a time here to this Iceberg.

INOOK: But why?

SPIRIT OF THE SUN: Because all things have their season — remember, Inook?

INOOK: Yes. A long time ago . . . When we started out on our hunt . . . My father! What about my father? Can he come with us?

SPIRIT OF THE ICE: No — he stays! Locked forever into the eternal ice.

FATHER: *(from within the ice block)* I am proud of you, Inook. You have become a mighty hunter.

INOOK: You will come back with us to the Land of the Aivilik, Father.

FATHER: No, Inook. Leave me to the peace of the dead. It is decreed that my struggles are over. Ayorama.

SPIRIT OF THE SUN: *He* cannot return, but *his* spirit will be reborn in our first son so that in time he can become the father of our grandchildren when you have gone to rest.

SUMNA: No earthly shape or creature can last. That is the law. Everything must forever change and go on changing, Inook.

FATHER: That's the law.

SPIRIT OF THE ICE: That's the law.

SUMNA: You may go now, Inook, and take the sun with you.

INOOK: I almost forgot. I made a promise . . .

SPIRIT OF THE SUN: . . . to the sea-monster. I know. You shall keep your promise. When I rise above the sea I shall throw a handful of sun-gold into his cave to light it up as bright as a spring morning. But whether it will cure his blindness . . .

INOOK: He'll feel the light if he can't see it.

INOOK:

O beautiful Spirit of the Sun
your light and your fire make me stronger
than whale, musk-ox, and polar bear
happier than seal and arctic hare.
I'm a shadow in a land of shadows no longer.
I'm Inook, a man now in his pride.
I bring to my people the sun as my bride.

(Music strikes up. The SPIRIT OF THE SUN and SUMNA dance a slow rhythmic round-dance with INOOK. The SPIRIT OF THE ICE stealthily gets hold of INOOK's harpoon and suddenly hurls it at INOOK. The harpoon misses him and instead strikes the frozen sun. There is a flash and a thunder-clap, and slowly the sun rises from its ice-block.
A quick change of scene without break.)

EPILOGUE

Same set as in the Prologue, only now the moon is setting and the sun rising. The wind is softer and the howling of the wolves more distant. The RAVEN flies in and circles the scene.

RAVEN:

Summer comes, winter must fly
the sun is climbing into the sky.
Snow wind, ice wind — pass away
Night must now make room for day.

Gull and goose come back with the sun
char and salmon start their run.
Herds of caribou return
Arctic shrew and arctic tern.

Summer comes and winter goes
winter comes and summer goes
man kills beast and beast kills man —
thus it was since time began.

(The RAVEN finishes his song when the sun has flushed the whole scene with her orange gold. Then he flies off. On his departing cackle the play ends.)

———————————— • ————————————

Inook and the Sun

Consider the Play

1. The *atmosphere* of a play is its emotional tone and overall effect. What atmosphere is created for this play through the Prologue?

2. In Episode 1, what reasons does Father give Inook for not following the sun?

3. In Episode 2, what reasons do Father and Mother give the Spirit of the Caribou when asking for help in killing caribou?

4. Episode 2 ends with a symbolic action. What is it? Explain its significance.

5. In Episode 3, what promise does the Spirit of the Wind make to Inook? What warning does the Spirit of the Dream give?

6. In Episode 5, the Spirit of the Moon and the Spirit of the Wind argue. Why and about what are they arguing?

7. What is the "Land of the Aivilik"?

8. The Goddess of the Sea puts three obstacles in Inook's path. What are they? How does he overcome them?

9. Some episodes begin with a passage of verse. What is the effect on the story when this technique is used?

10. The stage directions for Episode 10 specify colours to be used. What is the effect of these colours?

11. What does the Spirit of the Sun admire about Inook? What qualities does Inook find attractive about the Spirit of the Sun?

12. The play ends with an Epilogue. In your opinion, is this Epilogue necessary? Why? What other technique could have been used?

13. This play has many ingredients of the simple adventure tale. What are some of these ingredients? How are they used?

14. Comment on the poetry used in the play. Consider the rhythm, the rhyme (including the rhyming scheme), the stanzaic form, and the images created.

15. Why do you think the playwright chose to use both prose and poetry for this play?

16. If you were the playwright, would you choose to use prose only, poetry only, or a combination of prose and poetry? List reasons for and against each, and explain your choice.

17. What does the play suggest about the relationship between the Eskimos and the animals of the North?

18. Explore myths of other cultures, such as those of the ancient Greeks and Romans or the Indians of North America. Select one which you find particularly appealing. Discuss why you like this myth and suggest reasons why it has survived through the ages. Does the myth which you have selected have common threads with the myth of *Inook and the Sun?* What are they, and why do you think these common threads exist?

19. Current events have changed and are changing the culture and ways of living in the North. In your opinion, are these changes helpful or harmful? Conduct a survey to discover how other people view these changes. Make up a questionnaire and use it to question your classmates, other students in your school, or other people in your community. Write a summary of the results and compare your opinion with your findings.

20. What does the Arctic mean to you? Express your thoughts and feelings in the form of your choice, such as a collage, a poem, a sketch, a painting, a short story, or an essay.

Arms and the Man

by Bernard Shaw

The Playwright

George Bernard Shaw was born on July 26, 1856, in Dublin, Ireland. His family life was disturbed, poverty-stricken, and unpleasant because of his father's alcoholism. In 1872, his parents separated. His mother left Dublin, taking her two daughters to London. Shaw stayed behind but he left school, which he had always disliked, and went to work as a clerk in a land office. Four years later, however, he too left Dublin. He joined his mother and sisters in London, determined to make his name in the arts.

Shaw's literary career got off to a shaky start. He wrote five novels between 1879 and 1885, and all were rejected. But he found other interests in debating clubs, street corner oratory, the National Gallery, and the British Museum's reading room. He became a vegetarian and gave up alcohol and tobacco. Perhaps most important of all, he discovered the study of economics and the works of Karl Marx. He became a founding member of the British Socialist Fabian Society in 1885. That same year, he began his career as a playwright, journalist, book reviewer, and art critic. He soon established himself in other careers as well — as a music critic, drama critic, and public speaker.

In the 1890s, Shaw turned to writing plays in earnest. Although he was to become one of the most prolific and important British playwrights of modern times, he was not recognized as a bright new talent immediately. His earliest plays, which he characterized as "unpleasant", were performed only in obscure theatre clubs. His first play, *Widower's Houses,* was staged in 1892.

Arms and the Man, his fourth play, was the first to reach a larger audience. It was staged in London's West End (the equivalent of Broadway in New York City) on April 21, 1894. A few months later, on September 15, it was staged in New York. Both of those first stagings were small successes, but since then *Arms and the Man* has attracted increasingly large audiences.

During his long life, Shaw wrote extensively in many forms, served as a Member of Parliament, travelled around the world, won the Nobel Prize for Literature (in 1925), and carved a place for himself as one of the most important figures in twentieth century dramatic literature. In addition to shaping the theatre of his time and after, Shaw brought a bold new critical intelligence to his many other areas of interest. In the process, he helped mold the thought of three generations. By the time he died on November 2, 1950, he was regarded as perhaps the most extraordinary literary figure who had ever lived.

The Play

In some respects, George Bernard Shaw's public image was as famous as the plays he wrote. Tall, thin, and erect, he always wore the already long out of fashion Norfolk jacket and trousers that fastened just below the knee, exposing a pair of rather spindly stockinged shanks. He carried his head squarely on his shoulders and held his chin somewhat in, giving the impression both of keen attention to and lofty detachment from the world around him. He gave the impression, even in extreme old age, of exceptionally good health. Throughout his life, his eyes were clear and sprightly and his hair and beard well-groomed.

Shaw was as much an individualist in his writing as he was in his appearance. When asked why he wrote plays, he replied, "I am no ordinary playwright. I am a specialist in immoral and heretical plays. My reputation was gained by my persistent struggle to force the public to reconsider its morals. I write plays with the deliberate object of converting the nation to my opinion on sexual and social matters."

Shaw believed that one person (he himself) could be right and the rest of the world wrong, especially when it came to the state of British theatre at the end of the nineteenth century. His mission was, as he put it, to "bring English theatre into some sort of relationship with contemporary culture". He refused to write the traditional and popular comedy of manners. Instead, he wrote plays to unmask what he saw as the vices of society, and he dealt with serious social and economic problems — political vice, unsafe factories, unsanitary slums, workhouses, the rights of women, and the hypocrisy of the privileged classes. He developed a new form of play, which he called *thesis drama*.

Shaw found the thesis play valuable because through it he was able to set himself up as a teacher and a moralist. He was also able to make clear that he saw his task as a dramatist to set people thinking — in the "right" way — about worthwhile ideas. Most important of all, he found the thesis play the ideal vehicle for expounding his own views and for presenting his solutions to the social problems he saw around him.

Shaw aimed at a wide range of targets. He spared neither individuals nor whole social classes in his attacks on what he saw as evil or vice. The result was 50 plays which eventually earned him a reputation as the greatest dramatist in the English language since William Shakespeare.

Shaw did not confine his zeal as a reformer to his plays, however. In fact, writing plays was just one more commitment that had to be squeezed into busy days crowded with giving lectures, making speeches, attending and reviewing theatre and opera performances, writing newspaper columns, attending Fabian Society executive meetings, and taking French and German lessons. He always carried a small notebook in which he made notes at odd moments stolen from his hectic schedule. Many of these notes later saw life in his plays.

Arms and the Man was written for a new movement in the theatre — a movement aimed at bringing more reality and trueness to life into plays. Shaw declared his aim as "to put people on the stage as they are". The character of Bluntschli, for example, is Shaw's picture of a *real* soldier as opposed to the *stage* soldier of the plays of the 1890s. The stage soldier was obviously unreal. He was not frightened, and he gloried in exposing himself to danger. He had absolutely no common sense.

Shaw's picture of the soldier was based on his research into the question of what war was really like and his talks with soldiers who had seen active service in wartime. When critics complained that this picture was false and disgusting, Shaw pointed to a military writer, General Horace Porter, who said that the average soldier "stands his ground under a sense of duty and self-respect" but who does not enjoy the battle and is only too pleased when it stops. Like Bluntschli, the soldier fights when necessary but avoids fighting if possible.

Shaw did not believe that all good soldiers are brave and virtuous and that all bad soldiers are cowardly and evil. Nor did he believe that people in real life fall into neat categories, such as liar, truth-teller, sinner, or saint. And so Shaw's characters did not fit into these accepted categories. He wanted to put people on stage as they really are, and he demanded that the audience respect and accept human nature as it really is.

This is how Shaw explained his writing of *Arms and the Man:* "I created nothing; I invented nothing; I imagined nothing; I perverted nothing; I simply discovered drama in real life."

One can almost hear Shaw chuckling as he wrote this. Of course, he knew perfectly well how original his play was, but it tickled his sense of humour to pretend that all he had done was string together a few incidents from life and that anyone could do the same thing just as successfully.

During the first act of *Arms and the Man,* it is November 1885, a time when the Balkan States are being harassed by Turkey. The Balkans do not present a united front, however. Instead, they indulge in petty jealousies and disagreements. As the Turkish forces mass at the frontier, Serbia suddenly declares war on Bulgaria, hoping to take advantage of a difficult situation. At this dangerous moment, Russia withdraws its soldiers from the Bulgarian army. In spite of these difficulties, the poorly equipped Bulgarian army successfully resists the Serbian army and even captures Pirot in Serbia. Austria then intervenes to halt the Bulgarian advance.

The second and third acts take place on March 6, 1886, three days after the Treaty of Bucharest has restored peace.

In the 1890s, when Shaw wrote *Arms and the Man,* western Europeans tended to view the Balkan nations as comical rather than as sinister. Apparently, Shaw shared this view as he made a great deal of fun of the apparently haphazard actions of the Balkan states. It was another 20 years, in 1914, before the assassination of an Austrian archduke by a Serbian revolutionary, the spark that set off World War I, persuaded western Europeans to take events in the Balkans seriously.

Perhaps this explains Shaw's choice of title for the play. He used the opening words from Virgil's epic poem, *The Aeneid,* as an ironically fitting way to introduce the mock-epic tone of his play. Virgil's poem, which tells the story of Aeneas, the Trojan prince, after the fall of Troy, begins:

Of arms and the man I sing, who first from the shores of Troy,
Displaced by Fate, came to Italy and to the Livinian shores —
A man harassed much on both land and sea
By the power of the gods, through Juno's brooding ire,
And long in warfare suffering till be built
A City, and his deities enshrined
On Latian soil: whence came the Latin Race,
The Lords of Alba, and high-towering Rome.

These opening lines emphasize divine power and divine wrath as well as the quest of Aeneas after the fall of Troy. Shaw's use of words from the first line suggests a contrast between the noble, almost sacred quest of Aeneas and the down-to-earth, commonplace goals of Shaw's character, Bluntschli. The title may be interpreted, therefore, as a tongue-in-cheek allusion intended to prepare the audience for Shaw's attack on idealism in *Arms and the Man.*

George Bernard Shaw

Arms and the Man

Bernard Shaw

The First Production Was Staged
On April 21, 1894
At the Avenue Theatre
In London, England

With This Cast

Major Paul Petkoff ....James Welch
Major Sergius Saranoff ....Bernard Gould
Captain Bluntschli.............................Yorke Stephens
Major Plechanoff .............................A.E.W. Mason
Nicola ....Orlando Barnett
Catherine Petkoff ....Mrs. Charles Calvert
Raina Petkoff ....Alma Murray
Louka ....Florence Farr

Night: A lady's bedchamber in Bulgaria, in a small town near the Dragoman Pass, late in November in the year 1885. Through an open window with a little balcony a peak of the Balkans, wonderfully white and beautiful in the starlit snow, seems quite close at hand, though it is really miles away. The interior of the room is not like anything to be seen in the west of Europe. It is half rich Bulgarian, half cheap Viennese. Above the head of the bed, which stands against a little wall cutting off the left hand corner of the room, is a painted wooden shrine, blue and gold, with an ivory image of Christ, and a light hanging before it in a pierced metal ball suspended by three chains. The principal seat, placed towards the other side of the room and opposite the window, is a Turkish ottoman. The counterpane and hangings of the bed, the window curtains, the little carpet, and all the ornamental textile fabrics in the room are oriental and gorgeous; the paper on the walls is occidental and paltry. The washstand, against the wall on the side nearest the ottoman and window, consists of an enamelled iron basin with a pail beneath it in a painted metal frame, and a single towel on the rail at the side. The dressing table, between the bed and the windows, is a common pine table, covered with a cloth of many colours, with an expensive toilet mirror on it. The door is on the side nearest the bed; and there is a chest of drawers between. This chest of drawers is also covered by a variegated native cloth; and on it there is a pile of paper backed novels, a box of chocolate creams, and a miniature easel with a large photograph of an extremely handsome officer, whose lofty bearing and magnetic glance can be felt even from the portrait. The room is lighted by a candle on the chest of drawers, and another on the dressing table with a box of matches beside it.

The window is hinged doorwise and stands wide open. Outside, a pair of wooden shutters, opening outwards, also stand open. On the balcony a young lady, intensely conscious of the romantic beauty of the night, and of the fact that her own youth and beauty are part of it, is gazing at the snowy Balkans. She is in her nightgown, well covered by a long mantle of furs, worth, on a moderate estimate, about three times the furniture of the room.

Her reverie is interrupted by her mother, CATHERINE PETKOFF, a woman over forty, imperiously energetic, with magnificent black hair and eyes, who might be a very splendid specimen of the wife of a mountain farmer, but is determined to be a Viennese lady, and to that end wears a fashionable tea gown on all occasions.

---•---

CATHERINE *(entering hastily, full of good news):* Raina! *(she pronounces it Rah-eena, with the stress on the ee)* Raina! *(She goes to the bed, expecting to find RAINA there)* Why, where —? *(RAINA looks into the room)* Heavens, child! are you out in the night air instead of in your bed? Youll catch your death. Louka told me you were asleep.

RAINA *(dreamily):* I sent her away. I wanted to be alone. The stars are so beautiful! What is the matter?

CATHERINE: Such news! There has been a battle.

RAINA *(her eyes dilating):* Ah! *(She comes eagerly to CATHERINE).*

CATHERINE: A great battle at Slivnitza! A victory! And it was won by Sergius.

RAINA *(with a cry of delight):* Ah! *(They embrace rapturously)* Oh, mother! *(Then, with sudden anxiety)* Is father safe?

CATHERINE: Of course! he sends me the news. Sergius is the hero of the hour, the idol of the regiment.

RAINA: Tell me, tell me. How was it? *(Ecstatically)* Oh, mother! mother! mother! *(She pulls her mother down on the ottoman; and they kiss one another frantically).*

CATHERINE *(with surging enthusiasm):* You cant guess how splendid it is. A cavalry charge! think of that! He defied our Russian commanders — acted without orders — led a charge on his own responsibility — headed it himself — was the first man to sweep through their guns. Cant you see it, Raina: our gallant splendid Bulgarians with their swords and eyes flashing, thundering down like an avalanche and scattering the wretched Serbs and their dandified Austrian officers like chaff. And you! you kept Sergius waiting a year before you would be betrothed to him. Oh, if you have a drop of Bulgarian blood in your veins, you will worship him when he comes back.

RAINA: What will he care for my poor little worship after the acclamations of a whole army of heroes? But no matter; I am so happy! so proud! *(She rises and walks about excitedly).* It proves that all our ideas were real after all.

CATHERINE *(indignantly):* Our ideas real! What do you mean?

RAINA: Our ideas of what Sergius would do. Our patriotism. Our heroic ideals. I sometimes used to doubt whether they were anything but dreams. Oh, what faithless little creatures girls are! When I buckled on Sergius's sword he looked so noble; it was treason to think of disillusion or humiliation or failure. And yet — and yet — *(She sits down again suddenly)* Promise me youll never tell him.

CATHERINE: Dont ask for promises until I know what I'm promising.

RAINA: Well, it came into my head just as he was holding me in his arms and looking into my eyes, that perhaps we only had our heroic ideas because we are so fond of reading Byron and Pushkin, and because we were so delighted with the opera that season at Bucharest. Real life is so seldom like that! indeed never, as far as I knew it then. *(Remorsefully)* Only think, mother: I doubted him: I wondered whether all his heroic qualities and his soldiership might not prove mere imagination when he went into a real battle. I had an uneasy fear that he might cut a poor figure there beside all those clever officers from the Tsar's court.

CATHERINE: A poor figure! Shame on you! The Serbs have Austrian officers who are just as clever as the Russians; but we have beaten them in every battle for all that.

RAINA *(laughing and snuggling against her mother):* Yes: I was only a prosaic little coward. Oh, to think that it was all true! that Sergius is just as splendid and noble as he looks! that the world is really a glorious world for women who can see its glory and men who can act its romance! What happiness! what unspeakable fulfilment!

(They are interrupted by the entry of LOUKA, a handsome proud girl in a

pretty Bulgarian peasant's dress with double apron, so defiant that her servility to RAINA is almost insolent. She is afraid of CATHERINE, but even with her goes as far as she dares.)

LOUKA: If you please, madam, all the windows are to be closed and the shutters made fast. They say there may be shooting in the streets. *(RAINA and CATHERINE rise together, alarmed).* The Serbs are being chased right back through the pass; and they say they may run into the town. Our calvary will be after them; and our people will be ready for them, you may be sure, now theyre running away. *(She goes out on the balcony, and pulls the outside shutters to; then steps back into the room).*

CATHERINE *(businesslike, housekeeping instincts aroused):* I must see that everything is made safe downstairs.

RAINA: I wish our people were not so cruel. What glory is there in killing wretched fugitives?

CATHERINE: Cruel! Do you suppose they would hesitate to kill you — or worse?

RAINA *(to LOUKA):* Leave the shutters so that I can just close them if I hear any noise.

CATHERINE *(authoritatively, turning on her way to the door):* Oh no, dear, you must keep them fastened. You would be sure to drop off to sleep and leave them open. Make them fast, Louka.

LOUKA: Yes, madam. *(She fastens them).*

RAINA: Dont be anxious about me. The moment I hear a shot, I shall blow out the candles and roll myself up in bed with my ears well covered.

CATHERINE: Quite the wisest thing you can do, my love. Goodnight.

RAINA: Goodnight. *(Her emotion comes back for a moment).* Wish me joy *(They kiss).* This is the happiest night of my life — if only there are no fugitives.

CATHERINE: Go to bed, dear; and dont think of them. *(She goes out).*

LOUKA *(secretly to RAINA):* If you would like the shutters open, just give them a push like this *(she pushes them: they open: she pulls them to again).* One of them ought to be bolted at the bottom; but the bolt's gone.

RAINA *(with dignity, reproving her):* Thanks, Louka; but we must do what we are told. *(LOUKA makes a grimace).* Goodnight.

LOUKA *(carelessly):* Goodnight. *(She goes out, swaggering).*
(RAINA, left alone, takes off her fur cloak and throws it on the ottoman. Then she goes to the chest of drawers, and adores the portrait there with feelings that are beyond all expression. She does not kiss it or press it to her breast, or show it any mark of bodily affection; but she takes it in her hands and elevates it, like a priestess.)

RAINA *(looking up at the picture):* Oh, I shall never be unworthy of you any more, my soul's hero: never, never, never. *(She replaces it reverently. Then she selects a novel from the little pile of books. She turns over the leaves dreamily; finds her page; turns the book inside out at it; and, with a happy sigh, gets into bed and prepares to read herself to sleep. But before abandoning herself to fic-*

tion, she raises her eyes once more, thinking of the blessed reality, and murmurs)
My hero! my hero!

(A distant shot breaks the quiet of the night. She starts, listening; and two more shots, much nearer, follow, startling her so that she scrambles out of bed, and hastily blows out the candle on the chest of drawers. Then, putting her fingers in her ears, she runs to the dressing table, blows out the light there, and hurries back to bed in the dark, nothing being visible but the glimmer of the light in the pierced ball before the image, and the starlight seen through the slits at the top of the shutters. The firing breaks out again: there is a startling fusillade quite close at hand. Whilst it is still echoing, the shutters disappear, pulled open from without; and for an instant the rectangle of snowy starlight flashes out with the figure of a man silhouetted in black upon it. The shutters close immediately; and the room is dark again. But the silence is now broken by the sound of panting. Then there is a scratch; and the flame of a match is seen in the middle of the room.)

RAINA *(crouching on the bed):* Who's there? *(The match is out instantly).* Who's there? Who is that?

A MAN'S VOICE *(in the darkness, subduedly, but threateningly):* Sh—sh! Dont call out; or youll be shot. Be good; and no harm will happen to you. *(She is heard leaving her bed, and making for the door).* Take care: it's no use trying to run away.

RAINA: But who —

THE VOICE *(warning):* Remember: if you raise your voice my revolver will go off. *(Commandingly).* Strike a light and let me see you. Do you hear. *(Another moment of silence and darkness as she retreats to the chest of drawers. Then she lights a candle; and the mystery is at an end. He is a man of about 35, in a deplorable plight, bespattered with mud and blood and snow, his belt and the strap of his revolver case keeping together the torn ruins of the blue tunic of a Serbian artillery officer. All that the candlelight and his unwashed unkempt condition make it possible to discern is that he is of middling stature and undistinguished appearance, with strong neck and shoulders, roundish obstinate looking head covered with short crisp bronze curls, clear quick eyes and good brows and mouth, hopelessly prosaic nose like that of a strong minded baby, trim soldierlike carriage and energetic manner, and with all his wits about him in spite of his desperate predicament: even with a sense of the humor of it, without, however, the least intention of trifling with it or throwing away a chance. Reckoning up what he can guess about RAINA: her age, her social position, her character, and the extent to which she is frightened, he continues, more politely but still most determinedly)* Excuse my disturbing you; but you recognize my uniform? Serb! If I'm caught I shall be killed. *(Menacingly)* Do you understand that?

RAINA: Yes.

THE MAN: Well I dont intend to get killed if I can help it. *(Still more formidably)* Do you understand that? *(He locks the door quickly but quietly).*

RAINA *(disdainfully):* I suppose not. *(She draws herself up superbly, and looks him straight in the face, adding, with cutting emphasis)* Some soldiers, I know, are afraid to die.

THE MAN *(with grim goodhumor):* All of them, dear lady, all of them, believe me. It is our duty to live as long as we can. Now, if you raise an alarm —

RAINA *(cutting him short):*   You will shoot me. How do you know that *I* am afraid to die?

THE MAN *(cunningly):*   Ah; but suppose I dont shoot you, what will happen then? A lot of your cavalry will burst into this pretty room of yours and slaughter me here like a pig; for I'll fight like a demon: they shant get me into the street to amuse themselves with: I know what they are. Are you prepared to receive that sort of company in your present undress? *(RAINA, suddenly conscious of her nightgown, instinctively shrinks and gathers it more closely about her neck. He watches her and adds pitilessly)* Hardly presentable, eh? *(She turns to the otto-man. He raises his pistol instantly, and cries)* Stop! *(She stops).* Where are you going?

RAINA *(with dignified patience):*   Only to get my cloak.

THE MAN *(passing swiftly to the ottoman and snatching the cloak):* A good idea! I'll keep the cloak; and you'll take care that nobody comes in and sees you without it. This is a better weapon than the revolver, eh? *(He throws the pistol down on the ottoman).*

RAINA *(revolted):*   It is not the weapon of a gentleman!

THE MAN: It's good enough for a man with only you to stand between him and death. *(As they look at one another for a moment, RAINA hardly able to believe that even a Serbian officer can be so cynically and selfishly unchivalrous, they are startled by a sharp fusillade in the street. The chill of imminent death hushes the man's voice as he adds)* Do you hear? If you are going to bring those blackguards in on me you shall receive them as you are.
    (Clamor and disturbance. The pursuers in the street batter at the house door, shouting, "Open the door! Open the door! Wake up, will you!" A man servant's voice calls to them angrily from within, "This is Major Petkoff's house: you cant come in here"; but a renewal of the clamor, and a torrent of blows on the door, end with his letting a chain down with a clank, followed by a rush of heavy footsteps and a din of triumphant yells, dominated at last by the voice of CATHERINE, indignantly addressing an officer with, "What does this mean, sir? Do you know where you are?" The noise subsides suddenly.)

LOUKA *(outside, knocking at the bedroom door):*   My lady! my lady! get up quick and open the door. If you dont they will break it down.
    (The fugitive throws up his head with the gesture of a man who sees that it is all over with him, and drops the manner he has been assuming to intimidate RAINA.)

THE MAN *(sincerely and kindly):*   No use, dear; I'm done for. *(Flinging the cloak to her)* Quick! wrap yourself up; theyre coming.

RAINA: Oh, thank you. *(She wraps herself up with intense relief).*

THE MAN *(between his teeth):*   Dont mention it.

RAINA *(anxiously):*   What will you do?

THE MAN *(grimly):*   The first man in will find out. Keep out of the way; and dont look. It wont last long; but it will not be nice. *(He draws his sabre and faces the door, waiting.)*

RAINA *(impulsively):*   I'll help you. I'll save you.

THE MAN: You cant.

RAINA: I can. I'll hide you. *(She drags him towards the window).* Here! behind the curtains.

THE MAN *(yielding to her):* Theres just half a chance, if you keep your head.

RAINA *(drawing the curtain before him):* S-sh! *(She makes for the ottoman).*

THE MAN *(putting out his head):* Remember —

RAINA *(running back to him):* Yes?

THE MAN: — nine soldiers out of ten are born fools.

RAINA: Oh! *(She draws the curtain angrily before him).*

THE MAN *(looking out at the other side):* If they find me, I promise you a fight — a devil of a fight.
(She stamps at him. He disappears hastily. She takes off her cloak, and throws it across the foot of the bed. Then, with a sleepy, disturbed air, she opens the door. LOUKA enters excitedly.)

LOUKA: One of those beasts of Serbs has been seen climbing up the waterpipe to your balcony. Our men want to search for him; and they are so wild and drunk and furious. *(She makes for the other side of the room to get as far from the door as possible).* My lady says you are to dress at once and to — *(She sees the revolver lying on the ottoman and stops, petrified).*

RAINA *(as if annoyed at being disturbed):* They shall not search here. Why have they been let in?

CATHERINE *(coming in hastily):* Raina, darling, are you safe? Have you seen anyone or heard anything?

RAINA: I heard the shooting. Surely the soldiers will not dare come in here?

CATHERINE: I have found a Russian officer, thank Heaven: he knows Sergius. *(Speaking through the door to someone outside)* Sir: will you come in now? My daughter will receive you.
(A young Russian officer, in Bulgarian uniform, enters, sword in hand.)

OFFICER *(with soft feline politeness and stiff military carriage):* Good evening, gracious lady. I am sorry to intrude; but there is a Serb hiding on the balcony. Will you and the gracious lady your mother please to withdraw whilst we search?

RAINA *(petulantly):* Nonsense, sir: you can see that there is no one on the balcony. *(She throws the shutters wide open and stands with her back to the curtain where the man is hidden, pointing to the moonlit balcony. A couple of shots are fired right under the window; and a bullet shatters the glass opposite RAINA, who winks and gasps, but stands her ground; whilst CATHERINE screams, and the officer, with a cry of "Take care!" rushes to the balcony.)*

THE OFFICER *(on the balcony, shouting savagely down to the street):* Cease firing there, you fools; do you hear? Cease firing, damn you! *(He glares down for a moment; then turns to RAINA, trying to resume his polite manner)* Could anyone have got in without your knowledge? Were you asleep?

RAINA: No: I have not been to bed.

THE OFFICER (*impatiently, coming back into the room*): Your neighbors have their heads so full of runaway Serbs that they see them everywhere. (*Politely*) Gracious lady: a thousand pardons. Good night. (*Military bows, which RAINA returns coldly. Another to CATHERINE, who follows him out*).
(*RAINA closes the shutters. She turns and sees LOUKA, who has been watching the scene curiously.*)

RAINA: Dont leave my mother, Louka, until the soldiers go away.
(*LOUKA glances at RAINA, at the ottoman, at the curtain; then purses her lips secretively, laughs insolently, and goes out. RAINA, highly offended by this demonstration, follows her to the door, and shuts it behind her with a slam, locking it violently. The man immediately steps out from behind the curtain, sheathing his sabre. Then, dismissing the danger from his mind in a businesslike way, he comes affably to RAINA.*)

THE MAN: A narrow shave; but a miss is as good as a mile. Dear young lady: your servant to the death. I wish for your sake I had joined the Bulgarian army instead of the other one. I am not a native Serb.

RAINA (*haughtily*): No, you are one of the Austrians who set the Serbs on to rob us of our national liberty, and who officer their army for them. We hate them!

THE MAN: Austrian! not I. Dont hate me, dear young lady. I am a Swiss, fighting merely as a professional soldier. I joined the Serbs because they came first on the road from Switzerland. Be generous: youve beaten us hollow.

RAINA: Have I not been generous?

THE MAN: Noble! Heroic! But I'm not saved yet. This particular rush will soon pass through; but the pursuit will go on all night by fits and starts. I must take my chance to get off in a quiet interval. (*Pleasantly*) You dont mind my waiting just a minute or two, do you?

RAINA (*putting on her most genteel society manner*): Oh, not at all. Wont you sit down?

THE MAN: Thanks. (*He sits on the foot of the bed*).
(*RAINA walks with studied elegance to the ottoman and sits down. Unfortunately she sits on the pistol, and jumps up with a shriek. The man, all nerves, shies like a frightened horse to the other side of the room.*)

THE MAN (*irritably*): Dont frighten me like that. What is it?

RAINA: Your revolver! It was staring that officer in the face all the time. What an escape!

THE MAN (*vexed at being unnecessarily terrified*): Oh, is that all?

RAINA (*staring at him rather superciliously as she conceives a poorer and poorer opinion of him, and feels proportionately more and more at her ease*): I am sorry I frightened you. (*She takes up the pistol and hands it to him*). Pray take it to protect yourself against me.

THE MAN (*grinning wearily at the sarcasm as he takes the pistol*): No use, dear young lady: there's nothing in it. It's not loaded. (*He makes a grimace at it, and drops it disparagingly into his revolver case.*)

RAINA: Load it by all means.

THE MAN: Ive no ammunition. What use are cartridges in battle? I always carry chocolate instead; and I finished the last cake of that hours ago.

RAINA *(outraged in her most cherished ideals of manhood):* Chocolate! Do you stuff your pockets with sweets — like a schoolboy — even in the field?

THE MAN *(grinning):* Yes: isnt it contemptible? *(Hungrily)* I wish I had some now.

RAINA: Allow me. *(She sails away scornfully to the chest of drawers and returns with the box of confectionery in her hand).* I am sorry I have eaten them all except these. *(She offers him the box).*

THE MAN *(ravenously):* Youre an angel! *(He gobbles the contents).* Creams! Delicious! *(He looks anxiously to see whether there are any more. There are none: he can only scrape the box with his fingers and suck them. When that nourishment is exhausted he accepts the inevitable with pathetic goodhumor and says, with grateful emotion)* Bless you, dear lady! You can always tell an old soldier by the inside of his holsters and cartridge boxes. The young ones carry pistols and cartridges: the old ones, grub. Thank you. *(He hands back the box. She snatches it contemptuously from him and throws it away. He shies again, as if she had meant to strike him).* Ugh! Dont do things so suddenly, gracious lady. It's mean to revenge yourself because I frightened you just now.

RAINA *(loftily):* Frighten me! Do you know, sir, that though I am only a woman, I think I am at heart as brave as you.

THE MAN: I should think so. You havent been under fire for three days as I have. I can stand two days without shewing it much: but no man can stand three days; I'm as nervous as a mouse. *(He sits down on the ottoman, and takes his head in his hands).* Would you like to see me cry?

RAINA *(alarmed):* No.

THE MAN: If you would, all you have to do is to scold me just as if I were a little boy and you my nurse. If I were in camp now, theyd play all sorts of tricks on me.

RAINA *(a little moved):* I'm sorry. I wont scold you. *(Touched by the sympathy in her tone, he raises his head and looks gratefully at her: she immediately draws back and says stiffly)* You must excuse me: our soldiers are not like that. *(She moves away from the ottoman).*

THE MAN: Oh yes they are. There are only two sorts of soldiers: old ones and young ones. Ive served fourteen years: half of your fellows never smelt powder before. Why, how is it that youve just beaten us? Sheer ignorance of the art of war, nothing else. *(Indignantly)* I never saw anything so unprofessional.

RAINA *(ironically):* Oh! was it unprofessional to beat you?

THE MAN: Well, come! is it professional to throw a regiment of cavalry on a battery of machine guns, with the dead certainty that if the guns go off not a horse or man will ever get within fifty yards of the fire? I couldnt believe my eyes when I saw it.

RAINA *(eagerly turning to him, as all her enthusiasm and her dreams of glory rush back on her):*   Did you see the great cavalry charge? Oh, tell me about it. Describe it to me.

THE MAN: You never saw a cavalry charge, did you?

RAINA: How could I?

THE MAN: Ah, perhaps not. No: of course not! Well, it's a funny sight. It's like slinging a handful of peas against a window pane: first one comes; then two or three close behind him; and then all the rest in a lump.

RAINA *(her eyes dilating as she raises her clasped hands ecstatically):*   Yes, first One! the bravest of the brave!

THE MAN *(prosaically):*   Hm! you should see the poor devil pulling at his horse.

RAINA: Why should he pull at his horse?

THE MAN *(impatient of so stupid a question):*   It's running away with him, of course: do you suppose the fellow wants to get there before the others and be killed? Then they all come. You can tell the young ones by their wildness and their slashing. The old ones come bunched up under the number one guard: they know that theyre mere projectiles, and that its no use trying to fight. The wounds are mostly broken knees, from the horses cannoning together.

RAINA: Ugh! But I dont believe the first man is a coward. I know he is a hero!

THE MAN *(goodhumoredly):*   Thats what youd have said if youd seen the first man in the charge today.

RAINA *(breathless, forgiving him everything):*   Ah, I knew it! Tell me. Tell me about him.

THE MAN: He did it like an operatic tenor. A regular handsome fellow, with flashing eyes and lovely moustache, shouting his war-cry and charging like Don Quixote at the windmills. We did laugh.

RAINA: You dared to laugh!

THE MAN: Yes; but when the sergeant ran up as white as a sheet, and told us theyd sent us the wrong ammunition, and that we couldnt fire a round for the next ten minutes, we laughed at the other side of our mouths. I never felt so sick in my life; though Ive been in one or two very tight places. And I hadnt even a revolver cartridge, only chocolate. We'd no bayonets: nothing. Of course, they just cut us to bits. And there was Don Quixote flourishing like a drum major, thinking he'd done the cleverest thing ever known, whereas he ought to be court-martialled for it. Of all the fools ever let loose on a field of battle, that man must be the very maddest. He and his regiment simply committed suicide; only the pistol missed fire, thats all.

RAINA *(deeply wounded, but steadfastly loyal to her ideals):*   Indeed! Would you know him again if you saw him?

THE MAN: Shall I ever forget him!
(She again goes to the chest of drawers. He watches her with a vague hope that she may have something more for him to eat. She takes the portrait from its stand and brings it to him.)

RAINA: That is a photograph of the gentleman — the patriot and hero — to whom I am betrothed.

THE MAN *(recognizing it with a shock):*   I'm really very sorry. *(Looking at her)* Was it fair to lead me on? *(He looks at the portrait again)* Yes: thats Don Quixote: not a doubt of it. *(He stifles a laugh.)*

RAINA (quickly):   Why do you laugh?

THE MAN *(apologetic, but still great tickled):*   I didnt laugh, I assure you. At least I didnt mean to. But when I think of him charging the windmills and imagining he was doing the finest thing —*(He chokes with suppressed laughter).*

RAINA *(sternly):*   Give me back the portrait, sir.

THE MAN *(with sincere remorse):*   Of course. Certainly. I'm really very sorry. *(He hands her the picture. She deliberately kisses it and looks him straight in the face before returning to the chest of drawers to replace. He follows her, apologizing).* Perhaps I'm quite wrong, you know: no doubt I am. Most likely he had got wind of the cartridge business somehow and knew it was a safe job.

RAINA: That is to say, he was a pretender and a coward! You did not dare say that before.

THE MAN *(with a comic gesture of despair):*   It's no use, dear lady: I cant make you see it from the professional point of view. *(As he turns away to get back to the ottoman, a couple of distant shots threaten renewed trouble).*

RAINA *(sternly, as she sees him listening to the shots):*   So much the better for you!

THE MAN *(turning):*   How?

RAINA: You are my enemy; and you are at my mercy. What would I do if I were a professional soldier?

THE MAN: Ah, true, dear young lady: youre always right. I know how good youve been to me: to my last hour I shall remember those three chocolate creams. It was unsoldierly; but it was angelic.

RAINA *(coldly):*   Thank you. And now I will do a soldierly thing. You cannot stay here after what you have just said about my future husband; but I will go out on the balcony and see whether it is safe for you to climb down into the street. *(She turns to the window).*

THE MAN *(changing countenance):*   Down that waterpipe? Stop! Wait! I cant! I darent! The very thought of it makes me giddy. I came up it fast enough with death behind me. But to face it now in cold blood —! *(He sinks on the ottoman).* It's no use: I give up: I'm beaten. Give the alarm. *(He drops his head on his hands in the deepest dejection).*

RAINA *(disarmed by pity):*   Come, dont be disheartened. *(She stoops over him almost maternally: he shakes his head).* Oh, you are a very poor soldier: a chocolate cream soldier! Come, cheer up! it takes less courage to climb down than to face capture: remember that.

THE MAN *(dreamily, lulled by her voice):*   No: capture only means death; and death is sleep: oh, sleep, sleep, sleep, undisturbed sleep! Climbing down the pipe means doing something — exerting myself — thinking! Death ten times over first.

RAINA *(softly and wonderingly, catching the rhythm of his weariness):* Are you as sleepy as that?

THE MAN: Ive not had two hours undisturbed sleep since I joined. I havent closed my eyes for forty-eight hours.

RAINA *(at her wit's end):* But what am I to do with you?

THE MAN *(staggering up, roused by her desperation):* Of course. I must do something. *(He shakes himself; pulls himself together; and speaks with rallied vigor and courage).* You see, sleep or no sleep, hunger or no hunger, tired or not tired, you can always do a thing when you know it must be done. Well, that pipe must be got down: *(he hits himself on the chest)* do you hear that, you chocolate cream soldier? *(He turns to the window).*

RAINA *(anxiously):* But if you fall?

THE MAN: I shall sleep as if the stones were a feather bed. Goodbye. *(He makes boldly for the window; and his hand is on the shutter when there is a terrible burst of firing in the street beneath).*

RAINA *(rushing to him):* Stop! *(She seizes him recklessly and pulls him quite round).* Theyll kill you.

THE MAN *(coolly, but attentively):* Never mind: this sort of thing is all in my day's work. I'm bound to take my chance. *(Decisively)* Now do what I tell you. Put out the candle; so that they shant see the light when I open the shutters. And keep away from the window, whatever you do. If they see me theyre sure to have a shot at me.

RAINA *(clinging to him):* Theyre sure to see you: it's bright moonlight. I'll save you. Oh, how can you be so indifferent! You want me to save you, dont you?

THE MAN: I really dont want to be troublesome. *(She shakes him in her impatience).* I am not indifferent, dear young lady, I assure you. But how is it to be done?

RAINA: Come away from the window. *(She takes him firmly back to the middle of the room. The moment she releases him he turns mechanically towards the window again. She seizes him and turns him back, exclaiming)* Please! *(He becomes motionless, like a hypnotized rabbit, his fatigue gaining fast on him. She releases him and addresses him patronizingly).* Now listen. You must trust to our hospitality. You do not yet know in whose house you are. I am a Petkoff.

THE MAN: A pet what?

RAINA *(rather indignantly):* I mean that I belong to the family of the Petkoffs, the richest and best known in our country.

THE MAN: Oh yes, of course. I beg your pardon. The Petkoffs, to be sure. How stupid of me!

RAINA: You know you never heard of them until this moment. How can you stoop to pretend!

THE MAN: Forgive me: I'm too tired to think; and the change of subject was too much for me. Dont scold me.

RAINA: I forgot. It might make you cry. *(He nods, quite seriously. She pouts and then resumes her patronizing tone).* I must tell you that my father holds the highest command of any Bulgarian in our army. He is *(proudly)* a Major.

THE MAN *(pretending to be deeply impressed):* A Major! Bless me! Think of that!

RAINA: You shewed great ignorance in thinking that it was necessary to climb up to the balcony because ours is the only private house that has two rows of windows. There is a flight of stairs inside to get up and down by.

THE MAN: Stairs! How grand! You live in great luxury indeed, dear young lady.

RAINA: Do you know what a library is?

THE MAN: A library? A roomful of books?

RAINA: Yes. We have one, the only one in Bulgaria.

THE MAN: Actually a real library! I should like to see that.

RAINA *(affectedly):* I tell you these things to shew you that you are not in the house of ignorant country folk who would kill you the moment they saw your Serbian uniform, but among civilized people. We go to Bucharest every year for the opera season; and I have spent a whole month in Vienna.

THE MAN: I saw that, dear young lady. I saw at once that you knew the world.

RAINA: Have you ever seen the opera of Ernani?

THE MAN: Is that the one with the devil in it in red velvet, and a soldiers' chorus?

RAINA *(contemptuously):* No!

THE MAN *(stifling a heavy sigh of weariness):* Then I dont know it.

RAINA: I thought you might have remembered the great scene where Ernani, flying from his foes just as you are tonight, takes refuge in the castle of his bitterest enemy, an old Castilian noble. The noble refuses to give him up. His guest is sacred to him.

THE MAN *(quickly, waking up a little):* Have your people got that notion?

RAINA *(with dignity):* My mother and I can understand that notion, as you call it. And if instead of threatening me with your pistol as you did, you had simply thrown yourself as a fugitive on our hospitality, you would have been as safe as in your father's house.

THE MAN: Quite sure?

RAINA *(turning her back on him in disgust):* Oh, it is useless to try to make you understand.

THE MAN: Dont be angry: you see how awkward it would be for me if there was any mistake. My father is a very hospitable man: he keeps six hotels; but I couldnt trust him as far as that. What about your father?

RAINA: He is away at Slivnitza fighting for his country. I answer for your safety. There is my hand in pledge of it. Will that reassure you? *(She offers him her hand.)*

THE MAN *(looking dubiously at his own hand):*   Better not touch my hand, dear young lady. I must have a wash first.

RAINA *(touched):*   That is very nice of you. I see that you are a gentleman.

THE MAN *(puzzled):*   Eh?

RAINA: You must not think I am surprised. Bulgarians of really good standing — people in our position — was their hands nearly every day. So you see I can appreciate your delicacy. You may take my hand. *(She offers it again).*

THE MAN *(kissing it with his hands behind his back):*   Thanks, gracious young lady: I feel safe at last. And now would you mind breaking the news to your mother? I had better not stay here secretly longer than is necessary.

RAINA: If you will be so good as to keep perfectly still whilst I am away.

THE MAN: Certainly. *(He sits down on the ottoman).*
  (RAINA goes to the bed and wraps herself in the fur cloak. His eyes close. She goes to the door. Turning for a last look at him, she sees that he is dropping off to sleep.)

RAINA *(at the door):*   You are not going asleep, are you? *(He murmurs inarticulately: she runs to him and shakes him).* Do you hear? Wake up: you are falling asleep.

THE MAN: Eh? Falling aslee—? Oh no: not the least in the world: I was only thinking. It's all right: I'm wide awake.

RAINA *(severely):*   Will you please stand up while I am away. *(He rises reluctantly).* All the time, mind.

THE MAN *(standing unsteadily):*   Certainly. Certainly: you may depend on me.
  (RAINA looks doubtfully at him. He smiles weakly. She goes reluctantly, turning again at the door, and almost catching him in the act of yawning. She goes out.)

THE MAN *(drowsily):*   Sleep, sleep, sleep, sleep, slee— *(The words trail off into a murmur. He wakes again with a shock on the point of falling).* Where am I? That's what I want to know: where am I? Must keep awake. Nothing keeps me awake except danger: remember that: (intently) danger, danger, danger, dan— (trailing off again; another shock) Wheres danger? Mus' find it. (He starts off vaguely round the room in search of it). What am I looking for? Sleep — danger — dont know. (He stumbles against the bed). Ah yes: now I know. All right now. I'm to go to bed, but not to sleep. Be sure not to sleep, because of danger. Not to lie down either, only sit down. (He sits on the bed. A blissful expression comes into his face). Ah! (With a happy sigh he sinks back at full length; lifts his boots into the bed with a final effort; and falls fast asleep instantly).*
  (CATHERINE comes in, followed by RAINA.)

RAINA *(looking at the ottoman):*   He's gone! I left him here.

CATHERINE: Here! Then he must have climbed down from the —

RAINA *(seeing him):*   Oh! *(She points).*

CATHERINE *(scandalized):* Well! *(She strides to the bed, RAINA following until she is opposite her on the other side).* He's fast asleep. The brute!

RAINA *(anxiously):* Sh!

CATHERINE *(shaking him):* Sir! *(Shaking him again, harder)* Sir!! *(Vehemently, shaking very hard)* Sir!!!

RAINA *(catching her arm):* Dont, mamma: the poor darling is worn out. Let him sleep.

CATHERINE *(letting him go, and turning amazed to RAINA):* The poor darling! Raina!!! *(She looks sternly at her daughter).*
  (The man sleeps profoundly.)

————————————————— ACT: 2 ——————————————————

The sixth of March, 1886. In the garden of MAJOR PETKOFF's house. It is a fine spring morning: the garden looks fresh and pretty. Beyond the paling the tops of a couple of minarets can be seen, shewing that there is a valley there, with the little town in it. A few miles further the Balkan mountains rise and shut in the landscape. Looking towards them from within the garden, the side of the house is seen on the left, with a garden door reached by a little flight of steps. On the right the stable yard, with its gateway, encroaches on the garden. There are fruit bushes along the paling and house, covered with washing spread out to dry. A path runs by the house, and rises by two steps at the corner, where it turns out of sight. In the middle, a small table, with two bent wood chairs at it, is laid for breakfast with Turkish coffee pot, cups, rolls, etc.; but the cups have been used and the bread broken. There is a wooden garden seat against the wall on the right.

LOUKA, smoking a cigaret, is standing between the table and the house, turning her back with angry disdain on a man servant who is lecturing her. He is a middle-aged man of cool temperament and low but clear and keen intelligence, with the complacency of the servant who values himself on his rank in servitude, and the imperturbability of the accurate calculator who has no illusions. He wears a white Bulgarian costume: jacket with embroidered border, sash, wide knickerbockers, and decorated gaiters. His head is shaved up to the crown, giving him a high Japanese forehead. His name is NICOLA.

——————————————— • ———————————————

NICOLA: Be warned in time, Louka: mend your manners. I know the mistress. She is so grand that she never dreams that any servant could dare be disrepectful to her; but if she once suspects that you are defying her, out you go.

LOUKA: I do defy her. I will defy her. What do I care for her?

NICOLA: If you quarrel with the family, I never can marry you. It's the same as if you quarreled with me!

LOUKA: You take her part against me, do you?

NICOLA *(sedately):*   I shall always be dependent on the good will of the family. When I leave their service and start a shop in Sofia, their custom will be half my capital: their bad word would ruin me.

LOUKA: You have no spirit. I should like to catch them saying a word against me!

NICOLA *(pityingly):*   I should have expected more sense from you, Louka. But youre young: youre young.

LOUKA: Yes; and you like me the better for it, dont you? But I know some family secrets they wouldnt care to have told, young as I am. Let them quarrel with me if they dare!

NICOLA *(with compassionate superiority):*   Do you know what they would do if they heard you talk like that?

LOUKA: What could they do?

NICOLA: Discharge you for untruthfulness. Who would believe any stories you told after that? Who would give you another situation? Who in this house would dare be seen speaking to you ever again? How long would your father be left on his little farm? *(She impatiently throws away the end of her cigaret, and stamps on it).* Child, you dont know the power such high people have over the like of you and me when we try to rise out of our poverty against them. *(He goes close to her and lowers his voice).* Look at me, ten years in their service. Do you think I know no secrets? I know things about the mistress that she wouldnt have the master know for a thousand levas. I know things about him that she wouldnt let him hear the last of for six months if I blabbed them to her. I know things about Raina that would break off her match with Sergius if —

LOUKA *(turning on him quickly):*   How do you know? I never told you!

NICOLA *(opening his eyes cunningly):*   So thats your little secret, is it? I thought it might be something like that. Well, you take my advice and be respect-ful; and make the mistress feel that no matter what you know or dont know, she can depend on you to hold your tongue and serve the family faithfully. Thats what they like; and thats how youll make most out of them.

LOUKA *(with searching scorn):*   You have the soul of a servant, Nicola.

NICOLA *(complacently):*   Yes, thats the secret of success in service.
   (A loud knocking with a whip handle on a wooden door is heard from the stable yard.)

MALE VOICE OUTSIDE: Hollo! Hollo there! Nicola!

LOUKA: Master! back from the war!

NICOLA *(quickly):*   My word for it, Louka, the war's over. Off with you and get some fresh coffee. *(He runs out into the stable yard).*

LOUKA *(as she collects the coffee pot and cups on the tray, and carries it into the house):*   Youll never put the soul of a servant into me.
   (MAJOR PETKOFF comes from the stable yard, followed by NICOLA. He is a cheerful, excitable, insignificant, unpolished man of about 50, naturally unambitious except as to his income and his importance in local society, but just now greatly pleased with the military rank which the war has thrust on him

as a man of consequence in his town. The fever of plucky patriotism which the Serbian attack roused in all the Bulgarians has pulled him through the war; but he is obviously glad to be home again.)

PETKOFF *(pointing to the table with his whip):* Breakfast out here, eh?

NICOLA: Yes, sir. The mistress and Miss Raina have just gone in.

PETKOFF *(sitting down and taking a roll):* Go in and say Ive come; and get me some fresh coffee.

NICOLA: It's coming, sir. *(He goes to the house door. LOUKA, with fresh coffee, a clean cup, and a brandy bottle on her tray, meets him).* Have you told the mistress?

LOUKA: Yes: she's coming.
(NICOLA goes into the house. LOUKA brings the coffee to the table.)

PETKOFF: Well, the Serbs havnt run away with you, have they?

LOUKA: No, sir.

PETKOFF: Thats right. Have you brought me some cognac?

LOUKA *(putting the bottle on the table):* Here, sir.

PETKOFF: Thats right. *(He pours some into his coffee).*
(CATHERINE, who, having at this early hour made only a very perfunctory toilet, wears a Bulgarian apron over a once brilliant but now half worn-out dressing gown, and a colored handkerchief tied over her thick black hair, comes from the house with Turkish slippers on her bare feet, looking astonishingly handsome and stately under all the circumstances. LOUKA goes into the house.)

CATHERINE: My dear Paul, what a surprise for us! *(She stoops over the back of his chair to kiss him).* Have they brought you fresh coffee?

PETKOFF: Yes, Louka's been looking after me. The war's over. The treaty was signed three days ago at Bucharest; and the decree for our army to demobilize was issued yesterday.

CATHERINE *(springing erect, with flashing eyes):* Paul: have you let the Austrians force you to make peace?

PETKOFF *(submissively):* My dear: they didnt consult me. What could *I* do? *(She sits down and turns away from him).* But of course we saw to it that the treaty was an honorable one. It declares peace —

CATHERINE *(outraged):* Peace!

PETKOFF *(appeasing her):* — but not friendly relations: remember that. They wanted to put that in; but I insisted on its being struck out. What more could I do?

CATHERINE: You could have annexed Serbia and made Prince Alexander Emperor of the Balkans. Thats what I would have done.

PETKOFF: I dont doubt it in the least, my dear. But I should have had to subdue the whole Austrian Empire first; and that would have kept me too long away from you. I missed you greatly.

Arms and the Man

CATHERINE *(relenting):*   Ah! *(She stretches her hand affectionately across the table to squeeze his).*

PETKOFF: And how have you been, my dear?

CATHERINE: Oh, my usual sore throats: thats all.

PETKOFF *(with conviction):*   That comes from washing your neck every day. Ive often told you so.

CATHERINE: Nonsense, Paul!

PETKOFF *(over his coffee and cigaret):*   I dont believe in going too far with these modern customs. All this washing cant be good for the health: it's not natural. There was an Englishman at Philippopolis who used to wet himself all over with cold water every morning when he got up. Disgusting! It all comes from the English: their climate makes them so dirty that they have to be perpetually washing themselves. Look at my father! he never had a bath in his life; and he lived to be ninety-eight, the healthiest man in Bulgaria. I dont mind a good wash once a week to keep up my position; but once a day is carrying the thing to a ridiculous extreme.

CATHERINE: You are a barbarian at heart still, Paul. I hope you behaved yourself before all those Russian officers.

PETKOFF: I did my best. I took care to let them know that we have a library.

CATHERINE: Ah; but you didnt tell them that we have an electric bell in it? I have had one put up.

PETKOFF: Whats an electric bell?

CATHERINE: You touch a button; something tinkles in the kitchen; and then Nicola comes up.

PETKOFF: Why not shout for him?

CATHERINE: Civilized people never shout for their servants. Ive learnt that while you were away.

PETKOFF: Well, Ill tell you something Ive learnt too. Civilized people dont hang out their washing to dry where visitors can see it; so youd better have all that *(indicating the clothes on the bushes)* put somewhere else.

CATHERINE: Oh, thats absurd, Paul: I dont believe really refined people notice such things.

SERGIUS *(knocking at the stable gates):*   Gate, Nicola!

PETKOFF: Theres Sergius. *(Shouting)* Hollo, Nicola!

CATHERINE: Oh, dont shout, Paul: it really isnt nice.

PETKOFF: Bosh! *(He shouts louder than before)* Nicola!

NICOLA *(appearing at the house door):*   Yes, sir.

PETKOFF: Are you deaf? Dont you hear Major Saranoff knocking? Bring him round this way. *(He pronounces the name with the stress on the second syllable: Sarahnoff.)*

NICOLA: Yes, Major. *(He goes into the stable yard).*

PETKOFF: You must talk to him, my dear, until Raina takes him off our hands. He bores my life out about our not promoting him. Over my head, if you please.

CATHERINE: He certainly ought to be promoted when he marries Raina. Besides, the country should insist on having at least one native general.

PETKOFF: Yes; so that he could throw away whole brigades instead of regiments. It's no use, my dear: he hasnt the slighest chance of promotion until we're quite sure that the peace will be a lasting one.

NICOLA *(at the gate, announcing):* Major Sergius Saranoff! *(He goes into the house and returns presently with a third chair, which he places at the table. He then withdraws).*

(MAJOR SERGIUS SARANOFF, the original of the portrait in RAINA's room, is a tall romantically handsome man, with the physical hardihood, the high spirit, and the susceptible imagination of an untamed mountaineer chieftain. But his remarkable personal distinction is of a characteristically civilized type. The ridges of his eyebrows, curving with an interrogative twist round the projections at the outer corners; his jealously observant eye; his nose, thin, keen, and apprehensive in spite of the pugnacious high bridge and large nostril; his assertive chin would not be out of place in a Parisian salon, shewing that the clever imaginative barbarian has an acute critical faculty which has been thrown into intense activity by the arrival of western civilization in the Balkans. The result is precisely what the advent of nineteenth century thought first produced in England: to wit, Byronism. By his brooding on the perpetual failure, not only of others, but of himself, to live up to his ideals; by his consequent cynical scorn for humanity; by his jejune credulity as to the absolute validity of his concepts and the unworthiness of the world in disregarding them; by his wincings and mockeries under the sting of the petty disillusions which every hour spent among men brings to his sensitive observations, he has acquired the half tragic, half ironic air, the mysterious moodiness, the suggestion of a strange and terrible history that has left nothing but undying remorse, by which Childe Harold fascinated the grandmothers of his English contemporaries. It is clear that here or nowhere is RAINA's ideal hero. CATHERINE is hardly less enthusiastic about him than her daughter, and much less reserved in shewing her enthusiasm. As he enters from the stable gate, she rises effusively to greet him. PETKOFF is distinctly less disposed to make a fuss about him.)

PETKOFF: Here already, Sergius! Glad to see you.

CATHERINE: My dear Sergius! *(She holds out both her hands).*

SERGIUS *(kissing them with scrupulous gallantry):* My dear mother, if I may call you so.

PETKOFF *(drily):* Mother-in-law, Sergius: mother-in-law! Sit down; and have some coffee.

SERGIUS: Thank you: none for me. *(He gets away from the table with a certain distaste for PETKOFF's enjoyment of it, and posts himself with conscious dignity against the rail of the steps leading to the house).*

CATHERINE: You look superb. The campaign has improved you, Sergius. Everybody here is mad about you. We were all wild with enthusiasm about that magnificent cavalry charge.

SERGIUS *(with grave irony):*   Madam: it was the cradle and the grave of my military reputation.

CATHERINE: How so?

SERGIUS: I won the battle the wrong way when our worthy Russian generals were losing it the right way. In short, I upset their plans, and wounded their self-esteem. Two Cossack colonels had their regiments routed on the most correct principles of scientific warfare. Two major-generals got killed strictly according to military etiquette. The two colonels are now major-generals; and I am still a simple major.

CATHERINE: You shall not remain so, Sergius. The women are on your side; and they will see that justice is done you.

SERGIUS: It is too late. I have only waited for the peace to send in my resignation.

PETKOFF *(dropping his cup in his amazement):*   Your resignation!

CATHERINE: Oh, you must withdraw it!

SERGIUS *(with resolute measured emphasis, folding his arms):*   I never withdraw.

PETKOFF *(vexed):*   Now who could have supposed you were going to do such a thing?

SERGIUS *(with fire):*   Everyone that knew me. But enough of myself and my affairs. How is Raina; and where is Raina?

RAINA *(suddenly coming round the corner of the house and standing at the top of the steps in the path):*   Raina is here.
(She makes a charming picture as they turn to look at her. She wears an under-dress of pale green silk, draped with an overdress of thin ecru canvas embroidered with gold. She is crowned with a dainty eastern cap of gold tinsel. SERGIUS goes impulsively to meet her. Posing regally, she presents her hand; he drops chivalrously on one knee and kisses it.)

PETKOFF *(aside to CATHERINE, beaming with parental pride):*   Pretty, isnt it? She always appears at the right moment.

CATHERINE *(impatiently):*   Yes: she listens for it. It is an abominable habit.
(SERGIUS leads RAINA forward with splendid gallantry. When they arrive at the table, she turns to him with a bend of the head: he bows; and thus they separate, he coming to his place and she going behind her father's chair.)

RAINA *(stooping and kissing her father):*   Dear father! Welcome home!

PETKOFF *(patting her cheek):*   My little pet girl. *(He kisses her. She goes to the chair left by NICOLA for SERGIUS and sits down).*

CATHERINE: And so youre no longer a soldier, Sergius.

SERGIUS: I am no longer a soldier. Soldiering, my dear madam, is the coward's art of attacking mercilessly when you are strong, and keeping out of harm's way when you are weak. That is the whole secret of successful fighting. Get your enemy at a disadvantage; and never, on any account, fight him on equal terms.

PETKOFF: They wouldnt let us make a fair stand-up fight of it. However, I suppose soldiering has to be a trade like any other trade.

SERGIUS: Precisely. But I have no ambition to shine as a tradesman; so I have taken the advice of that bagman of a captain that settled the exchange of prisoners with us at Pirot, and given it up.

PETKOFF: What! that Swiss fellow? Sergius: Ive often thought of that exchange since. He over-reached us about those horses.

SERGIUS: Of course he over-reached us. His father was a hotel and livery stable keeper; and he owed his first step to his knowledge of horse-dealing. *(With mock enthusiasm)* Ah, he was a soldier: every inch a soldier! If only I had bought the horses for my regiment instead of foolishly leading it into danger, I should have been a field-marshal now!

CATHERINE: A Swiss? What was he doing in the Serbian army?

PETKOFF: A volunteer, of course: keen on picking up his profession. *(Chuckling)* We shouldnt have been able to begin fighting if these foreigners hadnt shewn us how to do it: we knew nothing about it; and neither did the Serbs. Egad, there'd have been no war without them!

RAINA: Are there many Swiss officers in the Serbian Army?

PETKOFF: No. All Austrians, just as our officers were all Russians. This was the only Swiss I came across. I'll never trust a Swiss again. He humbugged us into giving him fifty ablebodied men for two hundred worn out chargers. They weren't even eatable!

SERGIUS: We were two children in the hands of that consummate soldier, Major: simply two innocent little children.

RAINA: What was he like?

CATHERINE: Oh, Raina, what a silly question!

SERGIUS: He was like a commercial traveller in uniform. Bourgeois to his boots!

PETKOFF *(grinning):* Sergius: tell Catherine that queer story his friend told us about how he escaped after Slivnitza. You remember. About his being hid by two women.

SERGIUS *(with bitter irony):* Oh yes: quite a romance! He was serving in the very battery I so unprofessionally charged. Being a thorough soldier, he ran away like the rest of them, with our cavalry at his heels. To escape their sabres he climbed a waterpipe and made his way into the bedroom of a young Bulgarian lady. The young lady was enchanted by his persuasive commercial traveller's manners. She very modestly entertained him for an hour or so, and then called in her mother lest her conduct should appear unmaidenly. The old lady was equally fascinated; and the fugitive was sent on his way in the morning, disguised in an old coat belonging to the master of the house, who was away at the war.

RAINA *(rising with marked stateliness):* Your life in the camp has made you coarse, Sergius. I did not think you would have repeated such a story before me. *(She turns away coldly).*

CATHERINE *(also rising)*:   She is right, Sergius. If such women exist, we should be spared the knowledge of them.

PETKOFF: Pooh! nonsense! what does it matter?

SERGIUS *(ashamed)*:   No, Petkoff: I was wrong. *(To RAINA, with earnest humility)* I beg your pardon. I have behaved abominably. Forgive me, Raina. *(She bows reservedly)*. And you too, madam. *(CATHERINE bows graciously and sits down. He proceeds solemnly, again addressing RAINA)* The glimpses I have had of the seamy side of life during the last few months have made me cynical; but I should not have brought my cynicism here: least of all into your presence, Raina. I — *(Here, turning to the others, he is evidently going to begin a long speech when the MAJOR interrupts him)*.

PETKOFF: Stuff and nonsense, Sergius! Thats quite enough fuss about nothing: a soldier's daughter should be able to stand up without flinching to a little strong conversation. *(He rises)*. Come: it's time for us to get to business. We have to make up our minds how those three regiments are to get back to Philippopolis: theres no forage for them on the Sofia route. *(He goes towards the house)*. Come along. *(SERGIUS is about to follow him when CATHERINE rises and intervenes)*.

CATHERINE: Oh, Paul, cant you spare Sergius for a few moments? Raina has hardly seen him yet. Perhaps I can help you to settle about the regiments.

SERGIUS *(protesting)*:   My dear madam, impossible: you —

CATHERINE *(stopping him playfully)*:   You stay here, my dear Sergius: theres no hurry. I have a word or two to say to Paul. *(SERGIUS instantly bows and steps back)*. Now, dear *(taking PETKOFF's arm)*: come and see the electric bell.

PETKOFF: Oh, very well, very well.
(They go into the house together affectionately. SERGIUS, left alone with RAINA, looks anxiously at her, fearing that she is still offended. She smiles and stretches out her arms to him.)

SERGIUS *(hastening to her)*:   Am I forgiven?

RAINA *(placing her hands on his shoulders as she looks up at him with admiration and worship)*:   My hero! My king!

SERGIUS: My queen! *(He kisses her on the forehead)*.

RAINA: How I have envied you, Sergius! You have been out in the world, on the field of battle, able to prove yourself there worthy of any woman in the world; whilst I have had to sit at home inactive — dreaming — useless — doing nothing that could give me the right to call myself worthy of any man.

SERGIUS: Dearest: all my deeds have been yours. You inspired me. I have gone through the war like a knight in a tournament with his lady looking down at him!

RAINA: And you have never been absent from my thoughts for a moment. *(Very solemnly)* Sergius: I think we two have found the higher love. When I think of you, I feel that I could never do a base deed or think an ignoble thought.

SERGIUS: My lady and my saint! *(He clasps her reverently)*.

RAINA *(returning his embrace)*:   My lord and my —

SERGIUS: Sh—sh! Let me be the worshipper, dear. You little know how unworthy even the best man is of a girl's pure passion!

RAINA: I trust you. I love you. You will never disappoint me, Sergius. *(LOUKA is heard singing within the house. They quickly release each other).* I cant pretend to talk indifferently before her: my heart is too full. *(LOUKA comes from the house with her tray. She goes to the table and begins to clear it, with her back turned to them).* I will get my hat; and then we can go out until lunch time. Wouldnt you like that?

SERGIUS: Be quick. If you are away five minutes, it will seem five hours. *(RAINA runs to the top of the steps and turns there to exchange looks with him and wave him a kiss with both hands. He looks after her with emotion for a moment; then turns slowly away, his face radiant with the loftiest exaltation. The movement shifts his field of vision, into the corner of which there now comes the tail of LOUKA's double apron. His attention is arrested at once. He takes a stealthy look at her and begins to twirl his moustache mischievously, with his left hand akimbo on his hip. Finally, striking the ground with his heels in something of a cavalry swagger, he strolls over to the other side of the table, opposite her, and says)* Louka: do you know what the higher love is?

LOUKA *(astonished):* No, sir.

SERGIUS: Very fatiguing thing to keep up for any length of time, Louka. One feels the need of some relief after it.

LOUKA *(innocently):* Perhaps you would like some coffee, sir? *(She stretches her hand across the table for the coffee pot).*

SERGIUS *(taking her hand):* Thank you, Louka.

LOUKA *(pretending to pull):* Oh, sir, you know I didnt mean that. I'm surprised at you!

SERGIUS *(coming clear of the table and drawing her with him):* I am surprised at myself, Louka. What would Sergius, the hero of Slivnitza, say if he saw me now? What would Sergius, the apostle of the higher love, say if he saw me now? What would the half dozen Sergiuses who keep popping in and out of this handsome figure of mine say if they caught us here? *(Letting go her hand and slipping his arm dexterously round her waist)* Do you consider my figure handsome, Louka?

LOUKA: Let me go, sir. I shall be disgraced. *(She struggles: he holds her inexorably).* Oh, will you let go?

SERGIUS *(looking straight into her eyes):* No.

LOUKA: Then stand back where we cant be seen. Have you no common sense?

SERGIUS: Ah! thats reasonable. *(He takes her into the stable yard gateway, where they are hidden from the house).*

LOUKA *(plaintively):* I may have been seen from the windows: Miss Raina is sure to be spying about after you.

SERGIUS *(stung: letting her go):* Take care, Louka. I may be worthless enough to betray the higher love; but do not you insult it.

LOUKA *(demurely):* Not for the world, sir, I'm sure. May I go on with my work, please, now?

SERGIUS *(again putting his arm round her):* You are a provoking little witch, Louka. If you were in love with me, would you spy out of windows on me?

LOUKA: Well, you see, sir, since you say you are half a dozen different gentlemen all at once, I should have a great deal to look after.

SERGIUS *(charmed):* Witty as well as pretty. *(He tries to kiss her).*

LOUKA *(avoiding him):* No: I dont want your kisses. Gentlefolk are all alike: you making love to me behind Miss Raina's back; and she doing the same behind yours.

SERGIUS *(recoiling a step):* Louka!

LOUKA: It shows how little you really care.

SERGIUS *(dropping his familiarity and speaking with freezing politeness):* If our conversation is to continue, Louka, you will please remember that a gentleman does not discuss the conduct of the lady he is engaged to with her maid.

LOUKA: It's so hard to know what a gentleman considers right. I thought from your trying to kiss me that you had given up being so particular.

SERGIUS *(turning from her and striking his forehead as he comes back into the garden from the gateway):* Devil! devil!

LOUKA: Ha! ha! I expect one of the six of you is very like me, sir; though I am only Miss Raina's maid. *(She goes back to her work at the table, taking no further notice of him).*

SERGIUS *(speaking to himself):* Which of the six is the real man? Thats the question that torments me. One of them is a hero, another a buffoon, another a humbug, another perhaps a bit of a blackguard. *(He pauses, and looks furtively at LOUKA as he adds, with deep bitterness)* And one, at least, is a coward: jealous, like all cowards. *(He goes to the table).* Louka.

LOUKA: Yes?

SERGIUS: Who is my rival?

LOUKA: You shall never get that out of me, for love or money.

SERGIUS: Why?

LOUKA: Never mind why. Besides, you would tell that I told you; and I should lose my place.

SERGIUS *(holding out his right hand in affirmation):* No! on the honor of a— *(He checks himself; and his hand drops, nerveless, as he concludes sardonically)* — of a man capable of behaving as I have been behaving for the last five minutes. Who is he?

LOUKA: I dont know. I never saw him. I only heard his voice through the door of her room.

SERGIUS: Damnation! How dare you?

LOUKA *(retreating):* Oh, I mean no harm; youve no right to take up my words like that. The mistress knows all about it. And I tell you that if that gentleman ever comes here again, Miss Raina will marry him, whether he likes it or not. I know the difference between the sort of manner you and she put on before one another and the real manner.

(SERGIUS shivers as if she had stabbed him. Then, setting his face like iron, he strides grimly to her and grips her above the elbows with both hands.)

SERGIUS: Now listen you to me.

LOUKA *(wincing):* Not so tight: you're hurting me.

SERGIUS: That doesnt matter. You have stained my honor by making me a party to your eavesdropping. And you have betrayed your mistress.

LOUKA *(writhing):* Please —

SERGIUS: That shews that you are an abominable little clod of common clay, with the soul of a servant. *(He lets her go as if she were an unclean thing, and turns away, dusting his hands of her, to the bench by the wall, where he sits down with averted head, meditating gloomily).*

LOUKA *(whimpering angrily with her hands up her sleeves, feeling her bruised arms):* You know how to hurt with your tongue as well as with your hands. But I dont care, now I've found out that whatever clay I'm made of, youre made of the same. As for her, she's a liar; and her fine airs are a cheat; and I'm worth six of her. *(She shakes the pain off hardily; tosses her head; and sets to work to put the things on the tray).*

(He looks doubtfully at her. She finishes packing the tray, and laps the cloth over the edges, so as to carry all out together. As she stoops to lift it, he rises.)

SERGIUS: Louka! *(She stops and looks defiantly at him).* A gentleman has no right to hurt a woman under any circumstances. *(With profound humility, uncovering his head)* I beg your pardon.

LOUKA: That sort of apology may satisfy a lady. Of what use is it to a servant?

SERGIUS *(rudely crossed in his chivalry, throws it off with a bitter laugh, and says slightingly):* Oh! you wish to be paid for the hurt! *(He puts on his shako and takes some money from his pocket).*

LOUKA *(her eyes filling with tears in spite of herself):* No: I want my hurt made well.

SERGIUS *(sobered by her tone):* How?
(She rolls up her left sleeve; clasps her arm with the thumb and fingers of her right hand; and looks down at the bruise. Then she raises her head and looks straight at him. Finally, with a superb gesture, she presents her arm to be kissed. Amazed, he looks at her; at the arm; at her again; hesitates; and then, with shuddering intensity, exclaims "Never!" and gets away as far as possible from her.)

(Her arm drops. Without a word, and with unaffected dignity, she takes her tray and is approaching the house when RAINA returns, wearing a hat and jacket in the height of the Vienna fashion of the previous year, 1885. LOUKA makes way proudly for her and then goes into the house.)

RAINA: I'm ready. What's the matter? *(Gaily)* Have you been flirting with Louka?

SERGIUS *(hastily):* No, no. How can you think such a thing?

RAINA *(ashamed of herself):* Forgive me, dear: it was only a jest. I am so happy today.
(He goes quickly to her, and kisses her hand remorsefully. CATHERINE comes out and calls to them from the top of the steps.)

CATHERINE *(coming down to them):* I am sorry to disturb you, children; but Paul is distracted over those three regiments. He doesnt know how to send them to Philippopolis; and he objects to every suggestion of mine. You must go and help him, Sergius. He is in the library.

RAINA *(disappointed):* But we are just going out for a walk.

SERGIUS: I shall not be long. Wait for me just five minutes. *(He runs up the steps to the door).*

RAINA *(following him to the foot of the steps and looking up at him with timid coquetry):* I shall go round and wait in full view of the library windows. Be sure you draw father's attention to me. If you are a moment longer than five minutes, I shall go in and fetch you, regiments or no regiments.

SERGIUS *(laughing):* Very well. *(He goes in).*
(RAINA watches him until he is out of her sight. Then, with a perceptible relaxation of manner, she begins to pace up and down the garden in a brown study.)

CATHERINE: Imagine their meeting that Swiss and hearing the whole story! The very first thing your father asked for was the old coat we sent him off in. A nice mess you have got us into!

RAINA *(gazing thoughtfully at the gravel as she walks):* The little beast!

CATHERINE: Little beast! What little beast?

RAINA: To go and tell! Oh, if I had him here, I'd cram him with chocolate creams til he couldnt ever speak again!

CATHERINE: Dont talk such stuff. Tell me the truth, Raina. How long was he in your room before you came to me?

RAINA *(whisking round and recommencing her march in the opposite direction):* Oh, I forget.

CATHERINE: You cannot forget! Did he really climb up after the soldiers were gone; or was he there when that officer searched the room?

RAINA: No. Yes: I think he must have been there then.

CATHERINE: You think! Oh, Raina! Raina! Will anything ever make you straightforward? If Sergius finds out, it will be all over between you.

RAINA *(with cool impertinence):* Oh, I know Sergius is your pet. I sometimes wish you could marry him instead of me. You would just suit him. You would pet him, and spoil him, and mother him to perfection.

CATHERINE *(opening her eyes very widely indeed):* Well, upon my word!

RAINA *(capriciously: half to herself):* I always feel a longing to do or say something dreadful to him — to shock his propriety — to scandalize the five senses out of him. *(To CATHERINE, perversely)* I dont care whether he finds out about the chocolate cream soldier or not. I half hope he may. *(She again turns and strolls flippantly away up the path to the corner of the house).*

CATHERINE: And what should I be able to say to your father, pray?

RAINA *(over her shoulder, from the top of the two steps):* Oh, poor father! As if he could help himself! *(She turns the corner and passes out of sight).*

CATHERINE *(looking after her, her fingers itching):* Oh, if you were only ten years younger! *(LOUKA comes from the house with a salver, which she carries hanging down by her side)* Well?

LOUKA: There's a gentleman just called, madam. A Serbian officer.

CATHERINE *(flaming):* A Serb! And how dare he — *(checking herself bitterly)* Oh, I forgot. We are at peace now. I suppose we shall have them calling every day to pay their compliments. Well: if he is an officer why dont you tell your master? He is in the library with Major Saranoff. Why do you come to me?

LOUKA: But he asks for you, madam. And I dont think he knows who you are: he said the lady of the house. He gave me this little ticket for you. *(She takes a card out of her bosom; puts it on the salver; and offers it to CATHERINE).*

CATHERINE *(reading):* "Captain Bluntschli"? That's a German name.

LOUKA: Swiss, madam, I think.

CATHERINE *(with a bound that makes LOUKA jump back):* Swiss? What is he like?

LOUKA *(timidly):* He has a big carpet bag, madam.

CATHERINE: Oh Heavens! he's come to return the coat. Send him away: say we're not at home: ask him to leave his address and I'll write to him. Oh stop: that will never do. Wait! *(She throws herself into a chair to think it out. LOUKA waits).* The master and Major Saranoff are busy in the library, arnt they?

LOUKA: Yes, madam.

CATHERINE *(decisively):* Bring the gentleman out here at once. *(Peremptorily)* And be very polite to him. Dont delay. Here *(impatiently snatching the salver from her)*: leave that here; and go straight back to him.

LOUKA: Yes, madam. *(going).*

CATHERINE: Louka!

LOUKA *(stopping):* Yes, madam.

CATHERINE: Is the library door shut?

LOUKA: I think so, madam.

CATHERINE: If not, shut it as you pass through.

LOUKA: Yes, madam. *(going).*

CATHERINE: Stop! *(Louka stops).* He will have to go that way *(indicating the gate of the stable yard).* Tell Nicola to bring his bag here after him. Dont forget.

LOUKA *(surprised):* His bag?

CATHERINE: Yes: here: as soon as possible. *(Vehemently)* Be quick! *(LOUKA runs into the house. CATHERINE snatches her apron off and throws it behind a bush. She then takes up the salver and uses it as a mirror, with the result that the handkerchief tied round her head follows the apron. A touch to her hair and a shake to her dressing gown make her presentable).* Oh, how? how? how can a man be such a fool! Such a moment to select! *(LOUKA appears at the door of the house, announcing "Captain Bluntschli." She stands aside at the top of the steps to let him pass before she goes in again. He is the man of the midnight adventure in RAINA's room, clean, well brushed, smartly uniformed, and out of trouble, but still unmistakably the same man. The moment LOUKA's back is turned, CATHERINE swoops on him with impetuous, urgent, coaxing appeal).* Captain Bluntschli: I am very glad to see you; but you must leave this house at once. *(He raises his eyebrows).* My husband has just returned with my future son-in-law; and they know nothing. If they did, the consequences would be terrible. You are a foreigner: you do not feel our national animosities as we do. We still hate the Serbs: the effect of the peace on my husband has been to make him feel like a lion baulked of his prey. If he discovers our secret, he will never forgive me; and my daughter's life will hardly be safe. Will you, like the chivalrous gentleman and soldier you are, leave at once before he finds you here?

BLUNTSCHLI *(disappointed, but philosophical):* At once, gracious lady. I only came to thank you and return the coat you lent me. If you will allow me to take it out of my bag and leave it with your servant as I pass out, I need detain you no further. *(He turns to go into the house).*

CATHERINE *(catching him by the sleeve):* Oh, you must not think of going back that way. *(Coaxing him across to the stable gates)* This is the shortest way out. Many thanks. So glad to have been of service to you. Good-bye.

BLUNTSCHLI: But my bag?

CATHERINE: It shall be sent on. You will leave me your address.

BLUNTSCHLI: True. Allow me. *(He takes out his card-case and stops to write his address, keeping CATHERINE in an agony of impatience. As he hands her the card, PETKOFF, hatless, rushes from the house in a fluster of hospitality, followed by SERGIUS).*

PETKOFF *(as he hurries down the steps):* My dear Captain Bluntschli —

CATHERINE: Oh Heavens! *(She sinks on the seat against the wall).*

PETKOFF *(too preoccupied to notice her as he shakes BLUNTSCHLI's hand heartily):* Those stupid people of mine thought I was out here, instead of in the — haw! — library *(he cannot mention the library without betraying how proud he is of it).* I saw you through the window. I was wondering why you didnt come in. Saranoff is with me: you remember him, dont you?

SERGIUS *(saluting humorously, and then offering his hand with great charm of manner):* Welcome, our friend the enemy!

PETKOFF: No longer the enemy, happily. *(Rather anxiously)* I hope youve called as a friend, and not about horses or prisoners.

CATHERINE: Oh, quite as a friend, Paul. I was just asking Captain Bluntschli to stay to lunch; but he declares he must go at once.

SERGIUS *(sardonically):* Impossible, Bluntschli. We want you here badly. We have to send on three cavalry regiments to Philippopolis; and we dont in the least know how to do it.

BLUNTSCHLI *(suddenly attentive and businesslike):* Philippopolis? The forage is the trouble, I suppose.

PETKOFF *(eagerly):* Yes: thats it. *(To SERGIUS)* He sees the whole thing at once.

BLUNTSCHLI: I think I can shew you how to manage that.

SERGIUS: Invaluable man! Come along! *(Towering over BLUNTSCHLI, he puts his hand on his shoulder and takes him to the steps, PETKOFF following). (RAINA comes from the house as BLUNTSCHLI puts his foot on the first step.)*

RAINA: Oh! The chocolate cream soldier!
(BLUNTSCHLI stands rigid. SERGIUS, amazed, looks at RAINA, then at PETKOFF, who looks back at him and then at his wife.)

CATHERINE *(with commanding presence of mind):* My dear Raina, dont you see that we have a guest here? Captain Bluntschli: one of our new Serbian friends. *(RAINA bows: BLUNTSCHLI bows.)*

RAINA: How silly of me! *(She comes down into the centre of the group between BLUNTSCHLI and PETKOFF).* I made a beautiful ornament this morning for the ice pudding; and that stupid Nicola has just put down a pile of plates on it and spoilt it. *(To BLUNTSCHLI, winningly)* I hope you didnt think that you were the chocolate cream soldier, Captain Bluntschli.

BLUNTSCHLI *(laughing):* I assure you I did. *(Stealing a whimsical glance at her)* Your explanation was a relief.

PETKOFF *(suspiciously, to RAINA):* And since when, pray, have you taken to cooking?

CATHERINE: Oh, whilst you were away. It is her latest fancy.

PETKOFF *(testily):* And has Nicola taken to drinking? He used to be careful enough. First he shews Captain Bluntschli out here when he knew quite well I was in the library; and then he goes downstairs and breaks Raina's chocolate soldier. He must — *(NICOLA appears at the top of the steps with the bag. He descends; places it respectfully before BLUNTSCHLI; and waits for further orders. General amazement. NICOLA, unconscious of the effect he is producing, looks perfectly satisfied with himself. When PETKOFF recovers his power of speech, he breaks out at him with)* Are you mad, Nicola?

NICOLA *(taken aback):* Sir?

PETKOFF: What have you brought that for?

NICOLA: My lady's orders, Major. Louka told me that —

CATHERINE *(interrupting him):* My orders! Why should I order you to bring Captain Bluntschli's luggage out here? What are you thinking of, Nicola?

NICOLA *(after a moment's bewilderment, picking up the bag as he addresses BLUNTSCHLI with the very perfection of servile discretion):* I beg your pardon, captain, I am sure. *(To CATHERINE)* My fault, madam: I hope youll overlook it. *(He bows, and is going to the steps with the bag, when PETKOFF addresses him angrily).*

PETKOFF: Youd better go and slam that bag, too, down on Miss Raina's ice pudding! *(This is too much for NICOLA. The bag drops from his hand almost on his master's toes, eliciting a roar of)* Begone, you butter-fingered donkey!

NICOLA *(snatching up the bag, and escaping into the house):*   Yes, major.

CATHERINE: Oh, never mind. Paul: dont be angry.

PETKOFF *(blustering):*   Scoundrel! He's got out of hand while I was away. I'll teach him. Infernal blackguard! The sack next Saturday! I'll clear out the whole establishment — *(He is stifled by the caresses of his wife and daughter, who hang round his neck, petting him.)*

CATHERINE, RAINA *(together):*   Now, now, now, it mustnt be angry.
— Wow, wow, wow: not on your first day at home. I'll make another ice pudding. Tch-ch-ch!
— He meant no harm. Be good to please me, dear. Sh-sh-sh-sh!

PETKOFF *(yielding):*   Oh well, never mind. Come, Bluntschli: lets have no more nonsense about going away. You know very well youre not going back to Switzerland yet. Until you do go back youll stay with us.

RAINA: Oh, do, Captain Bluntschli.

PETKOFF *(to CATHERINE):*   Now, Catherine: it's of you he's afraid. Press him: and he'll stay.

CATHERINE: Of course I shall be only too delighted if *(appealingly)* Captain Bluntschli really wishes to stay. He knows my wishes.

BLUNTSCHLI *(in his driest military manner):*   I am at madam's orders.

SERGIUS *(cordially):*   That settles it!

PETKOFF *(heartily):*   Of course!

RAINA: You see you must stay.

BLUNTSCHLI *(smiling):*   Well, if I must, I must.
   (Gesture of despair from CATHERINE.)

───────────────── ❧ACT: 3❧ ─────────────────

In the library after lunch. It is not much of a library. Its literary equipment consists of a single fixed shelf stocked with old paper covered novels, broken backed, coffee-stained, torn and thumbed; and a couple of little hanging shelves with a few gift books on them: the rest of the wall space being occupied by trophies of war and the chase. But it is a most comfortable sitting room. A row of three large windows shows a mountain panorama, just now seen in one of its friendliest aspects in the mellowing afternoon light. In the corner next the right hand window a square earthenware stove, a perfect tower of glistening pottery, rises nearly to the ceiling and guarantees plenty of warmth. The ottoman is like that in

RAINA's room, and similarly placed; and the window seats are luxurious with decorated cushions. There is one object, however, hopelessly out of keeping with its surroundings. This is a small kitchen table, much the worse for wear, fitted as a writing table with an old canister full of pens, an eggcup filled with ink, and a deplorable scrap of heavily used pink blotting paper.

At the side of this table, which stands to the left of anyone facing the window, BLUNTSCHLI is hard at work with a couple of maps before him, writing orders. At the head of it sits SERGIUS, who is supposed to be also at work, but is actually gnawing the feather of a pen, and contemplating BLUNTSCHLI's quick, sure, businesslike progress with a mixture of envious irritation at his own incapacity and awestruck wonder at an ability which seems to him almost miraculous, though its prosaic character forbids him to esteem it. THE MAJOR is comfortably established on the ottoman, with a newspaper in his hand and the tube of his hookah within easy reach. CATHERINE sits at the stove, with her back to them, embroidering. RAINA, reclining on the divan, is gazing in a daydream out at the Balkan landscape, with a neglected novel in her lap.

The door is on the same side as the stove, farther from the window. The button of the electric bell is at the opposite side, behind BLUNTSCHLI.

———————————— • ————————————

PETKOFF (looking up from his paper to watch how they are getting on at the table):   Are you sure I cant help in any way, Bluntschli?

BLUNTSCHLI (without interrupting his writing or looking up):   Quite sure, thank you. Saranoff and I will manage it.

SERGIUS (grimly):   Yes, we'll manage it. He finds out what to do; draws up the orders; and I sign em. Division of labor! (BLUNTSCHLI passes him a paper). Another one? Thank you. (He plants the paper squarely before him; sets his chair carefully parallel to it; and signs with his cheek on his elbow and his protruded tongue following the movements of his pen). This hand is more accustomed to the sword than to the pen.

PETKOFF: It's very good of you, Bluntschli: it is indeed, to let yourself be put upon in this way. Now are you quite sure I can do nothing?

CATHERINE (in a low warning tone):   You can stop interrupting, Paul.

PETKOFF (starting and looking round at her):   Eh? Oh! Quite right, my love: quite right. (He takes his newspaper up again, but presently lets it drop). Ah, you havnt been campaigning, Catherine: you don't know how pleasant it is for us to sit here, after a good lunch, with nothing to do but enjoy ourselves. Theres only one thing I want to make me thoroughly comfortable.

CATHERINE: What is that?

PETKOFF: My old coat. I'm not at home in this one: I feel as if I were on parade.

CATHERINE: My dear Paul, how absurd you are about that old coat! It must be hanging in the blue closet where you left it.

PETKOFF: My dear Catherine, I tell you Ive looked there. Am I to believe my own eyes or not? (CATHERINE rises and crosses the room to press the button of the electric bell). What are you shewing off that bell for? (She looks at him majestically, and silently resumes her chair and her needlework). My dear: if you think the obstinacy of your sex can make a coat out of two old dressing gowns of Raina's, your waterproof, and my mackintosh, youre mistaken. That's exactly what the blue closet contains at present.

(NICOLA presents himself.)

CATHERINE: Nicola: go to the blue closet and bring your master's old coat here: the braided one he wears in the house.

NICOLA: Yes, madam. *(He goes out).*

PETKOFF: Catherine.

CATHERINE: Yes, Paul.

PETKOFF: I bet you any piece of jewellery you like to order from Sofia against a week's housekeeping money that the coat isnt there.

CATHERINE: Done, Paul!

PETKOFF *(excited by the prospect of a gamble):* Come: heres an opportunity for some sport. Wholl bet on it? Bluntschli: I'll give you six to one.

BLUNTSCHLI *(imperturbably):* It would be robbing you, major. Madame is sure to be right. *(Without looking up, he passes another batch of papers to SERGIUS).*

SERGIUS *(also excited):* Bravo, Switzerland! Major: I bet my best charger against an Arab mare for Raina that Nicola finds the coat in the blue closet.

PETKOFF *(eagerly):* Your best char—

CATHERINE *(hastily interrupting him):* Dont be foolish, Paul. An Arabian mare will cost you 50,000 levas.

RAINA *(suddenly coming out of her picturesque revery):* Really, mother, if you are going to take the jewellery, I dont see why you should grudge me my Arab.

(NICOLA comes back with the coat, and brings it to PETKOFF, who can hardly believe his eyes.)

CATHERINE: Where was it, Nicola?

NICOLA: Hanging in the blue closet, madame.

PETKOFF: Well, I am d—

CATHERINE *(stopping him):* Paul!

PETKOFF: I could have sworn it wasnt there. Age is beginning to tell on me. I'm getting hallucinations. *(To NICOLA)* Here: help me to change. Excuse me, Bluntschli. *(He begins changing coats, NICOLA acting as valet).* Remember: I didnt take that bet of yours, Sergius. Youd better give Raina that Arab steed yourself, since youve roused her expectations. Eh, Raina? *(He looks round at her; but she is again rapt in the landscape. With a little gush of parental affection and pride, he points her out to them, and says)* She's dreaming, as usual.

SERGIUS: Assuredly she shall not be the loser.

PETKOFF: So much the better for her. *I* shant come off so cheaply, I expect. *(The change is now complete. NICOLA goes out with the discarded coat).* Ah, now I feel at home at last. *(He sits down and takes his newspaper with a grunt of relief)*.

BLUNTSCHLI *(to SERGIUS, handing a paper):*   Thats the last order.

PETKOFF *(jumping up):*   What! Finished!

BLUNTSCHLI: Finished.

PETKOFF *(with childlike envy):*   Havnt you anything for me to sign?

BLUNTSCHLI: Not necessary. His signature will do.

PETKOFF *(inflating his chest and thumping it):*   Ah well, I think weve done a thundering good day's work. Can I do anything more?

BLUNTSCHLI: You had better both see the fellows that are to take these. *(SERGIUS rises)* Pack them off at once; and shew them that Ive marked on the orders the time they should hand them in by. Tell them that if they stop to drink or tell stories — if theyre five minutes late, theyll have the skin taken off their backs.

SERGIUS *(stiffening indignantly):*   I'll say so. *(He strides to the door)*. And if one of them is man enough to spit in my face for insulting him, I'll buy his discharge and give him a pension. *(He goes out)*.

BLUNTSCHLI *(confidentially):*   Just see that he talks to them properly, major, will you?

PETKOFF *(officiously):*   Quite right, Bluntschli, quite right. I'll see to it. *(He goes to the door importantly, but hesitates on the threshold)*. By the bye, Catherine, you may as well come too. They'll be far more frightened of you than of me.

CATHERINE *(putting down her embroidery):*   I daresay I had better. You would only splutter at them. *(She goes out, PETKOFF holding the door for her and following her)*.

BLUNTSCHLI: What an army! They make cannons out of cherry trees; and the officers send for their wives to keep discipline! *(He begins to fold and docket the papers)*.
   (RAINA, who has risen from the divan, marches slowly down the room with her hands clasped behind her, and looks mischievously at him.)

RAINA: You look ever so much nicer than when we last met. *(He looks up, surprised)*. What have you done to yourself?

BLUNTSCHLI: Washed; brushed; good night's sleep and breakfast. That's all.

RAINA: Did you get back safely that morning?

BLUNTSCHLI: Quite, thanks.

RAINA: Were they angry with you for running away from Sergius's charge?

BLUNTSCHLI *(grinning):*   No: they were glad because theyd all just run away themselves.

RAINA *(going to the table, and leaning over it towards him):*   It must have made a lovely story for them: all that about me and my room.

BLUNTSCHLI: Capital story. But I only told it to one of them: a particular friend.

RAINA: On whose discretion you could absolutely rely?

BLUNTSCHLI: Absolutely.

RAINA: Hm! He told it all to my father and Sergius the day you exchanged the prisoners. *(She turns away and strolls carelessly across to the other side of the room).*

BLUNTSCHLI *(deeply concerned and half incredulous):*   No! You dont mean that, do you?

RAINA *(turning, with sudden earnestness):*   I do indeed. But they dont know that it was in this house you took refuge. If Sergius knew, he would challenge you and kill you in a duel.

BLUNTSCHLI: Bless me! then dont tell him.

RAINA: Please be serious, Captain Bluntschli. Can you not realize what it is to me to deceive him? I want to be quite perfect with Sergius: no meanness, no smallness, no deceit. My relation to him is the one really beautiful and noble part of my life. I hope you can understand that.

BLUNTSCHLI *(sceptically):*   You mean that you wouldnt like him to find out that the story about the ice pudding was a — a — a — You know.

RAINA *(wincing):*   Ah, dont talk of it in that flippant way. I lied: I know it. But I did it to save your life. He would have killed you. That was the second time I ever uttered a falsehood. *(BLUNTSCHLI rises quickly and looks doubtfully and somewhat severely at her).* Do you remember the first time?

BLUNTSCHLI: I! No. Was I present?

RAINA: Yes; and I told the officer who was searching for you that you were not present.

BLUNTSCHLI: True. I should have remembered it.

RAINA *(greatly encouraged):*   Ah, it is natural that you should forget it first. It cost you nothing: it cost me a lie! A lie!
(She sits down on the ottoman, looking straight before her with her hands clasped around her knee. BLUNTSCHLI, quite touched, goes to the ottoman with a particularly reassuring and considerate air, and sits down beside her.)

BLUNTSCHLI: My dear young lady, dont let this worry you. Remember: I'm a soldier. Now what are the two things that happen to a soldier so often that he comes to think nothing of them? One is hearing people tell lies *(RAINA recoils):* the other is getting his life saved in all sorts of ways by all sorts of people.

RAINA *(rising in indignant protest):*   And so he becomes a creature incapable of faith and of gratitude.

BLUNTSCHLI *(making a wry face):*   Do you like gratitude? I dont. If pity is akin to love, gratitude is akin to the other thing.

RAINA: Gratitude! *(Turning on him)* If you are incapable of gratitude you are incapable of any noble sentiment. Even animals are grateful. Oh, I see now exactly what you think of me! You were not surprised to hear me lie. To you it was something I probably did every day! every hour? That is how men think of women. *(She paces the room tragically).*

BLUNTSCHLI *(dubiously):*   Theres reason in everything. You said youd told only two lies in your whole life. Dear young lady: isnt that rather a short allowance? I'm quite a straightforward man myself; but it wouldnt last me a whole morning.

RAINA *(staring haughtily at him):*   Do you know, sir, that you are insulting me?

BLUNTSCHLI: I cant help it. When you strike that noble attitude and speak in that thrilling voice, I admire you; but I find it impossible to believe a single word you say.

RAINA *(superbly):*   Captain Bluntschli!

BLUNTSCHLI *(unmoved):*   Yes?

RAINA *(standing over him, as if she could not believe her senses):*   Do you mean what you said just now? Do you know what you said just now?

BLUNTSCHLI: I do.

RAINA *(gasping):*   I! I!!! *(She points to herself incredulously, meaning "I, Raina Petkoff tell lies!" He meets her gaze unflinchlingly. She suddenly sits down beside him and adds, with a complete change of manner from the heroic to a babyish familiarity)* How did you find me out?

BLUNTSCHLI *(promptly):*   Instinct, dear young lady. Instinct, and experience of the world.

RAINA *(wonderingly):*   Do you know, you are the first man I ever met who did not take me seriously?

BLUNTSCHLI: You mean, dont you, that I am the first man that has ever taken you quite seriously?

RAINA: Yes: I suppose I do mean that. *(Cosily, quite at her ease with him)* How strange it is to be talked to in such a way! You know, I've always gone on like that.

BLUNTSCHLI: You mean the —?

RAINA: I mean the noble attitude and the thrilling voice. *(They laugh together).* I did it when I was a tiny child to my nurse. She believed in it. I do it before my parents. They believe in it. I do it before Sergius. He believes in it.

BLUNTSCHLI: Yes, he's a little in that line himself, isnt he?

RAINA *(startled):*   Oh! Do you think so?

BLUNTSCHLI: You know him better than I do.

RAINA: I wonder — I wonder is he? If I thought that —! *(Discouraged)* Ah, well: what does it matter? I suppose, now youve found me out, you despise me.

BLUNTSCHLI *(warmly, rising):*   No, my dear young lady, no, no, no a thousand times. It's part of your youth: part of your charm. I'm like all the rest of them: the nurse, your parents, Sergius: I'm your infatuated admirer.

RAINA (pleased):   Really?

BLUNTSCHLI (slapping his breast smartly with his hand, German fashion): Hand aufs Herz! Really and truly.

RAINA (very happy):   But what did you think of me for giving you my portrait?

BLUNTSCHLI (astonished):   Your portrait! You never gave me your portrait.

RAINA (quickly):   Do you mean to say you never got it?

BLUNTSCHLI: No. (He sits down beside her, with renewed interest, and says with some complacency) When did you send it to me?

RAINA (indignantly):   I did not send it to you. (She turns her head away and adds, reluctantly) It was in the pocket of that coat.

BLUNTSCHLI (pursing his lips and rounding his eyes):   Oh-o-oh! I never found it. It must be there still.

RAINA (springing up):   There still! for my father to find the first time he puts his hand in his pocket! Oh, how could you be so stupid?

BLUNTSCHLI (rising also):   It doesnt matter: I suppose it's only a photograph: how can he tell who it was intended for? Tell him he put it there himself.

RAINA (bitterly):   Yes: that is so clever! isnt it? (Distractedly) Oh! what shall I do?

BLUNTSCHLI: Ah, I see. You wrote something on it. That was rash.

RAINA (vexed almost to tears):   Oh, to have done such a thing for you, who care no more — except to laugh at me — oh! Are you sure nobody has touched it?

BLUNTSCHLI: Well, I cant be quite sure. You see, I couldnt carry it about with me all the time: one cant take much luggage on active service.

RAINA: What did you do with it?

BLUNTSCHLI: When I got through to Pirot I had to put it in safe keeping somehow. I thought of the railway cloak room; but thats the surest place to get looted in modern warfare. So I pawned it.

RAINA: Pawned it!!!

BLUNTSCHLI: I know it doesnt sound nice: but it was much the safest plan. I redeemed it the day before yesterday. Heaven only knows whether the pawn-broker cleared out the pockets or not.

RAINA (furious, throwing the words right into his face):   You have a low shop-keeping mind. You think of things that would never come into a gentleman's head.

BLUNTSCHLI (phlegmatically):   Thats the Swiss national character, dear lady. (He returns to the table).

RAINA: Oh, I wish I had never met you. (She flounces away, and sits at the window fuming.)
(LOUKA comes in with a heap of letters and telegrams on her salver, and crosses, with her bold free gait, to the table. Her left sleeve is looped up to the shoulder with a brooch, shewing her naked arm, with a broad gilt bracelet covering the bruise.)

LOUKA *(to BLUNTSCHLI):*   For you. *(She empties the salver with a fling on to the table).* The messenger is waiting. *(She is determined not to be civil to an enemy, even if she must bring him his letters).*

BLUNTSCHLI *(to RAINA):*   Will you excuse me: the last postal delivery that reached me was three weeks ago. These are the subsequent accumulations. Four telegrams: a week old. *(He opens one).* Oho! Bad news!

RAINA *(rising and advancing a little remorsefully):*   Bad news?

BLUNTSCHLI: My father's dead. *(He looks at the telegram with his lips pursed, musing on the unexpected change in his arrangements. LOUKA crosses herself hastily).*

RAINA: Oh, how very sad!

BLUNTSCHLI: Yes: I shall have to start for home in an hour. He has left a lot of big hotels behind him to be looked after. *(He takes up a fat letter in a long blue envelope).* Here's a whacking letter from the family solicitor. *(He pulls out the enclosures and glances them over).* Great Heavens! Seventy! Two hundred! *(In a crescendo of dismay)* Four hundred! Four thousand!! Nine thousand six hundred!!! What on earth am I to do with them all?

RAINA *(timidly):*   Nine thousand hotels?

BLUNTSCHLI: Hotels! nonsense. If you only knew! Oh, it's too ridiculous! Excuse me, I must give my fellow orders about starting. *(He leaves the room hastily with the documents in his hand).*

LOUKA *(knowing instinctively that she can annoy RAINA by disparaging BLUNTSCHLI):*   He has not much heart, that Swiss. He has not a word of grief for his poor father.

RAINA *(bitterly):*   Grief! A man who has been doing nothing but killing people for years! What does he care? What does any soldier care? *(She goes to the door, restraing her tears with difficulty).*

LOUKA: Major Saranoff has been fighting too; and he has plenty of heart left. *(RAINA, at the door, draws herself up haughtily and goes out).* Aha! I thought you wouldnt get much feeling out of your soldier. *(She is following RAINA when NICOLA enters with an armful of logs for the stove).*

NICOLA *(grinning amorously at her):*   Ive been trying all the afternoon to get a minute alone with you, my girl. *(His countenance changes as he notices her arm).* Why, what fashion is that of wearing your sleeve, child?

LOUKA *(proudly):*   My own fashion.

NICOLA: Indeed! If the mistress catches you, she'll talk to you. *(He puts the logs down, and seats himself comfortably on the ottoman).*

LOUKA: Is that any reason why you should take it on yourself to talk to me?

NICOLA: Come! dont be so contrairy with me. Ive some good news for you. *(She sits down beside him. He takes out some paper money. LOUKA, with an eager gleam in her eyes, tries to snatch it; but he shifts it quickly to his left hand, out of her reach).* See! a twenty leva bill! Sergius gave me that, out of pure swagger. A fool and his money are soon parted. Theres ten levas more. The Swiss gave me that for backing up the mistress's and Raina's lies about him. He's no fool, he isnt. You should have heard old Catherine downstairs as polite as you please to me, telling me not to mind the Major being a little impatient; for they knew what a good servant I was — after making a fool and a liar of me before them all! The twenty will go to our savings; and you shall have the ten to spend if youll only talk to me so as to remind me I'm a human being. I get tired of being a servant occasionally.

LOUKA: Yes: sell your manhood for 30 levas, and buy me for 10! *(Rising scornfully)* Keep your money. You were born to be a servant. I was not. When you set up your shop you will only be everybody's servant instead of somebody's servant. *(She goes moodily to the table and seats herself regally in SERGIUS's chair).*

NICOLA *(picking up his logs, and going to the stove):* Ah, wait til you see. We shall have our evenings to ourselves; and I shall be master in my own house, I promise you. *(He throws the logs down and kneels at the stove).*

LOUKA: You shall never be master in mine.

NICOLA *(turning, still on his knees, and squatting down rather forlornly on his calves, daunted by her implacable disdain):* You have a great ambition in you, Louka. Remember: if any luck comes to you, it was I that made a woman of you.

LOUKA: You!

NICOLA *(scrambling up and going to her):* Yes, me. Who was it made you give up wearing a couple of pounds of false black hair on your head and reddening your lips and cheeks like any other Bulgarian girl! I did. Who taught you to trim your nails, and keep your hands clean, and be dainty about yourself, like a fine Russian lady! Me: do you hear that? me! *(She tosses her head defiantly; and he turns away, adding more coolly)* Ive often thought that if Raina were out of the way, and you just a little less of a fool and Sergius just a little more of one, you might come to be one of my grandest customers, instead of only being my wife and costing me money.

LOUKA: I believe you would rather be my servant than my husband. You would make more out of me. Oh, I know that soul of yours.

NICOLA *(going closer to her for greater emphasis):* Never you mind my soul; but just listen to my advice. If you want to be a lady, your present behaviour to me wont do at all, unless when we're alone. It's too sharp and impudent; and impudence is a sort of familiarity: it shews affection for me. And dont you try being high and mighty with me, either. Youre like all country girls: you think it's genteel to treat a servant the way I treat a stableboy. Thats only your ignorance: and dont you forget it. And dont be so ready to defy everybody. Act as if you expected to have your own way, not as if you expected to be ordered about. The way to get on as a lady is the same as the way to get on as a servant: youve got to know your place: thats the secret of it. And you may depend on me to know my place if you get promoted. Think it over, my girl. I'll stand by you: one servant should always stand by another.

LOUKA *(rising impatiently):* Oh, I must behave in my own way. You take all the courage out of me with your coldblooded wisdom. Go and put those logs in the fire: thats the sort of thing you understand.

(Before NICOLA can retort, SERGIUS comes in. He checks himself a moment on seeing LOUKA; then goes to the stove.)

SERGIUS *(to NICOLA):* I am not in the way of your work, I hope.

NICOLA *(in a smooth, elderly manner):* Oh no, sir: thank you kindly. I was only speaking to this foolish girl about her habit of running up here to the library whenever she gets a chance, to look at the books. Thats the worst of her education, sir: it gives her habits above her station. *(To LOUKA)* Make that table tidy, Louka, for the Major. *(He goes out sedately).*

    (LOUKA, without looking at SERGIUS, pretends to arrange the papers on the table. He crosses slowly to her, and studies the arrangement of her sleeve reflectively.)

SERGIUS: Let me see: is there a mark there? *(He turns up the bracelet and sees the bruise made by his grasp. She stands motionless, not looking at him: fascinated, but on her guard)* Ffff! Does it hurt?

LOUKA: Yes.

SERGIUS: Shall I cure it?

LOUKA *(instantly withdrawing herself proudly, but still not looking at him):* No. You cannot cure it now.

SERGIUS *(masterfully):* Quite sure? *(He makes a movement as if to take her in his arms).*

LOUKA: Dont trifle with me, please. An officer should not trifle with a servant.

SERGIUS *(indicating the bruise with a merciless stroke of his forefinger):* That was no trifle, Louka.

LOUKA *(flinching, then looking at him for the first time):* Are you sorry?

SERGIUS *(with measured emphasis, folding his arms):* I am never sorry.

LOUKA *(wistfully):* I wish I could believe a man could be as unlike a woman as that. I wonder are you really a brave man?

SERGIUS *(unaffectedly, relaxing his attitude):* Yes: I am a brave man. My heart jumped like a woman's at the first shot; but in the charge I found that I was brave. Yes: that at least is real about me.

LOUKA: Did you find in the charge that the men whose fathers are poor like mine were any less brave than the men who are rich like you?

SERGIUS *(with bitter levity):* Not a bit. They all slashed and cursed and yelled like heroes. Psha! the courage to rage and kill is cheap. I have an English bull terrier who has as much of that sort of courage as the whole Bulgarian nation, and the whole Russian nation at its back. But he lets my groom thrash him, all the same. Thats your soldier all over! No, Louka: your poor men can cut throats; but they are afraid of their officers; they put up with insults and blows; they stand by and see one another punished like children: aye, and help to do it when they are ordered. And the officers!!! Well *(with a short harsh laugh)* I am an officer. Oh, *(fervently)* give me the man who will defy to the death any power on earth or in heaven that sets itself up against his own will and conscience: he alone is the brave man.

LOUKA: How easy it is to talk! Men never seem to me to grow up: they all have schoolboy's ideas. You dont know what true courage is.

SERGIUS *(ironically):*   Indeed! I am willing to be instructed. *(He sits on the ottoman, sprawling magnificently).*

LOUKA: Look at me! how much am I allowed to have my own will? I have to get your room ready for you: to sweep and dust, to fetch and carry. How could that degrade me if it did not degrade you to have it done for you? But *(with subdued passion)* if I were Empress of Russia, above everyone in the world, then!! Ah then, though according to you I could shew no courage at all, you should see, you should see.

SERGIUS: What would you do, most noble Empress?

LOUKA: I would marry the man I loved, which no other queen in Europe has the courage to do. If I loved you, though you would be as far beneath me as I am beneath you, I would dare to be the equal of my inferior. Would you dare as much if you loved me? No: if you felt the beginnings of love for me you would not let it grow. You would not dare: you would marry a rich man's daughter because you would be afraid of what other people would say of you.

SERGIUS *(bounding up):*   You lie: it is not so, by all the stars! If I loved you, and I were the Czar himself, I would set you on the throne by my side. You know that I love another woman, a woman as high above you as heaven is above earth. And you are jealous of her.

LOUKA: I have no reason to be. She will nevery marry you now. The man I told you of has come back. She will marry the Swiss.

SERGIUS *(recoiling):*   The Swiss!

LOUKA: A man worth ten of you. Then you can come to me; and I will refuse you. You are not good enough for me. *(She turns to the door).*

SERGIUS *(springing after her and catching her fiercely in his arms):*   I will kill the Swiss; and afterwards I will do as I please with you.

LOUKA *(in his arms, passive and steadfast):*   The Swiss will kill you, perhaps. He has beaten you in love. He may beat you in war.

SERGIUS *(tormentedly):*   Do you think I believe that she — she! whose worst thoughts are higher than your best ones, is capable of trifling with another man behind my back?

LOUKA: Do you think she would believe the Swiss if he told her now that I am in your arms?

SERGIUS *(releasing her in despair):*   Damnation! Oh, damnation! Mockery! mockery everywhere! everything I think is mocked by everything I do. *(He strikes himself frantically on the breast).* Coward! liar! fool? Shall I kill myself like a man, or live and pretend to laugh at myself? *(She again turns to go).* Louka! *(She stops near the door).* Remember: you belong to me.

LOUKA *(turning):*   What does that mean? An insult?

SERGIUS *(commandingly):*   It means that you love me, and that I have had you here in my arms, and will perhaps have you there again. Whether that is an insult I neither know nor care: take it as you please. But *(vehemently)* I will not be a coward and a trifler. If I choose to love you, I dare marry you, in spite of all Bulgaria. If these hands ever touch you again, they shall touch my affianced bride.

LOUKA: We shall see whether you dare keep your word. And take care. I will not wait long.

SERGIUS *(again folding his arms and standing motionless in the middle of the room):* Yes: we shall see. And you shall wait my pleasure.
(BLUNTSCHLI, much preoccupied, with his papers still in his hand, enters, leaving the door open for LOUKA to go out. He goes across to the table, glancing at her as he passes. SERGIUS, without altering his resolute attitude, watches him steadily. LOUKA goes out, leaving the door open.)

BLUNTSCHLI *(absently, sitting at the table as before, and putting down his papers):* Thats a remarkable looking young woman.

SERGIUS *(gravely, without moving):* Captain Bluntschli.

BLUNTSCHLI: Eh?

SERGIUS: You have deceived me. You are my rival. I brook no rivals. At six o'clock I shall be in the drilling-ground on the Kilssoura road, alone, on horseback, with my sabre. Do you understand?

BLUNTSCHLI *(staring, but sitting quite at ease):* Oh, thank you: thats a cavalry man's proposal. I'm in the artillery; and I have the choice of weapons. If I go, I shall take a machine gun. And there shall be no mistake about the cartridges this time.

SERGIUS *(flushing, but with deadly coldness):* Take care, sir. It is not our custom in Bulgaria to allow invitations of that kind to be trifled with.

BLUNTSCHLI *(warmly):* Pooh! dont talk to me about Bulgaria. You dont know what fighting is. But have it your own way. Bring your sabre along. I'll meet you.

SERGIUS *(fiercely delighted to find his opponent a man of spirit):* Well said, Switzer. Shall I lend you my best horse?

BLUNTSCHLI: No: damn your horse! thank you all the same, my dear fellow.
(RAINA comes in, and hears the next sentence). I shall fight you on foot. Horseback's too dangerous; I dont want to kill you if I can help it.

RAINA *(hurrying forward anxiously):* I have heard what Captain Bluntschli said, Sergius. You are going to fight. Why? *(SERGIUS turns away in silence, and goes to the stove, where he stands watching her as she continues, to BLUNTSCHLI)* What about?

BLUNTSCHLI: I dont know; he hasnt told me. Better not interfere, dear young lady. No harm will be done: I've often acted as sword instructor. He wont be able to touch me; and I'll not hurt him. It will save explanations. In the morning I shall be off home; and youll never see me or hear of me again. You and he will then make it up and live happily ever after.

RAINA *(turning away deeply hurt, almost with a sob in her voice):* I never said I wanted to see you again.

SERGIUS *(striding forward):* Ha! That is a confession.

RAINA *(haughtily):* What do you mean?

SERGIUS: You love that man!

Arms and the Man

RAINA *(scandalized):* Sergius!

SERGIUS: You allow him to make love to you behind my back, just as you treat me as your affianced husband behind his. Bluntschli: you knew our relations; and you deceived me. It is for that that I call you to account, not for having received favors *I* never enjoyed.

BLUNTSCHLI *(jumping up indignantly):* Stuff! Rubbish! I have received no favors. Why, the young lady doesnt even know whether I'm married or not.

RAINA *(forgetting herself):* Oh! *(Collapsing on the ottoman)* Are you?

SERGIUS: You see the young lady's concern, Captain Bluntschli. Denial is useless. You have enjoyed the privilege of being received in her own room, late at night —

BLUNTSCHLI *(interrupting him pepperily):* Yes, you blockhead! she received me with a pistol at her head. Your cavalry were at my heels. I'd have blown out her brains if she'd uttered a cry.

SERGIUS *(taken aback):* Bluntschli! Raina: is this true?

RAINA *(rising in wrathful majesty):* Oh, how dare you, how dare you?

BLUNTSCHLI: Apologize, man: apologize. *(He resumes his seat at the table.)*

SERGIUS: *(with the old measured emphasis, folding his arms):* I never apologize!

RAINA *(passionately):* This is the doing of that friend of yours, Captain Bluntschli. It is he who is spreading this horrible story about me. *(She walks about excitedly).*

BLUNTSCHLI: No: he's dead. Burnt alive.

RAINA *(stopping, shocked):* Burnt alive!

BLUNTSCHLI: Shot in the hip in a woodyard. Couldnt drag himself out. Your fellows' shells set the timber on fire and burnt him, with half a dozen other poor devils in the same predicament.

RAINA: How horrible!

SERGIUS: And how ridiculous! Oh, war! war! the dream of patriots and heroes! A fraud, Bluntschli. A hollow sham, like love.

RAINA *(outraged):* Like love! You say that before me!

BLUNTSCHLI: Come, Saranoff, that matter is explained.

SERGIUS: A hollow sham, I say. Would you have come back here if nothing had passed between you except at the muzzle of your pistol? Raina is mistaken about your friend who was burnt. He was not my informant.

RAINA: Who then? *(Suddenly guessing the truth)* Ah, Louka! my maid! my servant! You were with her this morning all that time after — after — Oh, what sort of god is this I have been worshipping! *(He meets her gaze with sardonic enjoyment of her disenchantment. Angered all the more, she goes closer to him, and says, in a lower, intenser tone)* Do you know that I looked out of the window as I went upstairs, to have another sight of my hero; and I saw something I did not understand then. I know now that you were making love to her.

SERGIUS *(with grim humor):*   You saw that?

RAINA: Only too well. *(She turns away, and throws herself on the divan under the center window, quite overcome).*

SERGIUS *(cynically):*   Raina: our romance is shattered. Life's a farce.

BLUNTSCHLI *(to RAINA, whimsically):*   You see: he's found himself out now.

SERGIUS *(going to him):*   Bluntschli: I have allowed you to call me a blockhead. You may now call me a coward as well. I refuse to fight you. Do you know why?

BLUNTSCHLI   No; but it doesnt matter. I didnt ask the reason when you cried on; and I dont ask the reason now that you cry off. I'm a professional soldier: I fight when I have to, and am very glad to get out of it when I havnt to. Youre only an amateur: you think fighting's an amusement.

SERGIUS *(sitting down at the table, nose to nose with him):*   You shall hear the reason all the same, my professional. The reason is that it takes two men — real men — men of heart, blood and honor — to make a genuine combat. I could no more fight with you than I could make love to an ugly woman. Youve no magnetism: youre not a man: youre a machine.

BLUNTSCHLI *(apologetically):*   Quite true, quite true. I always was that sort of chap. I'm very sorry.

SERGIUS: Psha!

BLUNTSCHLI: But now that youve found that life isnt a farce, but something quite sensible and serious, what further obstacle is there to your happiness?

RAINA *(rising):*   You are very solicitous about my happiness and his. Do you forget his new love — Louka? It is not you that he must fight now, but his rival, Nicola.

SERGIUS: Rival!! *(Bounding half across the room).*

RAINA: Dont you know that theyre engaged?

SERGIUS: Nicola! Are fresh abysses opening? Nicola!

RAINA *(sarcastically):*   A shocking sacrifice, isnt it? Such beauty! such intellect! such modesty! wasted on a middle-aged servant man. Really, Sergius, you cannot stand by and allow such a thing. It would be unworthy of your chivalry.

SERGIUS *(losing all self-control):*   Viper! Viper! *(He rushes to and fro, raging).*

BLUNTSCHLI: Look here, Saranoff: youre getting the worst of this.

RAINA *(getting angrier):*   Do you realize what he has done, Captain Bluntschli? He has set this girl as a spy on us; and her reward is that he makes love to her.

SERGIUS: False! Monstrous!

RAINA: Monstrous! *(Confronting him)* Do you deny that she told you about Captain Bluntschli being in my room?

SERGIUS: No; but —

RAINA *(interrupting):* Do you deny that you were making love to her when she told you?

SERGIUS: No; but I tell you —

RAINA *(cutting him short contemptuously):* It is unnecessary to tell us anything more. That is quite enough for us. *(She turns away from him and sweeps majestically back to the window).*

BLUNTSCHLI *(quietly, as SERGIUS, in an agony of mortification, sinks on the ottoman, clutching his averted head between his fists):* I told you you were getting the worst of it, Saranoff.

SERGIUS: Tiger cat!

RAINA *(running excitedly to BLUNTSCHLI):* You hear this man calling me names, Captain Bluntschli?

BLUNTSCHLI: What else can he do, dear lady? He must defend himself somehow. Come *(very persuasively):* dont quarrel. What good does it do?
  (RAINA, with a gasp, sits down on the ottoman, and after a vain effort to look vexedly at BLUNTSCHLI, falls a victim to her sense of humor, and actually leans back babyishly against the writhing shoulder of SERGIUS.)

SERGIUS: Engaged to Nicola! Ha! ha! Ah well, Bluntschli, you are right to take this huge imposture of a world coolly.

RAINA *(quaintly to BLUNTSCHLI, with an intuitive guess at his state of mind):* I daresay you think us a couple of grown-up babies, dont you?

SERGIUS *(grinning savagely):* He does: he does. Swiss civilization nurse-tending Bulgarian barbarism, eh?

BLUNTSCHLI *(blushing):* Not at all, I assure you. I'm only very glad to get you two quieted. There! there! let's be pleasant and talk it over in a friendly way. Where is this other young lady?

RAINA: Listening at the door, probably.

SERGIUS *(shivering as if a bullet had struck him, and speaking with quiet but deep indignation):* I will prove that that, at least, is a calumny. *(He goes with dignity to the door and opens it. A yell of fury bursts from him as he looks out. He darts into the passage, and returns dragging in LOUKA, whom he flings violently against the table, exclaiming)* Judge her, Bluntschli. You, the cool impartial man: judge the eavesdropper.
  (LOUKA stands her ground, proud and silent.)

BLUNTSCHLI *(shaking his head):* I mustnt judge her. I once listened myself outside a tent when there was a mutiny brewing. It's all a question of the degree of provocation. My life was at stake.

LOUKA: My love was at stake. I am not ashamed.

RAINA *(contemptuously):* Your love! Your curiosity, you mean.

LOUKA *(facing her and returning her contempt with interest):* My love, stronger than anything you can feel, even for your chocolate cream soldier.

SERGIUS *(with quick suspicion, to LOUKA):* What does that mean?

LOUKA *(fiercely):* It means —

SERGIUS *(interrupting her slightingly):*   Oh, I remember: the ice pudding. A paltry taunt, girl!

   (MAJOR PETKOFF enters, in his shirtsleeves.)

PETKOFF: Excuse my shirtsleeves, gentlemen. Raina: somebody has been wearing that coat of mine: I'll swear it. Somebody with a differently shaped back. It's all burst open at the sleeve. Your mother is mending it. I wish she'd make haste: I shall catch cold. *(He looks more attentively at them).* Is anything the matter?

RAINA: No. *(She sits down at the stove with a tranquil air).*

SERGIUS: Oh no. *(He sits down at the end of the table, as at first).*

BLUNTSCHLI *(who is already seated):*   Nothing. Nothing.

PETKOFF *(sitting down on the ottoman in his old place):*   Thats all right. *(He notices LOUKA).* Anything the matter, Louka?

LOUKA: No, sir.

PETKOFF *(genially):*   Thats all right. *(He sneezes)* Go and ask your mistress for my coat, like a good girl, will you?

   (NICOLA enters with the coat. LOUKA makes a pretence of having business in the room by taking the little table with the hookah away to the wall near the windows.)

RAINA *(rising quickly as she sees the coat on NICOLA's arm):*   Here it is, papa. Give it to me, Nicola; and do you put some more wood on the fire. *(She takes the coat and brings it to the MAJOR, who stands up to put it on. NICOLA attends to the fire).*

PETKOFF *(to RAINA, teasing her affectionately):*   Aha! Going to be very good to poor old papa just for one day after his return from the wars, eh?

RAINA *(with solemn reproach):*   Ah, how can you say that to me, father?

PETKOFF: Well, well, only a joke, little one. Come: give me a kiss. *(She kisses him).* Now give me the coat.

RAINA: No: I am going to put it on for you. Turn your back. *(He turns his back and feels behind him with his arms for the sleeves. She dexterously takes the photograph from the pocket and throws it on the table before BLUNTSCHLI, who covers it with a sheet of paper under the very nose of SERGIUS, who looks on amazed, with his suspicions roused in the highest degree. She then helps PETKOFF on with his coat).* There, dear! Now are you comfortable?

PETKOFF: Quite, little love. Thanks. *(He sits down, and RAINA returns to her seat near the stove).* Oh, by the bye, Ive found something funny. Whats the meaning of this? *(He puts his hand into the picked pocket).* Eh? Hallo! *(He tries the other pocket).* Well, I could have sworn —! *(Much puzzled, he tries the breast pocket).* I wonder — *(trying the original pocket).* Where can it —? *(He rises, exclaiming)* Your mother's taken it!

RAINA *(very red):*   Taken what?

PETKOFF: Your photograph, with the inscription: "Raina, to her Chocolate Cream Soldier: a Souvenir." Now you know theres something more in this than meets the eye; and I'm going to find it out. *(Shouting)* Nicola!

NICOLA (coming to him):   Sir!

PETKOFF: Did you spoil any pastry of Miss Raina's this morning?

NICOLA: You heard Miss Raina say that I did, sir.

PETKOFF: I know that, you idiot. Was it true?

NICOLA: I am sure Miss Raina is incapable of saying anything that is not true, sir.

PETKOFF: Are you? Then I'm not. (Turning to the others) Come: do you think I dont see it all? (He goes to SERGIUS, and slaps him on the shoulder). Sergius: youre the chocolate cream soldier, arnt you?

SERGIUS (starting up):   I! A chocolate cream soldier! Certainly not.

PETKOFF: Not! (He looks at them. They are all very serious and very self-conscious). Do you mean to tell me that Raina sends things like that to other men?

SERGIUS (enigmatically):   The world is not such an innocent place as we used to think, Petkoff.

BLUNTSCHLI (rising):   It's all right, Major. I'm the chocolate cream soldier. (PETKOFF and SERGIUS are equally astonished). The gracious young lady saved my life by giving me chocolate creams when I was starving: shall I ever forget their flavour! My late friend Stolz told you the story of Pirot. I was the fugitive.

PETKOFF: You! (He gasps). Sergius: do you remember how those two women went on this morning when we mentioned it? (SERGIUS smiles cynically. PETKOFF confronts RAINA severely). Youre a nice young woman, arnt you?

RAINA (bitterly):   Major Saranoff has changed his mind. And when I wrote that on the photograph, I did not know that Captain Bluntschli was married.

BLUNTSCHLI (startled into vehement protest):   I'm not married.

RAINA (with deep reproach):   You said you were.

BLUNTSCHLI: I did not. I positively did not. I never was married in my life.

PETKOFF (exasperated):   Raina: will you kindly inform me, if I am not asking too much, which of these gentlemen you are engaged to?

RAINA: To neither of them. This young lady (introducing LOUKA, who faces them all proudly) is the object of Major Saranoff's affections at present.

PETKOFF: Louka! Are you mad, Sergius? Why, this girl's engaged to Nicola.

NICOLA: I beg your pardon, sir. There is a mistake. Louka is not engaged to me.

PETKOFF: Not engaged to you, you scoundrel! Why, you had twenty-five levas from me on the day of your betrothal; and she had that gilt bracelet from Miss Raina.

NICOLA (with cool unction):   We gave it out so, sir. But it was only to give Louka protection. She had a soul above her station; and I have been no more than her confidential servant. I intend, as you know, sir, to set up a shop later on in Sofia; and I look forward to her custom and recommendation should she marry into the nobility. *(He goes out with impressive discretion, leaving them all staring after him).*

PETKOFF *(breaking the silence):* Well, I am — hm!

SERGIUS: This is either the finest heroism or the most crawling baseness. Which is it, Bluntschli?

BLUNTSCHLI: Never mind whether it's heroism or baseness. Nicola's the ablest man I've met in Bulgaria. I'll make him manager of a hotel if he can speak French and German.

LOUKA *(suddenly breaking out at SERGIUS):* I have been insulted by everyone here. You set them the example. You owe me an apology.
(SERGIUS, like a repeating clock of which the spring has been touched, immediately begins to fold his arms.)

BLUNTSCHLI *(before he can speak):* It's no use. He never apologizes.

LOUKA: Not to you, his equal and his enemy. To me, his poor servant, he will not refuse to apologize.

SERGIUS *(approvingly):* You are right. *(He bends his knee in his grandest manner)* Forgive me.

LOUKA: I forgive you. *(She timidly gives him her hand, which he kisses).* That touch makes me your affianced wife.

SERGIUS *(springing up):* Ah! I forgot that.

LOUKA *(coldly):* You can withdraw if you like.

SERGIUS: Withdraw! Never! You belong to me. *(He puts his arm about her).*
(CATHERINE comes in and finds LOUKA in SERGIUS's arms, with all the rest gazing at them in bewildered astonishment.)

CATHERINE: What does this mean?
(SERGIUS releases LOUKA.)

PETKOFF: Well, my dear, it appears that Sergius is going to marry Louka instead of Raina. *(She is about to break out indignantly at him: he stops her by exclaiming testily)* Dont blame me; Ive nothing to do with it. *(He retreats to the stove).*

CATHERINE: Marry Louka! Sergius: you are bound by your word to us!

SERGIUS *(folding his arms):* Nothing binds me.

BLUNTSCHLI *(much pleased by this piece of common sense):* Saranoff: your hand. My congratulations. These heroics of yours have their practical side after all. *(To LOUKA)* Gracious young lady: the best wishes of a good Republican! *(He kisses her hand, to RAINA's great disgust, and returns to his seat).*

CATHERINE: Louka: you have been telling stories.

LOUKA: I have done Raina no harm.

CATHERINE *(haughtily):* Raina!
(RAINA, equally indignant, almost snorts at the liberty.)

LOUKA: I have a right to call her Raina: she calls me Louka. I told Major Saranoff she would never marry him if the Swiss gentleman came back.

BLUNTSCHLI *(rising, much surprised):* Hallo!

LOUKA *(turning to RAINA):* I thought you were fonder of him than of Sergius. You know best whether I was right.

BLUNTSCHLI: What nonsense! I assure you, my dear Major, my dear Madame, the gracious young lady simply saved my life, nothing else. She never cared two straws for me. Why, bless my heart and soul, look at the young lady and look at me. She, rich, young, beautiful, with her imagination full of fairy princes and noble natures and cavalry charges and goodness knows what! And I, a commonplace Swiss soldier who hardly knows what a decent life is after fifteen years of barracks and battles: a vagabond, a man who has spoiled all his chances in life through an incurably romantic disposition, a man —

SERGIUS *(starting as if a needle had pricked him and interrupting BLUNT-SCHLI in incredulous amazement):* Excuse me, Bluntschli: what did you say had spoiled your chances in life?

BLUNTSCHLI *(promptly):* An incurably romantic disposition. I ran away from home twice when I was a boy. I went into the army instead of into my father's business. I climbed the balcony of this house when a man of sense would have dived into the nearest cellar. I came sneaking back here to have another look at the young lady when any other man of my age would have sent the coat back —

PETKOFF: My coat!

BLUNTSCHLI: — yes, thats the coat I mean — would have sent it back and gone quietly home. Do you suppose I am the sort of fellow a young girl falls in love with? Why, look at our ages! I'm thirty-four: I dont suppose the young lady is much over seventeen. *(This estimate produces a marked sensation, all the rest turning and staring at one another. He proceeds innocently)* All that adventure which was life or death to me, was only a schoolgirl's game to her — chocolate creams and hide and seek. Here's the proof! *(He takes the photograph from the table).* Now, I ask you, would a woman who took the affair seriously have sent me this and written on it "Raina, to her Chocolate Cream Soldier: a Souvenir"? *(He exhibits the photograph triumphantly, as if it settled the matter beyond all possibility of refutation).*

PETKOFF: Thats what I was looking for. How the deuce did it get there? *(He comes from the stove to look at it, and sits down on the ottoman).*

BLUNTSCHLI *(to RAINA, complacently):* I have put everything right, I hope, gracious young lady.

RAINA *(going to the table to face him):* I quite agree with your account of yourself. You are a romantic idiot. *(BLUNTSCHLI is unspeakably taken aback).* Next time, I hope you will know the difference between a schoolgirl of seventeen and a woman of twenty-three.

BLUNTSCHLI *(stupefied):* Twenty-three!
(RAINA snaps the photograph contemptuously from his hand; tears it up; throws the pieces in his face; and sweeps back to her former place.)

SERGIUS *(with grim enjoyment of his rival's discomfiture):* Bluntschli: my one last belief is gone. Your sagacity is a fraud, like everything else. You have less sense than even I!

BLUNTSCHLI *(overwhelmed):* Twenty-three! Twenty-three! *(He considers).* Hm! *(Swiftly making up his mind and coming to his host)* In that case, Major Petkoff, I beg to propose formally to become a suitor for your daughter's hand, in place of Major Saranoff retired.

RAINA: You dare!

BLUNTSCHLI: If you were twenty-three when you said those things to me this afternoon, I shall take them seriously.

CATHERINE *(loftily polite):* I doubt, sir, whether you quite realize either my daughter's position or that of Major Sergius Saranoff, whose place you propose to take. The Petkoffs and the Saranoffs are known as the richest and most important families in the country. Our position is almost historical: we can go back for twenty years.

PETKOFF: Oh, never mind that, Catherine. *(To BLUNTSCHLI)* We should be most happy, Bluntschli, if it were only a question of your position; but hang it, you know, Raina is accustomed to a very comfortable establishment. Sergius keeps twenty horses.

BLUNTSCHLI: But who wants twenty horses? We're not going to keep a circus.

CATHERINE *(severely):* My daughter, sir, is accustomed to a first-rate stable.

RAINA: Hush, mother: youre making me ridiculous.

BLUNTSCHLI: Oh well, if it comes to a question of an establishment, here goes! *(He darts impetuously to the table; seizes the papers in the blue envelope; and turns to SERGIUS).* How many horses did you say?

SERGIUS: Twenty, noble Switzer.

BLUNTSCHLI: I have two hundred horses. *(They are amazed).* How many carriages?

SERGIUS: Three.

BLUNTSCHLI: I have seventy. Twenty-four of them will hold twelve inside, besides two on the box, without counting the driver and conductor. How many tablecloths have you?

SERGIUS: How the deuce do I know?

BLUNTSCHLI: Have you four thousand?

SERGIUS: No.

BLUNTSCHLI: I have. I have nine thousand six hundred pairs of sheets and blankets, with two thousand four hundred eider-down quilts. I have ten thousand knives and forks, and the same quantity of dessert spoons. I have three hundred servants. I have six palatial establishments, besides two livery stables, a tea gardens, and a private house. I have four medals for distinguished services; I have the rank of an officer and the standing of a gentleman; and I have three native languages. Shew me any man in Bulgaria that can offer as much!

PETKOFF *(with childish awe):*   Are you Emperor of Switzerland?

BLUNTSCHLI: My rank is the highest known in Switzerland: I am a free citizen.

CATHERINE: Then, Captain Bluntschli, since you are my daughter's choice —

RAINA *(mutinously):*   He's not.

CATHERINE *(ignoring her):*   — I shall not stand in the way of her happiness. *(PETKOFF is about to speak)* That is Major Petkoff's feeling also.

PETKOFF: Oh, I shall be only too glad. Two hundred horses! Whew!

SERGIUS: What says the lady?

RAINA *(pretending to sulk):*   The lady says that he can keep his tablecloths and his omnibuses. I am not here to be sold to the highest bidder. *(She turns her back on him).*

BLUNTSHLI: I wont take that answer. I appealed to you as a fugitive, a beggar, and a starving man. You accepted me. You gave me your hand to kiss, your bed to sleep in, and your roof to shelter me.

RAINA: I did not give them to the Emperor of Switzerland.

BLUNTSCHLI: Thats just what I say. *(He catches her by the shoulders and turns her face-to-face with him).* Now tell us whom you did give them to.

RAINA *(succumbing with a shy smile):*   To my chocolate cream soldier.

BLUNTSCHLI *(with a boyish laugh of delight):*   Thatll do. Thank you. *(He looks at his watch and suddenly becomes businesslike).* Time's up, Major. Youve managed those regiments so well that youre sure to be asked to get rid of some of the infantry of the Timok division. Send them home by way of Lom Palanka. Saranoff: dont get married until I come back: I shall be here punctually at five in the evening on Tuesday fortnight. Gracious ladies *(his heels click)* good evening. *(He makes them a military bow and goes).*

SERGIUS: What a man! Is he a man!

———————— • ————————

Consider the Play

1. Analyse the character of Bluntschli as it is revealed in Act 1. Use the headings of physical appearance, social position, and mentality.

2. Consider the character of Raina as shown in Act 1. What are we told of her appearance, background, and mental outlook?

3. The character of Sergius does not come on stage until after Act 1 but other characters speak of him. Briefly describe the different impressions of Sergius given by Shaw himself and by the characters of Catherine, Raina, and Bluntschli.

4. "Perhaps we only had our heroic ideas because we are so fond of reading Byron and Pushkin." Explain the significance of Raina's statement.

5. Discuss Shaw's use of these stage techniques in Act 1:
   (A) The setting.
   (B) Catherine's manner.
   (C) Raina's mood.
   (D) Background sounds.

6. A number of props (moveable items) are used in Act 1. Explain why each of the following is essential:
   (A) The paperback novels.
   (B) The box of chocolates.
   (C) Sergius' photograph.
   (D) The candle and matches.

7. The character of Louka is introduced in Act 1 and becomes important later in the play. When Louka is first introduced, what qualities of character are suggested to lay the groundwork for Louka's later importance? Compare and contrast the characters of Louka and Nicola.

8. Good drama requires different characters who contrast one another. This is necessary to build conflict and tension. How did Shaw use contrasting characters in Act 2 to build conflict and develop the plot?

9. In Act 1, the attention of the audience is focussed on attitudes towards war. In Act 2, the attention of the audience is focussed on the love element of the plot. How does Shaw make sure that the audience does not forget the war focus of Act 1 during Act 2?

10. A *pivotal* character is one which remains constant. Other characters must change or develop around the pivotal character. Consider the characters in this play. Which do you think are pivotal? Why? Explain briefly.

11. Shaw had a habit of turning conventional situations upside down in order to startle and amuse the audience. Give two examples of how Shaw used this technique in *Arms and the Man*.

12. One way of using dramatic irony is to allow some characters to keep secrets from other characters. Give two examples of how Shaw used this technique.

13. The problem Shaw faced in Act 3 was to keep the audience interested after an early climax. How did Shaw solve this problem? Explain briefly the purpose served by Petkoff's coat and Raina's photograph in solving the problem.

14. How does the subplot of the Nicola-Louka love affair represent the clash of ideals?

15. Shaw takes aim at many subjects in this play. List at least three. In your opinion, does Shaw do this in the spirit of reform or simply for comic effect? Explain your point of view. Cite evidence from the play to support your opinion.

16. Shaw expresses his annoyance with idealists in this play, both in the introduction and in the play itself. Is his tone different in these two sections? Explain your opinion briefly.

17. One theme in this play is romantic love. Write the script for a one-minute television commercial promoting *Arms and the Man* as a play about romantic love *or* a commercial promoting any other play or novel on that basis. Include drawings to clarify the intent and appearance of your commercial.

18. Is romantic love a realistic possibility today? Will it be a realistic possibility ten years from now? Why? Explain your point of view.

19. How does North American society view romantic love today? Survey newspapers and magazines for advertisements that use romantic appeal to sell products. Select and clip at least five. Use the clippings as evidence to support your opinion of how society views romantic love today.

20. What do you think courtship, marriage, and love will be like in the year 2000? Discuss. Compare and contrast your view with Shaw's view in *Arms and the Man* and with society's views today.

───────────── • ─────────────

Glossary

This glossary contains words and phrases commonly found in works on dramatic literature, dramatic theory, and the history of drama. Although many of these terms are also used in literature in general, the definitions here have been limited to specific applications to dramatic literature. Additional meanings for these terms may be found in standard dictionaries and literary references.

A

Act. A major section or subdivision of the action of a drama. In classical Greek drama, there were usually five acts, and each major division was indicated by the appearance of the chorus. Elizabethan playwrights also tended to present dramas in five acts. Most modern full-length plays are presented in three acts, although some have only two or even one. A one-act play may or may not be divided into scenes.

Action. An event or series of real or imagined happenings which form the subject of a play. Although action is sometimes used to refer to the physical activity in a drama, it may also refer to the process of change effected during the course of the play. In this sense, the action of a drama may not be physical at all although it may be seen partly through physical activity.

Actor. A performer who impersonates, in the theatre, the fictional character in a drama. Actor and character are not synonymous, although the two are seen by the audience as a single living being. In this text, actor is used to refer to both male and female performers. Note that female roles have not always been played by women, however. Women were unknown on the ancient Greek stage, on the classical Japanese stage, and on the English stage before 1660.

Antecedent action. The portion of a dramatic story that is presumed to have occurred before the action of the drama itself begins. Antecedent action of which the audience must be aware is usually revealed in dialogue.

Anticlimax. A drop, either intentional or accidental, in the tension or excitement generated by the climax of a play. The anticlimax usually occurs near the end. If accidental, it represents a serious flaw in the structure of the play because the attention and interest of the audience will decrease and the final effect of the work will not be satisfying. A skilful playwright, however, can use anticlimax to good effect by making a subdued closing part of the total plan. An example of the effective artistic use of anticlimax is found in Henrik Ibsen's *A Doll's House,* written in 1879.

Antihero. A character who lacks the qualities needed for heroism. An antihero is not noble in life or mind and does not have an attitude marked by high purpose or lofty aim. King Claudius in Shakespeare's *Hamlet* is an example of an antihero.

Aside. A stage convention used to indicate words spoken by a character but heard only by the audience and not by other characters on stage. The aside is a comment for the benefit of the audience. It may be spoken either directly to the audience or in an offhand way as if the character were speaking to himself or herself.

Atmosphere. The overall effect of a play. This meteorological term refers to the dominant mood of a drama as created by setting, description, and dialogue.

B

Burlesque. A form of comic art. Burlesque is an imitation intended to ridicule by exaggeration. In general, it is a dramatic composition that makes fun of, or satirizes, some other specific work or general form of theatre.

C

Character. A person represented in a play. Character also refers to the dispositions, traits, or behaviour patterns which the dramatist gives to the agents, or characters, of the drama.

Chorus. In classical Greek drama, a group of singers and dancers who participated in religious festivals and dramatic performances. The chorus occasionally commented on the deeds of characters and interpreted the significance of events for the audience. By Elizabethan times, the active role of the chorus had been taken over by a single actor who recited the prologue and epilogue and who sometimes provided commentary between acts as well.

Climax. The high point of emotional excitement in a drama *or* the turning point of the plot. Climax is most often used to mean the emotional high point — the moment in the play when the crisis comes to its point of greatest intensity and is then resolved in some way. When discussing drama, it is important to determine in which sense the term climax is being used.

Collaboration. When two or more dramatists work together to produce a play or a number of plays. Collaboration also refers to the play written in that way. The practice was especially strong during Elizabethan times. One of the most famous dramatic teams was that of John Fletcher (1579-1635) and Francis Beaumont (1584-1616) who together produced at least 14 plays between 1606 and 1615. Fletcher also collaborated with several other writers, including, it is believed, William Shakespeare. Collaboration is also fairly common in modern theatre. For example, George S. Kaufman (1889-1961), the fine American comic dramatist, wrote almost all of his many successes in collaboration with others, most notably with Moss Hart (1904-1961).

Comedy. A major form of drama which aims at provoking laughter by exposing human folly. The term is also applied specifically to a play of light and amusing character with a happy ending. The comedies of any society reflect its accepted modes of behaviour and ethical standards. Thus, the appreciation of a comedy is often limited to the society that produced it. Sometimes, however, comedies go beyond time and place.

Comedy of humours. A comic play involving characters whose actions are controlled by some whim or humour.

Comedy of manners. A comic play involving the conventions and manners of artificial, sophisticated society.

Comedy of situation. A comic play which depends on plot more than on characterization for its humour.

Comic relief. A humourous scene, incident, or remark within an essentially serious or even tragic drama. It is placed there in order to evoke laughter as a release from the tension of the serious action. Comic relief is designed deliberately by a playwright to relieve emotional intensity and, at the same time, to heighten, increase, and highlight the seriousness or tragedy of the action. Shakespeare, for example, used comic relief in many of his plays. Famous examples are Mercutio in *Romeo and Juliet,* the gravedigger scene in *Hamlet,* and the drunken porter episode in *Macbeth.*

Conflict. The element of struggle in a dramatic action which results from the interplay between opposing forces in the plot. Dramatic conflict may occur between the protagonist and the forces of nature, between the protagonist and another character, between the protagonist and society as a whole, or within the protagonist (an internal struggle).

D

Dialogue. A conversation or speaking together. In general, dialogue refers to the parts of a dramatic text intended to be spoken by the actors. More specifically, dialogue is an interchange of speech between two characters. Thus, dialogue is different from soliloquy, the chorus, and narration. Dialogue is the essential language of drama. Constructing effective dialogue is often considered to be the crucial testing of the skill of a playwright.

Diction. The style of speaking and writing reflected in the choice and use of words. Diction refers to the selection and arrangement of words in statements. It also refers to the accuracy, emphasis, and distinction with which they are spoken and written.

Drama. A composition in prose or verse presenting in pantomime and dialogue a narrative involving conflict and usually designed for presentation on a stage. The term *drama* comes from the Greek *dran,* meaning "to do". Drama is also used to refer to a play of serious rather than comic nature. This major literary form dates back to the fifth century B.C.

Dramatis personae. A Latin term for characters of the drama. The printed version of a play almost always includes a list of the characters at the front of the text. From the Renaissance until roughly the mid-1800s, the term *dramatis personae* was used as the heading for these lists, regardless of the language used for the play itself. Today, the terms characters or cast are generally used instead.

Dramatist. The author of a dramatic work. The classical Greeks called the dramatist a poet. Later, the terms dramatist or playwright came into general use. Dramatists works with verbal tools (words), human tools (the bodies, faces, voices, and movements of the actors), and mechanical tools (the theatre stage and machinery).

Drawingroom comedy. A type of play popular in the 1800s. Often called "cup and saucer drama", the drawingroom comedy features realistic, domestic ac   and situations set in upperclass drawingrooms. These plays earned their name through the mundane, commonplace actions indicated in the scripts, such as the serving of tea.

E

Epilogue. A closing speech, following the action of a drama, delivered by one of the actors directly to the audience. Epilogues first appeared in plays of the Renaissance. In the 1700s, they were considered essential to close both comedies and tragedies. Often, important literary people wrote epilogues for one another's plays. As a rule, the epilogue would ask for the audience's applause. It was not uncommon for the dramatist to use the epilogue as a means to insult the audience by suggesting in it that if the audience did not care for the play it was because the audience lacked taste, not because the play itself was faulty.

Episode. An incident or scene in the course of the action of a drama. Occasionally, an episode is a digression. Usually, however, it is a unified narrative passage integrated within the main plot. Modern drama critics often look upon an episode as that part of a scene that changes with the entrance or exit of a character.

F

Falling action. The part of the play that follows the climax. It is the equivalent of the resolution or denouement of a drama, which leads to the catastrophe. The protagonist's fortunes decline and the counterplayers begin their ascendancy over him or her.

Fantasy. An extravagant and unrestrained imagination. This term is applied to any dramatic work in which the action occurs in a nonexistent and unreal world. A fantasy transcends the bounds of known reality. It introduces human beings into a world where the ordinary laws of human nature are suspended.

Farce. A form of comedy that relies mainly on artificial manipulations of plot and comic situations rather than on character development. Farce is popular because it makes audiences laugh while making little demand on the intellect. It is a mainstay of many television and motion picture comedians.

I

Inciting action. The early point in a drama at which the rising action is set in motion. Sometimes referred to as the *exciting force*, the inciting action may take the form of an idea, commitment, or resolution on the part of the protagonist *or* it may take the form of some external force imposed on the protagonist. For example, the inciting action in Shakespeare's *Hamlet* occurs when the Ghost tells the young prince how his father was murdered. As a result, Hamlet vows to get revenge. The inciting action may be a single moment or an entire scene. It comes early in the play, however, since it serves as the transition from the introduction to the rising action.

K

Kabuki drama. A popular classical drama of the Japanese theatre. Based on popular legends and myths or on historical events, Kabuki dramas are performed on a wide shallow stage with a sort of causeway running from the left-hand side to the back of the hall along which the actors make their entrances and exits. The plays are not thought of as literary works so much as texts for performance. By Western standards, they are episodic, sprawling, and often narrative rather than dramatic. In the 1600s, a single performance could last for 12 hours. Today, acts from favourite plays are usually selected, thus reducing the performance time to two or three hours.

M

Marionettes. Dolls or puppets that perform in a form of dramatic entertainment known as puppet theatre. Technically, a *puppet* is a doll manipulated by the hand of the operator, while a *marionette* is a doll detached from the operator and controlled by strings or wires. Puppets and marionettes date back to the earliest times of drama. They were popular folk entertainment, often presented by travelling players in temporary, open-air theatres. During the 1500s and 1600s, more refined versions were developed for aristocratic audiences and indoor theatres. In this century, there has been a rebirth of puppet and marionette entertainments. Although sometimes regarded as mainly for children, there is a growing awareness that puppet theatre is suitable for all ages.

Melodrama. A form of play that intensifies sentiment, exaggerates emotion, and relates sensational and thrilling action. The term comes from the Greek words for song and drama. Originally, melodramas were romantic plays with music, singing, and dancing. During the 1700s, they evolved into plays with elaborate but oversimplified plots stuffed with coincidence and which always had happy endings. The structure was designed to lead the audience's expectations one way, only to end in a different or opposite conclusion, usually through the use of the *deus ex machina* (an artificial, forced, or improbable device used to resolve the difficulties of plot). Although moral and ethical issues are raised, they are never explored as deeply in melodrama as in tragedies because the characters in melodrama are always clearly drawn as good or evil. The tone of melodrama is idealistic, and its action reaffirms the commonly accepted moral and ethical beliefs of the day. The sensational elements of melodrama are common today in Gothic novels and in modern films, literature, and television drama. Melodrama will remain a major form of serious drama because it allows audiences to release emotions through its emphasis on sentiment. Melodrama idealizes the world and allows audiences to escape, however briefly, the harsh realities of life.

Mime. A classical Greek and Roman form of comedy which presented events of everyday life through dances, gestures, and dialogue. With the advent of Christianity, mime was driven from the public theatres. It was preserved, however, by wandering entertainers, and the tradition of semi-dramatic performances continued through the Middle Ages. Mime influenced later dramatic forms, such as the miracle play and the pantomime. (Pantomime is the art of portraying a character or mood by the use of gestures, facial expressions, and bodily movements.) Mime may be thought of as an ancestor of vaudeville. Today, mime is a style of performance which depends solely on gesture. No speech is used. The term mime is also used as a verb (meaning to imitate or copy in action) and as a noun (meaning an entertainer who is clever in mimicking or imitating others).

Miracle play. A medieval dramatic form dealing with Biblical stories or the lives of saints. Usually presented in a series, miracle plays dealt with such events as the creation of the world. In England, the miracle plays were presented on moveable wagons, called pageants, in connection with the Corpus Christi celebration. Thus, they became known as Corpus Christi plays.

Mock epic. A literary work which makes fun of the conventions and traditions of epic poetry by treating some trivial subject in a grand manner. Mock epic drama describes a type of play which is intended to mock serious, heroic drama.

Monologue. A speech by one person. *Monologue* comes from the Greek term meaning "one word" or "one speech". It is sometimes used interchangeably with soliloquy. A soliloquy should be understood as a part of a drama in which a character, alone, utters his or her thoughts. A monologue, however, may be complete in itself and is usually addressed to someone — either the audience or an imagined second character.

Morality play. An allegory in dramatic form. Morality plays were common from the 1300s to the 1500s. Most used personified abstractions of vices and virtues (such as Shame, Lust, Mercy, and Faith). Unlike miracle and mystery plays, morality plays did not necessarily use Biblical or strictly religious material. They were more concerned with morality than spirituality. They portrayed an invented hero who was faced with some problem or temptation of the type which faced people in real life. The characters in morality plays were little more than symbolic representations of abstract concepts in keeping with the style of allegory.

Mystery play. A play which dealt with Biblical stories, such as the "mystery" of the birth, life, death, and resurrection of Jesus Christ. Especially popular during the Middle Ages, the mystery play got its name from the French word *mystère*, meaning "craft". Many mystery plays were performed by members of craft guilds, such as the shipwrights' or wheelwrights' guild. Today, as a rule, the terms mystery play and miracle play are used interchangeably.

N

Narration/Narrative. A form of conversation in which the main purpose is to relate an event or series of events. *Narration* comes from the Latin word meaning "tell". Narration is also called *narrative*, which may be used as an adjective or a noun. Narration (or narrative) appears in history, news stories, biography, autobiography, etc. In all drama, some narration is necessary, if only to aid the exposition. Excessive use of narration, however, can detract from the effectiveness of a play.

Noh drama. The oldest Japanese dramatic form, dating back to the middle of the 1300s. Some 500 Noh (or No) plays have survived. They are performed on a square stage raised slightly from the ground. The audience sits on two sides of the stage. To one side is a balcony housing a chorus of ten singers. At the back there is another smaller stage occupied by four musicians and two stage hands. The actors make their entrances and exits along a long slanting walk which recedes from the left-hand side of the stage. There is no scenery on stage. Locations are represented by a small conventionalized framework with a roof which is used to indicate the presence of a building. The plays, which consist of highly formalized dances, are performed by two actors, although they have companions in various scenes. Noh dramas are grounded in Buddhist thought and often show the salvation of the soul of a dead person. Ghosts and tormented spirits meet Buddhist monks and find peace. The texts of the Noh plays are quite brief and are essentially poetic rather than dramatic.

O

One-act play. A fairly short drama, usually with a continuous action which is complete in itself and achieves its effect through economy and intensity. The one-act play developed at the turn of the century and served as a method for encouraging new playwrights by allowing their works to be staged with a minimum expenditure of time and money. The typical one-act play runs from about 20 minutes to about one hour. Thus, two or more one-act plays are usually staged for one evening's entertainment.

P

Pageant. Originally, a moveable stage on which scenes of medieval religious plays were performed. Later, an entertainment performed on a moveable stage. Today, pageant is used to describe a procession made up of spectacularly costumed groups of people and usually including songs, dances, and dramatic scenes based on some event of local historical interest. The historical pageant was very popular during the early 1900s.

Passion play. A religious drama concerning the crucifixion of Christ. In the Middle Ages, passion plays were widely performed on Good Friday. After the Reformation, they survived mainly in Switzerland, Austria, and southern Germany. Today, the most famous passion play is presented every ten years at Oberammergau, Bavaria (Germany). An American version is staged regularly in the Black Hills of South Dakota.

Pathos. The ability in drama to call forth feelings of pity, compassion, and sadness. *Pathos* comes from the Greek word meaning "suffering". Aristotle (384-322 B.C.) claims (in Chapter XI of the *Poetics*) that pathos is one of the three types of incidents in tragic plots, the other two being recognition and reversal. He defined an incident of pathos as one embodying "destructive or painful actions such as death on the stage, scenes of very great pain, the infliction of wounds, and the like".

Playwright. One who writes plays. In English, the suffix "wright" means "maker". So a playwright, or dramatist, is a playmaker rather than simply a playwriter. The playwright must design, shape, and build the narrative as well as write the dialogue.

Prologue. Any introductory speech preceding the action of a play. In ancient Greek tragedy, the prologue was the part of the play that set forth the subject of the drama before the chorus entered. The ancient Roman comic writers followed this tradition by writing prologues for their comedies. Prologues were considered essential in English drama of the 1600s and 1700s. During the 1700s, writers often wrote prologues for each other's plays. Alexander Pope (1688-1744), Samuel Johnson (1709-1784), and David Garrick (1717-1779) are known to have done so.

Proscenium arch. That part of the stage in a modern theatre which lies between the orchestra and the curtain. It is often a decorative structure that separates the stage from the auditorium. Proscenium is often used as a synonym for the stage itself.

Puppetry. The art of making artificial figures perform on a miniature stage. Derived from the Latin word for "doll", puppetry involves manipulating small figures representing persons or animals through the use of rods, wires, strings, or fingers. A puppet show is a dramatic performance in which the characters are made to act by manipulators who speak the words.

R

Rising action. The second main part of the plot in which most of the complications occur. Rising action begins with the inciting force and represents the tangling of incidents and the conflict between the protagonist and the opposing forces. It leads to the climax, the highest point of excitement. In much classical Greek and Elizabethan drama, rising action occurs in the first two acts of a five-act play.

S

Scene. A subdivision of a play or of an act of a play. Although the idea of what constitutes a scene varies from period to period and from culture to culture, it is generally considered to be a unit of dramatic action in which a single point is made. The term scene is often used with a qualifying adjective to describe the function of a dramatic unit. Examples are love scene, expository scene, transitional scene, and messenger scene.

Setting. The fictional location of a dramatic action as it is represented on the stage. Setting also refers to the scenery and properties used. As well, it refers to the locale or period in which the action of a play takes place. The time period in which an action is placed may also be considered as part of the setting, for example, a medieval setting, an eighteenth century setting, and so on.

Situation comedy. A version of farce in which the comedy of the action depends almost exclusively on plot twists and exploiting ridiculous situations. Also called *sitcoms*, these comedies serve as standard fare on television today, but they have also been popular on the stage throughout the history of drama.

Social drama. A play which deals primarily with social questions and problems. The social drama focusses on environmental and cultural factors more than on personal and psychological characteristics. It centres attention on the society in which the play's characters live, the effects of society on them, and the social forces that control the action. These plays develop a thesis but are not necessarily an all-out effort in propaganda.

Soliloquy. A speech made by a character while he or she is alone on the stage. It is the utterance of a character who is talking to himself or herself and who is unaware of any hearers who may be present. The term comes from the Latin meaning "talking to oneself". It is often used in drama to allow the audience insight into a character's innermost feelings or to give the audience essential information. Soliloquys were derived from classical Greek tragedies and widely used in Renaissance drama. Many famous passages in Shakespeare's plays are soliloquys. Today, soliloquys are rarely used in stage plays, but they have become an acceptable feature in films, usually in the form of voice-overs. In a voice-over, the character's thoughts are spoken but the actor's lips remain still.

Spectacle. A drama presented to the sight or view, especially something striking, unusual, or impressive. Spectacle usually refers to a display on a grand scale. Spectacle is the sum of the visual implications in a drama and one of the integral parts of a play. It permeates every aspect of the action, beginning with the words of the dialogue. For the reader of a playscript, the elements of spectacle cause the reader to visualize the action and are often so obvious that the reader takes them for granted.

Stage direction. Any part of a dramatic script not intended to be spoken in performance. This includes directions for entrances and exits, descriptions of the characters and setting, comments on how lines are to be read (for example, "moodily" or "angrily"), and speech tags (which specify which character is to speak the line). Classical Greek drama texts contain few stage directions, the necessary action being indicated in the dialogue itself. Elizabethan drama texts also contain few stage directions. Modern plays, on the other hand, tend to include substantial stage directions. Many stage direction terms in use today are derived from Latin terms. Examples are *exit* (he or she goes off), *exeunt* (they go off), *solus* (alone), *manent* (remaining), and *omnes* (speaking together).

Style. The sum of the characteristic techniques used by a playwright to express his or her ideas, that is, how a dramatist writes. *Style* comes from the Latin meaning "writing instrument". The techniques include dramatic structure, characterization, diction, imagery, and so on. Style is what makes a dramatist distinctive and individual.

Subplot. A minor or secondary line of action in a drama. Also called *double plot* or *underplot,* the subplot usually contrasts or reinforces the main plot. The subplot is a distinguishing feature of English drama since Elizabethan times. It is not unusual to find plays with two or even three subplots interwoven with the main plot. This device gives English drama much of its variety and richness.

T

Theatre of the absurd. The name given to a body of dramatic works which developed in the 1950s and were closely connected to existentialist thought. In this type of drama, the conventions of structure, plot, and characterization are distorted. For example, an irrational quality of nature is stressed, and the isolation of the human being is treated as the central element of conflict. In Theatre of the Absurd, *absurd* is defined as senseless, illogical, and contrary to common sense. Thus, characters may appear in different forms and identities, the action may have no fixed setting, and the sequence of time may be fluid and indefinite.

Tragedy. Prose or verse drama which is serious in nature. A tragedy possesses the power to affect the reader or the audience by dealing with the stresses of being human and the nobility of the human spirit in the face of this stress. The term *tragedy* comes from the Greek meaning "goat song". The tragic drama involves death just as the sacrifice of goats in ancient rituals involved death. The term tragedy is applied to a dramatic work that traces the career of a noble person whose character is flawed in some way and whose actions cause him or her to break some moral precept, resulting in the character's downfall and destruction.

Turning point. The point of crisis in a play. The turning point is the point at which one of two forces or characters suddenly gets the advantage. It is the most dramatic scene in the play.

V

Vaudeville. A variety show consisting of individual performances of dancing, singing, dramatic sketches, acrobatics, and other unrelated stunts. The term comes from *Vau-de-Vire,* a valley in France noted for satirical songs. Vaudeville shows consisted of a variety of acts performed on the same bill. Featured players were known as headliners. Many noted twentieth century entertainers began their careers in vaudeville.

W

Well-made play. A term used to describe a tightly structured play that emphasizes principles of construction rather than content or significant subject matter. This term, which comes from the French *pièce bien faîte,* was developed during the late 1800s. The well-made play depends upon suspense and surprises and is basically a formula for melodrama. It depends on scenes of tearful emotion, discoveries, misunderstandings, reversals, and poetic justice. With the arrival of Henrik Ibsen's naturalism and George Bernard Shaw's social drama, the well-made play fell into disrepute. To this day, the term is used to indicate a type of slick, superficial, mechanically efficient drama which deals with a trivial subject.

Wit. The clever and appropriate expression of ideas providing amusement and pleasure. The term *wit* is derived from the Old English *witan,* meaning "to know". Thus, wit is defined primarily as a matter of sense and understanding. It is mainly intellectual, appealing to the mind's ability to perceive relationships, see similarities, and make comparisons. Wit is an intellectual display of cleverness, while humour refers more to the nature of character as a source of laughter. Wit depends wholly on clever phrasing, while humour rises from situations and does not depend on sharpness of expression.

———————————•———————————

Index

S

Satire, 115
Scene, 6
Scott, Sir Walter, 118
Shaw, George Bernard, 301-303
Shearer, Norma, 119
Shelley, Percy Bysshe, 118-119
Simard, André, 271

T

Tennyson, Lord, Alfred, 118, 190
Theatre, definition of, 6
Thesis drama, 302
Thomas, Lillian Beynon, 12, 53-54
Thousand Clowns, A, 55-117

V

Vesey, Desmond I., 194-195
Virgil, 303

W

Women's Christian Temperance Union
  (WCTU), 12, 53
Women's suffrage movement, 11-13, 54

Y

Young Women's Christian Association
  (YWCA), 12